MW00800740

RECIPE
the
Healing in the Age of Aquarius

Lynnie Nichols and Don Tolman

photography…
Michelle McKoy Photography, Tuuli Kaunisluonto, Rebecca May

book cover illustration…
Rebecca Ashcroft

illustration…
Dora Debrecini

book design…
Adi Bustaman

THE RECIPE -
HEALING IN THE AGE OF AQUARIUS

Copyright © 2021 Lynnie Nichols and Don Tolman

All rights reserved.

The contents of this book are derived from Lynnie Nichols' personal research/study and first-hand experience/pure observation facilitating health/healing retreats for the past 10 years, along with the immense first-hand experience of Healing with Wholefoods Medicine Man Don Tolman, who has supported thousands of people worldwide to heal naturally from disease, along with the ancient wisdom gained during his 40+ year search for Truest Truths. No warranties or claims are made as to the accuracy of the information provided and this extends to all aspects of the book contents. Lynnie Nichols and Don Tolman claim no formal health credentials; therefore, we must tell you that the content is for informational purposes only and not intended to be a substitute for professional medical advice, diagnosis or treatment and you should therefore check with your doctor before following any of the guidance in the contents of this book!

If you choose to follow this guidance, no responsibility will be accepted. Lynnie Nichols and Don Tolman are not responsible for any third-party websites, materials or products recommended throughout this book; these are purely resources for your convenience and are not endorsed in any way by Lynnie Nichols or Don Tolman.

Because of the dynamic nature of the internet, any web addresses or links contained in this book may have changed since publication and may no longer be valid. The views expressed in this work are solely those of the author and do not necessarily reflect the views of the publisher, and the publisher hereby disclaims any responsibility for them.

CONTENTS

Michelle McKoy Photography

FOREWORD *by Lynnie*

I feel it so necessary, before we even begin to get into this book, to acknowledge the brilliance of my co-author, friend and mentor, the most incredibly wise man, known to most as **The Wholefoods Medicine Man or Cowboy Don Tolman!** This man truly is a genius; his wisdom reaches far beyond the confines of Wholefood Medicine and, in fact, encompasses many of the unknown mysteries of the Cosmos!

I cannot even begin to imagine what life must have felt like for Don, awakened long before the masses and ostracised as a child for his intuitiveness. My heart hurts to think how lonely that must have felt, and yet I'm grateful this catalysed his connectedness to nature, in turn synchronising the events and experiences that initiated downloads of incredible information and instigated Don's 40+ year search for Truest Truths. This worldwide search through ancient catacombs, pyramids, libraries and more finally rewarded Don with his lifelong dream to discover the recipe for 'The Meal of Hercules,' which ancient tribes such as the Essene Hebrews believed to be the most sacred food that could be offered as a single meal to the 'Sacred Living Temple' (body). This meal, specifically translated from ancient Hebrew scrolls into English, is now called Pulse and dates back over 2,600 years when students of the Pythagorean Academy, at the completion of 40 days of fasting on water, air and sunshine, were given a shoulder strap pouch filled with a 'millstone crushed hand assembled Golden Measured Meal' that Pythagoras himself referred to as the Meal of Hercules. This meal is specifically based on measures of 1:1.6 X 3.14 phi pi, and thanks to Don's brilliance, here we are, millennia later, with access to not just this information but the Meal of Hercules (Pulse) itself.

Don's brilliance extends to the creation of many other products such as 3D Theta posters that work on different areas of consciousness, assisting you to grow spiritually and mentally. He also brought back the Carillon bowl, which is a large crystal bowl based on an original artifact that was found in Egypt. It is said that the original bowl was used in hierosonic chambers by priests in order to tune into other states of consciousness, as well as for healing purposes. Don has recreated the original from 100% pure Grade A quartz crystal. It is set in the Key of David (G Gb/F#) and is used to create balance in the mind and body. The special vibrations of the bowl, combined with the power of your voice, can be used to promote healing within your mind and body to bring about new states of consciousness, transforming you physically, mentally, and emotionally. Along with these products, Don has a wide range of organic natural health products.

Over the years, many unawakened Beings have ridiculed Don's teachings. He's had two attempts on his life and yet, determinedly, he continues his mission to 'wake up' the world, educating thousands upon thousands of people in regards to the corruptness of the pharmaceutical industry. Don has helped thousands of people heal naturally from minor to major health issues including cancer. He is the author of many books including Magnus Opus, Gaia Speaks- A Mother's Call and The Farmacist Desk References 1, 2 and 3. I truly believe that Don has contributed beyond measure to the awareness level of the collective consciousness today. To have knowledge of all that has been presented to us recently as truth, and have no way of changing this situation, he must truly have felt like banging his head against a brick wall! I remember asking him once, 'How do you cope with knowing what you know?' His answer was, 'I drink beer!' 😊

Thanks to Don, we are privy to many ancient 'nuggets of wisdom' that have since been hidden away behind lock and key, simply because they're not in the best interest of the governing bodies whose entire agenda is to keep us small and whose entire power structure only exists because we are ignorant to the truth of who we really are!

Don has confirmed much of my own intuitive knowing in regards to health and healing and has absolutely blown my mind on innumerable topics outside of this.

From the bottom of my heart and soul, Don Tolman; on behalf of the whole world, I seriously cannot thank you enough for your wisdom, guidance, teachings, resilience and bravery.

You have given us incredible hope for a better world in the Age of Aquarius.

We Love You xxx

FOREWORD *by Don*

For the last three generations, using wholefoods as medicines has been lost to the masses thanks to the pharmaceutical industry's global push for toxic cut, burn and poisons. Today it's coming back to more and more people that healing themselves with foods and embracing the Seven Principles of Health taught through the ages are much better and safer than the magic bullets of big pharma that all have 'side-effects' and create recurrent health problems that build their business with on-going 'Treatments'... The Truest Truth is that **'NATURE'S COMPLEX SO THAT WE DON'T HAVE TO BE!'**

AN APPLE A DAY KEEPS THE DOCTOR AWAY IS CORRECT AND TRUE ... and other foods target body organs and physiological functions in the same way. Lynnie's Healing Recipes are AWESOME! So, grab some Fruits, Veggies, Nuts, Seeds and organic non-GMO Grains and start Reading and Eating your way to Health!

But first, one more thing:

My experience with this Beautiful Goddess of Life and Enlightenment is that she instinctively is fulfilling the ancient history of her name. The ancestors of the Duthie family (Lynnie's birth name) were part of an ancient Scottish tribe called the Picts. They also had Gaelic and Celtic backgrounds. The name Duthie is derived from the Gaelic name Dudhthaigh, which means 'Dark'... The Ancient Alpha Numeric code of Duthie is 11, which means 'Doorway'. The Duthie families focused on teaching people how to come out of the Darkness of ignorance and not knowing to see the Light of Truth and Knowledge about Health and Longevity by Embracing the Physics of Nature that our bodies are made of. In Britain these people were called 'the Tolmans' and 'the Duthies'—the Doorway to Life and Health and Healing.

The name Nichols goes back pre-1066 A.D. when people were forced to take on first and last names for purposes of control and taxation by identifying individuals. The Nicholses were the ones who embraced the idea of 'Power to the People' by giving gifts and teaching Wisdom of the Ages that had been handed down 'Mouth to Ear' from one generation to the next. Eventually even Christianity embraced Old Saint Nicolas, later spelled Nicholas because of a Saint bringing back the Giving and Teaching of his family name being Nichols.

The Matriarchal meaning of the name Lynnie, Lyn, Lynnette, etc. literally means: a brook, stream, a waterfall cascading into a pool, and this magic in nature was symbolised as a Songbird, singing and walking gracefully, bringing joy to those listening and watching the movement of the Waters of Life. This is exactly what Lynnie has captured in this book, Healing in the Age of Aquarius. When we embrace the Physics of Nature around us and avoid toxic chemicals, fake foods, poisonous commercially prepared drinks, and toxic personal care products that are absorbed through our skin into our bloodstream and interstitial tissues, creating dis-comforts that today pharma/medica call diseases, avoiding all of this and getting back to Nature-made foods and products, we clear toxins and overcome deficiencies, which are the only cause of disease and discomforts in your Sacred House or Living Temple, your Abode or Body—it's where you live.

Your health is your responsibility and Lynnie gives you brilliant Recipes of Health and Healing. Mother Earth and Father Sun will bless you with energy and health and restoration of lost or weakened function capacities even at the cellular level.

This book is a retro-futuris Gift, bringing the Past Wisdom of Health and Healing back to the People to empower them with knowledge and let you Radiate with Light, Joy and Happiness.

Thank you, Lynnie Nichols, for living up to your Name and Soul's Purpose. This book will Bless many lives.

Cowboy Don Tolman,
the Wholefood Medicine Man.
www.thedontolman.com

PREFACE *by Don*

Is it Man's destiny to carry around a body of nothing more than 'flesh and blood,' hoping to leave it in order to join the 'one-ness' of Spirit? The body by many is thought of as heavy, painful and ugly, wishing 'it' could be dropped off at the local body shop for cleaning, shaping and repairing, much as we would a suit of clothes or an automobile. All this negativity ... and yet, from the most ancient of civilizations, manuscripts, tablets and icons point at a compelling mystery about 'matter'. Man's physical body was considered a sacred 'vessel', a 'ship', even a 'spaceship', a 'cup', 'chalice', a 'house' because it is your abode (which is where the word 'body' comes from); it is where one 'fasts', offers up prayers (the desires of the heart) and truly lives. Consider also the 'temple', the most sacred of all 'buildings', where God/Goddess dwells and where He/She maintains and sets the foundations for all life, yet allows you to build how you will.

'The body machine' is the label given to 'us' by those whom we choose to be our doctors, whose predecessors over a hundred years ago looked through a microscope and saw 'animalcules' (later named bacteria) for the very first time. It wasn't long before 'they' began to predict the end of disease and suffering because now they believed they saw and knew the source of illness. They believed they could repair, fix and even replace parts, just like any machine, and not worry about the animalcules... 'They' would just declare open war and 'kill them all'. Yet here we are, 2020, and we are in a period of even more dire concern over those same 'animalcules' that are now mutating, getting stronger and attacking us (we are told). The medical profession is stymied! They pretend they have answers. Cut, Burn, and Poisons is their war cry, but, at the same time, they're still always looking for new drugs, new procedures, and new diseases, giving old drugs new names and ever new uses in order to make more money. It's capitalism at its finest and its worst.

There's something uncomfortable about the invasiveness of cutting out and drilling into of our bodies; we aren't a body machine regardless of what's said about it. We're more than a kidney, a heartbeat, a temperature! We're much more; we're members of a large extended family stretching from one continent to another, Children of the Earth. Actually, still more, we're 'born' from (brought forth from and for) and also 'borne' by (carried/upheld/supported by) the cosmos; we're made of stardust, made from the same elements as all life, born/borne for joy and pleasure, to seek and find our purpose, to fulfill the measure of our creation as all life does. We are Children of Light.

I remember an ancient mystery about Matter, an Earth Mother, even called 'a Goddess' by many, the Matriarch, the only one whose Principles of Life and Laws of Nature set the Body Temple free of pain, disease and encumbrances. Gaea, or Mother Earth, was the great goddess of the early Greeks. She represented the earth and was worshipped as the 'Mother of All Living'. In Greek mythology, she was given birth by, or created by her mother, 'Cosmos', originally meaning 'Beautiful Goddess' and later defined as 'Ordered Beauty'; then Her daughter 'Gaea' gave birth to both the first race of gods (the Titans) and the first humans... Then a breast of the mother appeared from the Earth Mother's blood (the ocean), an Island of Mystery and Wonder, they named it the 'Isle of Cosmos'. They studied the principles of enhanced beauty and named them the Art Cosmetics. Milk bathing was an anti-aging, beautifying Life Ritual.

In some records of the creation story of the ancient Greeks, Chaos came before everything else, even before Cosmos. Chaos was made of Void, Mass, and Darkness (Set) in confusion. Then the earth, in the form of Gaea, came into existence. From Mother Earth sprang the starry heavens in the form of the sky god Uranus. From Gaea also came the mountains, plains, seas and rivers that make up the earth as we know her today. Everything came into existence through the feminine. Galaxy means: 'Mother's Milk'... Gala is the Festivals of Seasons or Holidays; Gala means, 'Celebration of 'Mother's Milk'. This is why our galaxy is named the 'Milky Way'.

Gaea, Mother Earth, was, to some, the oldest of the gods/goddesses of the early Greeks. She was known as the Supreme Goddess by humans and gods alike. She presided over marriages and oaths and was honoured as the source of all growth, learning and knowledge. From this came the modern academic (meaning trivia) publishing of the postulates (guessing) of what they call the 'Big Bang Theories.'

What if... MOST SCIENCE IS NOT REALLY SCIENTIFIC? SCIENCE MEANS KNOWLEDGE, NOT BOUGHT AND

PAID FOR CLINICAL STUDIES THAT HAVE TO PUBLISH A PRE-SELECTED RESULT CHOSEN BY THE $$$MONEY-FUNDERS$$$ AND GIVEN THE (GOOD OLD BOYS') 'PEER REVIEWED' STATUS OF 'EMPIRICAL EVIDENCE'. What if... In the process of multinational corporations grouping together to create for themselves 'Authoritative Control' by using financial infiltration of Politics, Institutionalised Religions, Pharma/Medical Industries, World Banking and more, we the 'masses' have been indoctrinated into 'Blind Trust' ... and to focus our attention on the material realm of existence to the exclusion of the Three Subtle Realms, we have virtually consciously rid the Cosmos of Nature, rid Nature of Spirit/intelligence, and, in a sense, denied the 'existence of all life' other than that which is physically observable here on this earth?

What if... for example, the encounter of a UFO phenomenon was 'subtle' in the sense that it may manifest in the optic physical world of sight of some but derives from a source which by its very nature could not provide the kind of hard evidence that would satisfy 'academically indoctrinated 'scientific' sceptics, for whom reality is limited to their studies and chanting memorised preselected answers? They can only perceive 'material forms' from the perspective of formal educational training in physics from bought and paid for multinational corporate curriculums. 'We don't want you to think; we want you to be a puppet (without you knowing) with a bloated sense of self for your academic (which means trivia) achievement and for the job we will hire you for, for 'being a good little chant learner.'

What if... On the other hand, we were to acknowledge that the phenomenon is beyond our present framework of knowledge? Might not such an attitude of humility become, paradoxically, a way to enlarge upon what could then be learned from our curiosity and our sense of wonder that sparks imagination ... that is always a 'preview' of what is coming? Is it possible that adopting an open attitude toward the testimony of witnesses could enable us to learn of 'unseen realities' now obscured by our too limited epistemology, allowing us to rediscover the sacred and the divinity in Nature in ourselves and our absolute connection to all of Cosmic design and existence?

I think of these experiences as a crossing over between the material world and what in Eastern philosophy is called the subtle realms. Experiencers describe being brought into another dimension of reality from which a new Perspective of Life on Earth is possible. Sensitivity to our dysfunctional ecological and social conditions emerges as many come to feel that every living system is connected to what many call 'Source', 'Home' and 'Cosmic Mother'. An awareness of this relationship must be regained, the 'Experiencers' say, if we are to create a sustainable, peaceful world wherein this could be an Age of Imagination taken to Cosmic Proportions.

If this whole notion of 'other realms' ... 'other life on other worlds' is bad science, it may nonetheless be good medicine. Yet, is it bad science, or is it simply walking at the edge of greater experience? What if... Experiencers can also speak of 'empiricism, reason, logic, and empathy'? Maybe it is all simply a process of finding the experiences of other realms in order to be 'Informationally Transformative' and in this rise to ever higher levels of thought capacities.

NOTE. The following dialogue predates the 3rd century Catholic Essene brotherhood's retranslation of a manuscript some monks called 'The lost Alchemy of Physical Immortality'. The scroll was subsequently retranslated by three different monks from 1851 to the 1950s. The 1851 scroll is called the Slovakian Scriptorium; the 1901 translation is called the Lithuanian Archivia; while the most popularly read edition was translated in the 1950s and is owned by the International Biogenic Society and is called 'The Essene Gospel of Peace'. I love the Christian slant on the scroll because it re-establishes what most apocryphal texts say of the Vegetarian Healer called Jesus of Nazareth. I met the modern-day translator of the scroll at his home/spa in Baja California in 1977 on Mount Kuchumaa. Our mutual passions bonded us immediately. I love the Credo below that he put together for his fans and followers.

International Biogenic Society Credo...

The credo of the International Biogenic Society states the following: • We believe that our most precious possession is Life. • We believe we shall mobilize all the forces of Life against the forces of death. • We believe mutual understanding leads toward mutual cooperation; that mutual cooperation leads toward Peace; and that Peace is the only way of survival for mankind. • We believe that we shall preserve instead of waste our natural resources, which are the heritage of our children. • We believe that we shall avoid the pollution of our air, water and soil, the basic preconditions of life. • We believe that we shall preserve the vegetation of our planet: the humble grass which came 50 million years ago and the majestic trees which came 20 million years ago, to prepare our planet for mankind. • We believe that we shall eat only fresh, natural, pure, wholefoods without chemicals and artificial processing. • We believe that we shall lead a simple, natural, creative life, absorbing all the sources of energy, harmony and knowledge in and around us. • We believe that the improvement of life and mankind on our planet must start with individual efforts, as the whole depends on the atoms composing it.

The following presentation goes back to a time when God/Good was Female, when men and women were god-lings, and their daily business was to be about HER work, 'The great work'—the Magnus (not magnum) Ma-gnus Opus of Cosmic Enterprise: To become, over time and distance, IMMORTALS, GODS & GODDESSES: Earthly bodies transmuted into temples of intelligence that shine as bright as a thousand Suns/Sons … body vehicles that through embracing Principles of Living Temple Work – a 'reconstruction' of the original inherited building materials of the Womb – 'alchemically transmute' or 'translate' into something much Higher. A 'rebirth' wherein you are Borne Again upon the Waters of Life or Mother Nature's Milk for 40 days and 40 nights... Then you learn to Walk the RainBow Bridge into the 'Heavens' in order to learn how to step through time and space, body vehicle intact, and do so at will at supra-luminal speeds of thought … to learn how to build worlds then acclimate yourself to that world by stepping out of your Garden Enclosure (a wandering Planetary Pod) for periods of time till you are accustomed and ready to plant your own seed in order to populate the new world … and in this help to bring to pass the perpetuation of all life and the human experience through the fulfillment of eternal progression of the 'Cosmological Anatomica Materia Templum'.

FORGOTTEN KNOWLEDGE BECOMES A MYSTERY...

The Phoenix and it's Bearer, The Philosophers' Stone, Alpheus: The Underground River in the Peloponnesus, the Cintamani of the Buddhists, the Farr of the Persians, The Shekkinah of the Jews, the Syamantaka of the Hindus, the Orphic Egg of the Greeks, the Pearl of Perfection of the Chinese, The Golden Fleece, the Ark of the Covenant, the Holy Grail, Etc. An egg-shaped gem of Wonder and Power. Buddha, Jesus, Osiris, Moses, Orpheus, Krishna, and hundreds of other Legends speak of this Emitting Light.

WHAT IF...

Knowing the Principles of Living Temple Work, and Doing those Principles, causes your Body/Temple to 'become' the answer and the sought for 'object' to this Lost Mystery? WHAT IF... Your only reason for 'being' is to get a body so as to gain further Light and Knowledge in any given Life Time? WHAT IF... When you do Living Temple work, it's not just for you but for those before you and for those who will follow you? WHAT IF... we follow each other through 'Seed' in and out of LIFE/TIMES? We came here from seed as all things physical do; what if that's how we return into Life/Time? 'And this is the Spirit of Elijah, to turn the Hearts of the Father's to the Children and the Hearts of the Children to the Father's' so that the bodies inherited are more whole and further ahead in a given lifetime. In this is found Eternal Progression, intelligence is Light and it permeates all Matter; any principle of intelligence gained in a given lifetime rises with you upon your return. Living Temple work removes the Veil of Forgetfulness, and in this you can gain the knowledge and experience of a thousand lifetimes in ONE lifetime.

21st Century; A Feminine Focus: Keep in mind Ancient Scholars taught that each one of us is created both Male and Female (epicenes), Left and Right Hemispheres, Left and Right sides of the Body, Yin and Yang. A return to a focus on the feminine is not putting women in charge but rather each of us balancing the qualities of Male and Female within ourselves by focusing on the feminine values of loving, nurturing, caring kindness to ourselves and all other living things.

In a tantrum, I threw myself on the bed, bawling my eyes out, angry and frustrated, feeling helpless in my desperate desire for the world to 'wake up' to the truth as the words of the prediction I'd just heard and the sickening reality of this replayed over and over in my mind... 'ONE IN TWO PEOPLE IN AMERICA/AUSTRALIA WILL BE DIAGNOSED WITH CANCER DURING THEIR LIFETIME!' Overwhelmed by this statement and the barrage of emotions that raged through my body, I lay sobbing until my mascara resembled a sick version of Goth lipstick and a wave of calmness and clarity rose from somewhere deep within, accompanied by the words, 'Pull yourself together Girl, stop sooking and bloody well do something about it!' AND SO HERE I AM!

HONESTLY... IT DOESN'T HAVE TO BE THIS WAY! I mean that's a crazy, ridiculous 50% of people getting diagnosed with cancer! Do you realise that there are cultures around the world that are long-lived and dis-ease free and in some instances have never experienced a single case of cancer to this day? So how is this even possible, what do they do differently to us? Well, the answer is unbelievably simple—they follow the laws of nature, the principles of health and the wisdom of our ancestors!

Knowledge is power and, unfortunately for most in our Western world, thanks to past false indoctrination, that power has been stolen from us! It is my passionate desire that each and every person has the knowledge and tools to empower themselves with the courage, trust and self-confidence to change that cancer prediction via PREVENTION, to cure dis-ease before it ever manifests into physical form, to let go of the fears that have kept so many running back and forth to the doctor time and time again, suppressing the symptoms yet never truly healing. We are powerful, self-healing, self-creating Beings and, when we embrace this truth, miraculous healings and transformations take place! We can heal our body of any disease when we offer it the correct healing environment, and if you choose to read on, you will discover testimonials in proof of this. We are more than just a physical body; therefore, true healing must take place holistically—mind, body and spirit.

It's not enough to focus purely on the physical body if the core of the dis-ease is emotional toxicity, just as it's not enough to focus solely on our emotions if the physical body is overwhelmed with toxicity and crying out for nutrients! It's time to get back to basics and the ancient wisdom still practised in cultures around the world that are long-lived and disease-free! It's time to embrace the physics of nature and the principles of health! It's time to embrace 'Self-Care'.

There's a quote by Henry Ford that says, 'If you always do what you've always done, you will always get what you've always got.' Stop for a moment and think about that in relation to your health and your life in general for that matter... Are you ready to do something different? Are you ready to start living and loving life again?

People everywhere are awakening to the truth, awakening to the mistruths we have been indoctrinated with since the day money became more important than a human being's life, mistruths that have kept us small, powerless, misinformed and without choice. The time has come to challenge everything you have ever been told or taught... Go deeper, 'feel' into the innate wisdom of your own body and ask, 'Does this FEEL like my truth?' and then trust your body; don't let fear and past programming keep you in those patterns you've been playing out all these years. Contemplate your health and then open your mind to the possibility that maybe you've had it wrong; maybe those people you have been putting up on pedestals don't have all the answers after all! I mean all we have to do is take a look at the state of our Western society and it's pretty damn obvious!

Quantum science has proven that everything in the Cosmos is energy vibrating at varying resonances. If this is the case it seems conclusive to say that 'we' are energy, and 'that' which we originated from (known by most as God) is energy, and therefore, if we are the same as that which we originated from, on some level, we must also be gods and goddesses, and, to some degree, have access to a similar creative and healing energy/power!

Long ago, our ancestors understood this. They knew of their Divine origin and embraced a direct connection to Spirit (God), to the land, to the celestial bodies and all that is provided for us here on Earth by nature in order to optimise our human experience, including plants with their individual healing properties. They understood that the wisdom we needed to live a vibrant existence was inherently within us, including the knowledge and power to heal ourselves nature's way. Our ancestors understood the connection between all things and knew that everything in the Cosmos was designed to work together in the most perfect way. They understood that just as the moon affects the tides, so too does it affect the waters within us, as well as the times for planting and cultivating crops, and, therefore, our ancestors would plant and cultivate in accordance with the 13 lunar cycles (13 months) and the specific times for planting, pruning, and picking.

It was understood that there was a 'best time' to plant each fruit and vegetable; for instance, no planting should take place between black moon until the first crescent appears—then, as the moon is waxing towards the 1st quarter, it is time to plant leafy greens such as spinach, cabbage, lettuce etc. as the energy is directed into the leaves of the plant. The waxing moon in the 1st quarter is also a great time for planting cereal and grain crops, sewing seeds and transplanting seedlings. Taking it one step even further than this, they understood that the best time to carry out any of these processes was when the moon was in the astrological water signs of Cancer, Scorpio and Pisces. It was understood that between the 1st quarter and full moon was the perfect time to plant crops with seeds inside the fruit/vegetable such as tomatoes, cucumber, zucchini, capsicum etc, and that two days prior to full moon is the ideal time for the grafting of fruit trees. The best time during this phase for these actions is, once again, when the moon is in the water signs of Cancer, Scorpio and Pisces. And on it goes throughout the complete lunar cycle!

As with so much of our ancestral wisdom, this knowledge has been lost to the masses due to circumstances out of our control. From the moment of birth, our modern day 'system' begins to disconnect the newborn god/goddess from the Source of that which we truly are ... we leave the womb that has nourished and nurtured us for nine full months, opening our eyes to the clinical surrounds of a hospital room, cord cut before we can receive the final nourishing benefits of the placental blood, removed from our mother, whisked away by a stranger, and, not too long afterward, jabbed with a needle full of chemicals! In no time whatsoever our existence is full of artificial elements. Many of us are fed processed, foodless foods and drinks whilst breathing polluted air and drinking chemically contaminated water, further continuing the disconnection from our one true Source. Off to school we go where it is demanded we do exactly as we are told and think exactly as the curriculum demands via chant memorising the answers expected of us. If we get the answers incorrect we are made to feel like a failure and possibly even shamed in front of our classmates, concreting the belief in our mind that we really are a failure and, with this, disconnecting even further from the perfect Being we really are!

When are we ever taught to think and feel and question? If for some reason we even dare to do these things in school we are punished, made out to be a 'smart ass' and ostracised as one of the 'naughty kids' ... and so the separation from one's true nature and the degradation of pure thoughts continues. Somewhere along the line, many of us are introduced to 'religion', which even further encourages disconnection from our true Source, burdening us with controlling, fear-based rules and regulations! We are encouraged to worship idols outside of ourselves whilst visiting the confines of four concrete walls, making monetary donations that line the pockets of institutions, and, from here, the idea of direct communication with Spirit no longer even enters our head. By now, any inkling of the truth of who we really are is well and truly forgotten, buried deep beneath a mound of negative core beliefs, lies and deception. Fear and control is the result, and we begin to feel a sense of separation, suppression, and loss; of being lost, unloved, unworthy, hopeless, helpless and abandoned.

Our ancestors understood that 'human thought' was the most powerful energy in the Universe and when combined with visualisation and emotion, resulted in materialisation. Unfortunately, our negative core belief programming makes for a much less than perfect basis for pure positive thoughts, hence resulting in the manifestation of poverty, struggle and dis-ease.

So, what if the sole purpose of being here in this physical reality was to reclaim our Divinity, to reclaim our direct connection to Spirit and our innate creative and healing powers, in order to materialise the heavenly life we desire? What if WE ARE the sole Creators of our own reality and everything we see and experience in our life is in fact a consequence of our own conscious and subconscious thoughts, beliefs and cellular memories?

Nature is healing because it is the true source of all Man. When we spend time in the simplicity of nature, nourishing our physical body and soul, we heal and thrive. Our ancestors understood this, just as they understood the ancient alchemy of AFEW... Air–Breathe the freshest of air; Fire–we receive energy and healing from the Sun; Earth–eat only that which is provided by Mother Nature and make use of the healing clays that detoxify the body; Water–drink and fast on pristine, unpolluted, electrified water!

What if, once we detoxify our body, mind and spirit, the key to a beautiful, vibrant, healthy life really is that simple?

My 'Awakening' to the truth – my passion for natural health, healing and spirituality – began 26 years ago when my two-year-old daughter developed eczema on her feet and legs accompanied by an unrelenting, chronic itchiness that forced her to scratch uncontrollably until her feet and legs were red raw and bleeding day and night. At the onset of the eczema I immediately cut all foods with preservatives, colourings, dairy, sugar and wheat from her diet, feeding her purely on fruit, vegetables and meat; yet this seemed to make no difference whatsoever, so I turned to the doctor in hope of gaining some answers.

Completely disillusioned, with no hope whatsoever of a cure, just a bag full of medication in the form of steroid creams, antihistamine and antibiotics to supress the symptoms, I returned home a short time later. I knew that none of this medication was good long term, but I had no idea what alternatives I had. We researched far and wide, trying every natural cream and cure we could find to no avail. In our desperate attempt to protect her from her continuous desire for relief we resorted to clothing her in cotton long pants during the day and all-in-one cotton pyjamas at night, along with ankle-length boots laced up as tight as we could get them for 24 hours a day, bar a brief moment at anti-itch bath time. The 15 ml adult's dose of antihistamine we were advised to give her each night did little at all in the way of relief and I would constantly be woken by Jess sobbing in bed, somehow succeeding in tearing her boots and pyjamas off, resulting in hands feet legs and sheets covered in blood. I literally could not take my eyes off her for more than a few seconds during the day and, if I did, I would find her hiding behind the furniture, in cupboards or anywhere else she could find for that matter, in order to steal a few blissful moments alone scratching in peace.

At one stage her legs became so infected they actually stank like rotten meat. Back to the doctor I went, only to be told the exact same thing: 'There is nothing you can do except wait for her to grow out of it; here's another dose of antibiotics!' Feeling completely helpless and hopeless, I would leave the doctor's surgery in tears time and time again.

After several extremely long, stressful months, it was suggested by someone that I try a dietician for answers. Unbelievably, within minutes of entering the consultation room the dietician had diagnosed the CAUSE of Jess's eczema as a natural form of MSG called salicylates and amines found in fruits and vegetables and given me a very basic diet to get her started on. Well, I am not exaggerating when I say that 24 hours later Jess was a completely different child! ALL of her itchiness had totally ceased and, after months and months of being driven crazy by the incessant irritation, we were finally able to strip off her long pants and lace-up ankle boots, allowing her to run barefoot and fancy free like every other child... I could not believe that in as little as 24 hours, the problem that had devastated our lives for months on end was gone, just like that, just like magic!

I was disgusted that, on one hand, the doctors were telling me that there was absolutely nothing we could do—that we would just have to wait until she grew out of it, which, according to them, might take years, and in the meantime give the little two-year-old girl an adult's dose of Phenergan every night and keep her smothered in steroid cream to supress the symptoms—and yet, within minutes in a dietician's consultation room, by diagnosing the actual CAUSE of the eczema and a simple diet change, we had been given our lives back.

As you can imagine, my life had been changed forever and over the next 20 years my interest in natural health and spirituality became my passion, leading me to some incredible teachers such as Louise Hay, Brandon Bays and Don Tolman. After battling my own emotional demons of chronic anxiety for many years, I was inspired to delve deeper into the cause of dis-ease and the steps necessary in order to heal from conditions both physical and emotional, concluding without doubt that everything is connected—body systems, beliefs, emotions and dis-ease; therefore, to truly heal we must take a holistic approach, body, mind and spirit. My determination to conquer anxiety led me down the path of emotional healing and through my personal process work I discovered first-hand the power of forgiveness and the importance of gaining awareness of our core belief system, which is the subconscious driving force behind our emotions and behaviours.

As a Journey Healing Practitioner and Voice Dialogue Facilitator I was guided to help others with the knowledge I'd gained over the years in regards to emotions and physical health and began running holistic healing retreats, offering a healing environment to detoxify the body and mind via raw foods, emotional healing therapies, and, most recently, water fasting. My faith in the body's healing ability during this time was confirmed over and over again as I witnessed miraculous healings and transformations take place before my very eyes. It was not long after I began the retreats, that I discovered our Healing with Wholefoods Cowboy, Don Tolman. Finally, I had substance for my beliefs/knowing. I was in absolute resonance with what Don was teaching and the knowledge he had gained over his 40-year search for truest truths, backed up by scientific proof and ancient scrolls, etc. Don's books and website information, including many recorded webinars, have helped me to support so many people searching for natural ways to heal themselves from dis-ease ... and so, to me, the obvious thing to do was to get together with Don and share the powerful information that has been lost to the masses over the last few centuries and, in fact, is our birthright!

© Michelle McKoy

So here it is! May this resource be treasured and passed down through the generations in order for us to 'take back our power' and live the way nature intended.

This is your life; you didn't take this physical form to be unhappy, to struggle, to spend your life sick and tired! Here is THE RECIPE to holistic healing – body, mind and spirit – consistently proven to be transformational. It's time to be the most empowered, vibrant version of YOU and, in doing so, inspire and empower your children and all of those around you to be the healthiest and best version of themselves! Don't wait until you've become yet another medical statistic; begin embracing 'self-care' today and you will soon discover how amazing and powerful your body is. You will soon discover the TRUTH.

Cowboy Don's INTRODUCTION

The Age of Aquarius

Planets line up on the same side of the Sun every 13 Ages or 26,000 years. Most of you know that happened in 2012. We are now going into the Age of Aquarius (an Air Sign) and according to ancient writings, the Age of Aquarius (13 letters) was officially entered into on the 26th of January 2020. These numbers all add up to 13... 1+2+6+2+0+2+0=13.

Plants that symbolize the number 13 are: Cannabis, Magic Mushrooms, Hops and Dark Organic Chocolate. These are all part of the same botanical family of emotional health, healing, happiness and creativity. All of these plants originated from Planet 13, according to ancient records, and floated here on solar winds, falling into our atmosphere. Planet means, 'Wandering Rock'; Plant means 'Wandering Seeds.'

The number 13 was called 'The Most Precious, Sacred Number' on this earth and throughout the Cosmos. In this Age of the Air Sign, 'Humanity will flip into Greater EnLightenment, a Breath of Fresh Air'. For instance, the ancient knowledge of our Sun having 13 planets, and their names will return: Mercury, Venus, Earth, Mars, Jupiter, Saturn, Uranus, Neptune, Pluto, Ceres, Make Make, Haumea, and Eris (the 13th planet).

People will awaken to the 13 doorways (enterology) of the human body: Two-Eyes, Two-Ears, Two-Nostrils, One-Mouth, Two-Nipples, One-pee door, One-poop door, One- Skin, One-Brain (our thoughts create emotions; emotions create behaviours; behaviours create results).

The Ancients weren't primitive and stupid; they were Scholastic Geniuses (those who observe out of interest). They found the brilliance of the 13 Astrological Birth Signs, 13 Birthstones, 13 Flower signs, and 13 animal symbolisms. This is total scholastic genius, they are all spot on!

Air, Fire (Sun) Earth, Water—A. F. E. W. Few there be that find it! 'Find what?' you ask. Few there will be that find and embrace the Four Birth Signs of Air, Fire, Earth and Water! Embrace these things and Lift your Mind, Emotions, and Physical Health and better your Social Relationships.

Most Religions and Academics (which means those who study trivia and obsolete educational curriculums) are people who think that all the Ancient Wisdom of the 13s is Parascience (unprovable by scientific theories). But even Religious Bibles have the number 13 in them; however, the number 13 was done away with and changed to be the 12+1; for example, Jesus-1 and his 12 Apostles = 13. Moses-1 and the 12 Tribes = 13. The 12-Sons of Jacob-1 = 13 etc. Even court rooms have a Judge-1 and a 12-Man Jury = 13 this can go on and on... But let's get to the Age of Aquarius and Eris, the 13th Planet.

So, what exactly is the Age of Aquarius? It's many things, but basically Planet Earth has entered a new vernal equinox and constellation called Aquarius. It's about how humanity will experience the energy that rules that constellation. Many astrologers have different perspectives based on when we exactly enter this new age, certainly the 2012 Planet line-up is the start of the entrance of the Age of Aquarius, but Jan 26th, 2020 confirms it! 1/26/2020 adds up to 13. Right now, we are noticing a shift on the planet in terms of consciousness, morals, values and awakening. Some will agree we are still experiencing a blend of the Age of Pisces and the Age of Aquarius. Age of Pisces, ruled by the fish, is a symbol of religion. Christianity and religion (which created governments) ruled humanity during this era. If you've ever been to Europe you can see all the destruction and corruption that religion has caused. Religion even led to the murder of Hundreds of Thousands. One such event was The Spanish Inquisition.

The representation of Aquarius, the water bearer, shows a woman pouring water from a pot into a body of water. The water is indeed water, but if you look closely the waves also represent brain waves, the brain is 93% water. Aquarius is a highly intellectual and open-minded sign. It's been recorded that the Age of Aquarius is the 'Dumping of Water to move the fish (Pisces) down the River of the Past'. So with awakened, enlightened intellectual pursuits, Aquarius is 'washing away the old mentality' and is the 'Dawn of the new Awakening.' Even Water Fasting and Liquid Juice Fasting has returned and many are doing it to Clarify their Body, Mind and Emotions.

Aquarius is a fixed Air sign. Every sign has positive and negative traits. Like yin-yang, the world cannot exist without both. Aquarius rules scientific/mental pursuits, metaphysical beliefs, philanthropic interests, humanity, truth, idealism, rebellion, logic, equality and inventions. Some negatives include extremism, militant revolution, anger, rebellion, stubbornness, inflexibility and radicalism. Aquarius pushes humanity to live in a better society, therefore it's no surprise the New Age has started off dodgy! Rebellion has peaked as humanity protests government taking the Rights of the People away via forced vaccinations etc. When looking at the energy shift between Pisces and Aquarius, it's no surprise that extremism in the Middle East has led to rebellion or radical acts based off religious views of what is 'right and wrong'. Humanity is still pushing forward to protect women's rights and to diminish the false reality of the feminine energy. A big part of this age will be to recreate equality amongst men and women. Since Aquarius is a mental sign, overthinking or not thinking at all is what hinders the world. It's no surprise that mental health and depression/suicide rates have increased. We are becoming highly mental creatures and when we cannot connect to the values of society, we lose our minds. We are at the beginning of this age and there is a long way to go for some to evolve their minds.

But in a more positive light, the past is making a comeback. Natural and ancient methods of Foods and Plants as medicine are gaining popularity and research is showing how yoga, meditation and healing practices benefit one's health. People care more about animals now and try alternative methods of eating for ethical reasons. Research is now proving that metaphysics (shunned during the Age of Pisces) is 'real.' From telepathy to quantum physics, people are better accepting concepts such as astral traveling, shamanism and intuition.

Aquarius rules technology and individuality. It's no surprise that Steve Jobs (a creative Pisces) not only revolutionised the world with technology but labelled it with the 'I' branding, which boasts the Aquarian desire for 'individuality'. Have you ever heard of New Age music? In terms of music and culture, digital music such as electronic and techno-based rhythms (ruled by Aquarius) is also gaining popularity, especially in the electronic music dance scene. Technology, inventions, drones and robots are all inspired by this new age of critical thinking. But can these inventions do more harm than good? Absolutely, if the person is not in control of the betterment of him or herself and the world. Aquarius is based on hopes and wishes. The goal of this age is to look deeper at humanity, find its truth and create the ideal world that humans want to live in. It sounds ideal, but already more and more self-sustaining villages are forming.

The biggest lesson in this new age is to improve one's self to better the world. We need to learn how to balance logic with idealism. The ideal aspect of the Age of Aquarius is a true Utopia. The negative aspect of this age is ugly, messy and destructive. We, as Souls on this planet, have a role to play and we must live with awareness to make better choices for the world and ourselves. So, everything we are currently experiencing and noticing is based on the positive and negative qualities of Aquarius. The one thing the Age of Aquarius can learn from is the balanced thought processes from its sister air sign, Libra. The more balanced Aquarius gets, the more magical life will become.

More and more people in today's modern world of thousands of diseases need to learn to have a warm, personal and refreshing combination of logic, reason and clarity of the simple practical wisdom of the healers throughout the ages.

In the earliest dynasties of Egypt, they taught and wrote about the expansion and contraction principles behind all of existence. They named these two energy patterns Phi and Pi, which the Polymaths called the two transcendental (infinite) numbers.

They knew that the entire cosmos expands and contracts; that galaxies expand and contract; that planets in their orbit in solar systems expand and contract. Even our earth, every 40 to 60 years, goes into expansion, which is an elliptical orbit around the Sun, and the earth goes into global cooling or freezing. Then, 40 to 60 years later, it goes into a spherical orbit that heats the earth up/global warming. Even our atmosphere expands and contracts; ocean tides expand and contract; the winds even expand and contract. The seasons are based on expansion and contraction. Your body is based upon expansion and contraction. Your lungs expand and contract; the heart expands and contracts. Peristaltic action in the intestines is expansion and contraction. All of your muscles expand and contract. You can open your hand and you can close it into a fist. All of the cells, molecules and atoms work on expansion and contraction. The ancient healers taught there is only one disease and that is chaos at the atomic level, which creates chaos at the molecular level, which creates chaos at the cellular level. When enough cells are in chaos, you feel it as a discomfort, later called dis-ease or disease. No disease or discomfort was a mystery. They knew there are only two causes of atomic, molecular and cellular chaos.

Number 1: Toxicities … Number 2: Deficiencies

This creates magnified or depleted chaos in the balance of expansion and contraction energy forces in the body, today called physiological function of anatomical structures and organs. Today this energy movement is called inflammation (expansion) and anti-inflammation (contraction).

Inflammation and anti-inflammation is actually a critical part of the body's auto-genic system meaning: self-healing response. There are two types of inflammation/expansion: acute and chronic. Acute inflammation is an accident or a puncture, like stubbing your toe, breaking a bone, getting a sun burn, spraining an ankle, getting an insect bite, or cutting your hand. The injury site will become red, swollen and inflamed, and this acute inflammation is how the body heals.

Chronic inflammation is the problem in the world today. Chronic inflammation makes itself known through the symptoms and discomforts of illness and diseases that it causes. There is no doubt that chronic inflammation is at the root of most major health concerns.

Here are some of the diseases linked to chronic inflammation according to published medical journals:

Age-Related Macular Degeneration, Alzheimer's Disease, Arthritis, Autoimmune Diseases, Dozens of Cancers, Cardiovascular Disease, Chronic Kidney Disease, Depression, Type 1 and Type 2 Diabetes, Obesity, Parkinson's Disease and on and on into hundreds and hundreds of diseases.

Stop eating refined synthetic sugars and processed, manufactured fake foods; stop eating fast foods. These all create chronic inflammation. Poor sleep creates higher levels of inflammatory substances. Obesity creates high levels of chronic inflammation. Fat cells are produced to protect you from these toxic substances in the diet and personal care products. Stress and feeling fatigued and frazzled creates high levels of inflammation. Diet, what you eat and drink, can have huge effects on chronic inflammation.

Preventing and clearing chronic inflammation is the building block of healthy living. It's time to discover a proven and delicious diet and pleasurable lifestyle that is the Path of Health, Freedom from Diseases and Expanded Happiness. I call it the 'Balanced Expansion/Contraction' Diet. The BEC diet. The word diet comes of the word Deity, meaning Offerings (meals) and Tithes (snacks-1/10th of a meal), Sacraments (Sacred Ferments) to the body that are good.

Ancient Healers of Human Diseases…

Whole Plant Foods, Herbs, Flowers and the recorded Seven Principles of Health and Longevity played a huge role in Ancient Egyptian medicine, which was also shared with communal tribes on other continents. Proof comes from burial sites, tombs and underground temples where archaeologists have found extensive sets of healing documents and scrolls, including what today is called the Ebers Papyrus, the Edwin Smith Papyrus, the Hearst Papyrus, and the London Medical Papyrus, which contained the earliest documented awareness of discomforts in the body, now called symptoms, which today are diagnosed as diseases (originally meaning Dis-ease or Dis-comforts). The most famous plant - medicine 'encyclopaedia' is the Ebers Papyrus, a 110-page scroll that rolls out to be about 20 meters long.

Egyptians consumed raw red radishes, garlic and onions for endurance and to heal asthma and bronchial-pulmonary issues. Many of their herbs and plant foods were steeped in wine and used as oral medicine. These were natural herbs, fruits, vegetables, nuts seeds and grains that were untainted by fungicides, pesticides, herbicides, insecticides, or fluoridated water. The Egyptians documented use of myrrh, frankincense, fennel, cassia, thyme, juniper, aloe and many more. Fresh garlic cloves were peeled, mashed and macerated in a mixture of organic apple cider vinegar and water and used as a rinse for sore throats and toothaches.

The Goddess of Sweetness and Healing was called by some 'The Land of Milk and Honey'... Egyptians knew about the healing powers of milk (the juices of plants) and of honey. In fact, the first official recognition of the importance of honey dates back to the First Egyptian Dynasty and the 'Sealer of the Honey.' In Niuserre's Sun temple, bee-keepers are shown in hieroglyphics blowing smoke into hives as they are removing honeycombs. The honey was immediately jarred and sealed and could therefore be kept for years, and it was used for the production of medicines and ointments. They even used it as one of nature's protector inhibitors; today, it would be called nature's antibiotics. Even the milk of cows and goats, etc. is the juice made of grass and water. Today the milk or juice of plants is called herbal teas, organic coffees, organic wines, organic beers, etc.

The main land for bee-keeping was in Lower Egypt where there was extensive irrigation feeding thousands of flowering plants. The bee was chosen as a symbol for the country and the gods and angels were associated with the bee. One pharaoh's title was Bee King and his royal archers protected the bees like they were his holy temple. The temples were actually homes for the bees, in order to satisfy the desire of the gods. Canaan was called the 'Land of Milk and Honey' in the Hebrew tradition. Ambrosia was the drink of the gods and goddesses.

Egyptian methods of health and healing are some of the oldest ever documented. From the 33rd century BC until the Persian invasion in 525 BC, the Egyptian healers' – called the SWNWT – practices remained consistent in their highly advanced methods for the time. Homer even wrote in the Odyssey, 'In Egypt, the women and men are more skilled in healing than any of human kind,' and, 'The Egyptians were skilled in plant medicines and principles of health more than any other art.'

The Edwin Smith papyrus is, we are told, still being studied by pharmaceutical chemists, but in my experience of seeing ancient collections and then seeing today's modern version of the Edwin Smith Papyrus, which is viewed as a learning manual, I can see it has been rewritten to fit today's chemistry; it's not the alchemy of the genius of the past. The Ebers Papyrus is the largest record of ancient Egyptian medicine known today. The scroll contains some 700 remedies including empirical practice and observation. The papyrus actually contains a 'treatise

on the heart,' which recognizes the heart as the centre of the blood supply with vessels attached.

Even mental disorders, depression and dementia were detailed in one of the chapters. The Egyptians were treating intestinal disease and parasites, eye and skin problems, and even abscesses and tumours, as well as hundreds of other discomforts.

• Aloe vera was used to alleviate burns, ulcers, skin diseases and allergies, • Basil was written up as heart medicine, • Bayberry was prescribed for diarrhoea, ulcers and haemorrhoids, • Dill was recognised for laxative and diuretic properties, • Frankincense was used for throat and larynx infections and to stop bleeding and vomiting. • Garlic was given to the Hebrew slaves daily to give them vitality and strength for building the pyramids, • Licorice was utilised as a mild laxative, to expel phlegm, and to alleviate chest and respiratory problems, • Onion and citrus were taken to prevent colds and to address cardiovascular problems, • Parsley was prescribed as a diuretic, • Thyme was given as a pain reliever and turmeric for open wounds, • Cherries were used to heal bursitis, • Poppy was used to relieve insomnia, as an anaesthetic, and to deaden pain, • Coriander was taken as a tea for urinary complaints, including cystitis, • Pomegranate root was strained with water and drunk to address 'snakes of the belly' (tapeworms). The alkaloids contained in pomegranate paralysed the worms' nervous systems and they relinquished their hold

Disease and Natural Cures in Ancient Egypt...

Disease was not uncommon in Ancient Egypt. There were many skin afflictions and parasites from the Nile river waters. Worms and tuberculosis were common, sometimes transmitted from eating dead animals, especially pigs and cattle. Pneumonia struck people who breathed too much sand into the lungs during sand storms. But the Egyptian healing physicians took full advantage of the physics of nature, the natural resources all around them, in order to treat common ailments. Many of their methods are still very viable today and are considered part of holistic medicines.

Scholars have been able to translate the scrolls and appreciate what the Egyptians knew back then about Anatomy, Physiological Functions, Hygiene (the goddess Hygeia) and Healing. Those scrolls, without question, paved the way for modern medicine before the Cut, Burn and Poison put into place by the Pharmakeia (Greek for Poisons) Pharmaceutical, meaning poison makers.

The ancient healers never embraced chemical poisons (which create side effects) as remedies. 'Healthy comes of a Happy Heart' is Ancient Egyptian wisdom. Epicure meant: Pleasure of Health.

Among the thousands of different plant foods that Mother Nature and Father Sun provide us, they all contain every known nutritional component in varying amounts. For instance, citrus has the highest vitamin C, yet all plants have vitamin C. Every plant food has all 200,000 identifiable proteins and they are quick-delivery proteins to the cells of the body. This is why animals that only eat grass and other plants are the STRONGEST LAND ANIMALS on the earth. Gorillas are 99% fruitarian and are the strongest of all land animals. Most of today's fastest and strongest athletes are vegan and vegetarian.

We should try to eat only Organic Non-GMO Foods; they are not only the healthiest for people but are the healthiest for the planet also. Get them locally and in season so they are the freshest and at best quality. Seeing, Smelling, Tasting, and Touching Your Foods Activates the Brain and the Body's Entire Nerve System, Which Awakens the Cells to Uptake the Nutritional Delivery for Health, Healing and Happiness.

INSIGHT INTO DIS-EASE

THE MIND...

At the core of ALL of our behaviours is subconscious programming, the beliefs and behaviours passed down generationally and/or brought through at birth from past life experiences and the collective consciousness, along with the programming we have taken on ourselves via our perception of life and the indoctrination we have received from parents, teachers and other influential Beings during our younger years. It is said that from the moment of conception we have a mind that perceives life outside of the womb and forms beliefs surrounding this and that our subconscious programming, both negative and positive, is embedded deeply within the psyche by the time we are seven years old. Bit scary, huh?

The thing to realise here is that this belief system is created solely from the **perception** of the experiences that foetus and child endure and not necessarily the truth. From these beliefs we then create behaviours based on our particular belief system. We create these behaviours as a form of protection, as a survival mechanism, whilst we are young. As we grow older, however, the very same behaviours that once helped to protect us often keep us stuck in disempowering, inhibiting cycles that prevent us from achieving our goals and attracting the things we most desire in life such as love, abundance, trust, happiness, freedom, faith and peace. Our belief system works on a subconscious level 24 hrs a day, seven days a week, constantly attracting to us, via the Law of Attraction, people and experiences that affirm these beliefs. This is absolutely awesome when it comes to the positive, empowering beliefs we have created; yet the perception of a young child quite often gets things wrong and so when it comes to the negative core belief system, it's a completely different story! I believe THE most powerful thing we can do for our own healing and personal growth is to find out what our negative core belief system is and do the work necessary to change this programming...

So what is a negative core belief system?

A negative core belief system is the disempowering beliefs we have created via our perception of the world during childhood. For example, if a baby within the mother's womb perceives via the emotional vibrations it is experiencing time and time again that it is unwanted, there's a huge chance that baby will grow up believing at a cellular level, I am not wanted, I am not worthy of love, I am unlovable. Even if the mother grows to love the baby/child over time, if that belief has already been created by the foetus, the programming is embedded within the subconscious where it plays out forever more by sabotaging friendships, relationships and love in general due to the belief that, At a core level, I am unlovable. If a child spends her life watching her mother being mistreated or abused by men, one of two things may happen. Either she will perceive this as, Women are not worthy of love and respect, or something along those lines, or, alternatively, Men cause pain, men only hurt you, etc. Either way, this subconscious belief then sabotages her relationships by drawing to her, via the Law of Attraction, people and experiences that affirm the belief. If a male child watches this behaviour, he may perceive this as normal and therefore later in life recreate the same behavioural pattern of his father.

A scenario that I've witnessed time and time again as an emotional healing practitioner and have found absolutely fascinating, reassuring my belief that everything comes back to PERCEPTION, is the experience of a female who in younger years was sexually abused by a male. Depending on 'perception' she will create a belief around this. She may perceive this as 'being loved' and therefore have no real adverse effects from the experience or she may perceive herself as being to blame in some way, creating a belief along the lines of, *I deserve to be mistreated/abused, or, I'm undeserving of love, I'm unlovable,* etc. and going through life carrying a huge amount of shame regardless of the fact that she was a completely innocent victim. These negative core beliefs then attract to her scenarios that affirm her beliefs in the way of abusive relationships or she may become promiscuous at an early age, allowing men to use and abuse her because she believes subconsciously that she does not deserve any better than this. It all comes back to the core belief system and subconscious programming and, unfortunately, UNTIL we gain awareness, it's not something we have control over. This is why people attract the same types of experiences and people into their life over and over again until eventually they gain a degree of awareness about their programming and make change. The belief system in conjunction with the Law of Attraction is very powerful and works in all areas of life.

One way to discover a little about your belief system is to take a good hard look at life... What's happening in the finance department? What's happening in the area of love and relationships? Are you living and loving life or is every day a struggle? Are you living a victim mentality of, Poor me, it's not fair? Look for the patterns and then go deeper... Do you believe you are unlovable, that money is evil, I don't deserve, life is scary, people are dangerous, men/women just abuse you, life wasn't meant to be easy, I'm not good enough, not worthy, I have to be perfect, I have to be the best? And on and on it goes...

So why is this SO important? Our belief system/subconscious programming determines our behaviour and our underlying emotional state. For instance, as I delved into the core of my own chronic anxiety, I discovered a massive 'fear of the unknown' combined with a 'fear of what others thought', all of which led back to a negative core belief: If I am not perfect, I'm not good enough! Holy shite... No wonder I lived my life in a constant state of fight or flight for so many years! If being perfect was what I had to achieve in order to feel inner peace, it was never going to happen! Through reprogramming my mind, however, I now find peace in the belief that 'my imperfection is perfect' and the anxiety that held me prisoner to my own home for so many years no longer has that power over me. Don't get me wrong, I still have moments of feeling anxious and fearful like everybody else, but I now experience them in a normal, balanced way.

Emotions/Cellular Memories...

At the height of any powerful emotion, if we do not allow ourselves to fully express the feeling it becomes stored away in the body along with the memory accompanying it. Over time, these stored emotions become exhausting. Imagine trying to hold a beach ball under water, how exhausted your arm becomes holding it down, keeping it hidden beneath the surface. This is what it's like for the body. Supressed emotions are a huge burden for the body to lug around each day. The more we push them down the more burdensome they become until, eventually, we feel like we may explode or have a breakdown, depending on the particular emotions being supressed (hence my tantrum at the introduction of this book ... better out than in I say!). The stored cellular memory is triggered time and time again when something happening in life today subconsciously or consciously reminds us in some way of the initial stored experience.

This resurfacing of a stored emotion is shown quite obviously at times when we experience an 'extreme' reaction to something or someone and have awareness that our reaction was uncalled for. For instance, someone who has experienced a car accident and not found closure through expressing the emotion and finding forgiveness with all concerned may have a major panic attack at the slightest indication of another person braking in front of them, etc. These 'extreme' reactions are a sign that something is wrong; there is dis-ease on the energetic/emotional level that needs healing and if we intentionally or unintentionally ignore these signs, eventually the blocked cellular memory/emotion manifests into a stronger signal in the form of physical dis-ease in the body.

Our cells are constantly replacing themselves and as each new cell comes along to replace the old, the memory stored in that cell is passed on to the new cell where it continues to express itself when triggered, initially via strong emotional reactions, as mentioned, and then, if this is continually ignored and supressed, it is manifested physically. This might be as simple as an ache or pain to begin with as the body tries to gain our attention, manifesting into more serious dis-ease if we continue to ignore the body's warning signals. Dis-ease in any form is our teacher, it's our body's way of giving us a symptom in order to show us that there's something we need to look at on a deeper level. In fact, the word 'symptom' actually means a sign or signal of something deeper.

Now, this is where everything goes terribly wrong...

The body has done a brilliant job so far of trying to tell us that there's something deeper, something energetically, emotionally or subconsciously that is affecting us, a deeper emotional toxicity or physical toxicity that needs attention in order to bring back the balance. However, instead of listening to our body, taking notice of its intelligent warning signs and working with our innate wisdom to find the CAUSE of the symptom, we have been wrongly taught to trot off to the doctor and get a pill or medicine. What we haven't been taught, however, is that this only supresses the symptom, which, I will say again, is the body's way of showing us there is something wrong! The symptom goes away because the medication is designed to SUPRESS this, but it doesn't get rid of the initial problem; a pill can't make emotional or physical toxicity go away! Now the body has to look for another way of expressing a signal in order to get our attention and so more dis-ease and toxicity is created and our overall state of health deteriorates.

If, instead, we embraced the body's intelligence and the power of our own innate healing ability and took the time to go deeper, to find the CAUSE of the symptom by discovering the supressed memory/emotion/subconscious belief causing the physical or emotional manifestation, we would find closure and healing. When authentic forgiveness takes place, the cellular memory is released forever more and when the new cell comes along, there is no degenerative memory to pass on. This is why seemingly miraculous healings can occur in the time a particular organ or body part takes to renew its cells. Brandon Bays, the creator of the very powerful 'The Journey' emotional healing process, discovered this first-hand when she embarked upon her own journey of healing from a basketball-sized cancerous tumour of the uterus. By discovering the degenerative memory at the core of her tumour and doing the forgiveness work on this memory to bring absolute closure, combined with detoxifying the physical body, her cancer was completely gone in just 6 ½ weeks and has never returned!

Science has proven that our cells hold memories and this is shown clearly in case studies of donor recipients taking on the traits of their donors. Studies have shown recipients who were suddenly able to speak another language and recipients craving foods they would never previously have eaten and having memories of people they had never met, discovering, after research, that these were family or friends of their particular organ transplant donor.

See how amazing our bodies are! Pretty incredible, huh? As an emotional healing practitioner I've been privileged to witness many miraculous physical and emotional transformations for which emotional healing has been the catalyst.

RECIPE *the*
HEALING THE MIND...

Changing your negative core belief programming...

So how do we change our oftentimes detrimental negative belief system?

Well, you will be ecstatic to know that the recipe is really very simple. It does take a little time to reprogramme a belief system that has been working seven days a week, 24 hours a day our whole life! In fact, neuroscientists have studied the brain in relation to this and concluded that in some cases we are able to change a belief in as little as 30 days whilst other subconscious reprogramming can take up to 200 days. Either way, this is a very small timeframe when you consider the incredible, positive, life-changing effect that ridding yourself of unhealthy, negative core beliefs will have on your body and life. Commitment and determination are the keys to empowering yourself with a brand-spankin'-new, positive belief system...

OK, so let's start at the beginning...

To discover what your core belief system is, in particular your negative core beliefs, all you really have to do is take a good HONEST look at life... Start to monitor your thoughts, behaviours and emotions. Think about the patterns or cycles you know play out time and time again. See them in the light of what they really are, the body's symptoms of a deeper cause, the outward signs or manifestation of the Negative Core Belief System and/or blocked cellular memories.

1. Ask the people closest to you what cycles or patterns they see you playing out and what statements you say to you and others time and time again. Ask them to be completely honest—and promise them you won't get upset if they tell you something you don't want to hear! The only way to make change is to accept and embrace the truth, however hard it might be to hear. From here anything and everything is possible!

2. Find a quiet space and breathe deeply until your body feels soft and relaxed. If you feel tenseness in the body, direct your breath into this area and allow yourself to 'let go'. Once you're feeling relaxed, think about your relationships, both intimate and platonic, then notice how this makes you feel in your body. If you start to feel uneasy it's a sure sign there is some sort of emotional baggage/blockage here. Tune into this feeling and notice exactly what emotion is arising and who is popping into your mind or what pattern you see. What sort of people are you attracting into your life time and time again? How do they treat you and how does that make you feel? Pay attention to the words popping into your head, the belief you have about yourself or others. Honour yourself by giving yourself the time to delve deeper, remembering that this is possibly THE most powerful thing you can do to change your life.

3. Explore other areas of your life. Spend one session at a time on each aspect of your life or on the areas you feel are not positive or flowing the way you would like. Ask the Innate Wisdom of your body to show you what your negative core belief system is, remembering that you are more than just a physical body. Stay focused down into your body, out of the mind, and feel. Your body wants you to heal and will help you to do this if you can just stay out of those stories of the mind long enough to give it a chance. Remember, those stories were created most often by a younger you, the one that 'perceived' life to be a certain way when this was not necessarily the truth. As you 'feel' your emotions, be aware of the words or memories popping into your mind.

4. Each time you uncover a negative belief about yourself, about other people or about life in general, write it down so you have a basis to work from.

5. Now, this step is VERY IMPORTANT... Take the time to create a new counteracting, positive statement. For example, if your

belief is, I'm not good enough, create a statement such as, 'I am perfect just the way I am.'

6. Say this statement aloud over and over every day (it's said to be 300 times more powerful saying it aloud rather than just in your head) starting from the moment you open your eyes and finishing before you go to sleep at night. Bring emotion into it as if you already believe it. Now bring visualisation into the recipe. Your body doesn't know whether this is taking place in real life or in a visualisation; the chemical changes in your body/mind will be exactly the same. Write your statement down every day. See yourself living with this new truth; feel it and affirm it over and over. Remember, you are working with the Law of Attraction here. Words accompanied by emotion, accompanied by visualisation increase the power of the word a hundred fold! Remember, it only takes 30 days in some cases to really embed this new programming! Write the statement down every day so you are not just saying it but seeing it visually as well as feeling it.

Emotional Healing…

Healing emotional and physical dis-ease/degenerative blocked cellular memories.

The recipe to healing is very simple, however not always easy to accomplish alone, so it is an area that I would highly recommend seeking extra help with, especially when traumatic situations have been experienced in the past. Saying that, it can only assist your healing journey to allow yourself to feel the suppressed emotions; yet this can sometimes be frightening and when it comes to forgiveness, extra help will most likely be needed. Forgiveness is the key to true, authentic healing so I highly recommend finding a Journey Emotional Healing Practitioner to assist you with your process as they will have extra tools to help quieten the mind chatter and come to peaceful resolution.

If you would like to give it a go yourself, here's a simple emotional healing recipe based on 'The Journey'. For a more in-depth, step-by-step process I highly recommend Brandon Bays' book, The Journey.

When working to heal a strong reoccuring emotion or behaviour…

Sit quietly with your eyes closed and think for a moment about that emotion/behaviour. How does it make you feel?

Allow yourself to fully feel the emotion that rises in your body; focus on the area of the body in which you feel this the strongest and just stay in that emotion until it moves through the body like a wave on the ocean.

What's the feeling rising into this? Again, feel this emotion until it moves through. Be present, in the moment, eyes turned down into the body in order to keep you out of the mind. 'Feel'—ignore the chatter of the mind as this will tell you bullshit story after bullshit story, all based on your past programming, which you now know is not necessarily the truth. Stay focused in the body. Be aware of who or what memory pops into your mind during this emotional drop-through. Don't try to work it out with the mind; if nothing pops into your mind organically just stay with the emotional feelings until a memory, a vision or an innate knowing does come to mind.

Stay with the emotions, allowing yourself to express the feelings that have been supressed and stored away in the body. If you are completely present to these feelings and open to all that arises, eventually you will find yourself nearing 'TRUTH', the Source of who you really are beneath personality/ego. This is the level of the Soul and is often felt as true, authentic peace! For most, this feeling is completely new and it can be absolutely life-changing just to even glimpse this side of you…

Rest here, getting to know yourself as this Truth for a few minutes before moving on with the process.

*If you already have awareness regarding a certain person or experience that you hold un-forgiveness toward, or that you need to forgive you, allow yourself to be present to that memory and fully embrace the 'feeling' accompanying this, regardless how painful it may be. (What we resist persists; what we bring into the light of truth will be released from the body)

Keep your focus in the body and out of the stories of the mind and really allow yourself to fully experience the emotional feelings. Let yourself cry; let yourself be angry; let yourself feel the guilt, shame and hate; let your body release the burdensome weight of the emotions it's been storing as you watch, like the ebb and flow of an ocean, the emotions rising in waves and releasing from the body before another emotion arises. Remember, it's coming up for freedom. Your body wants you to heal! Move through the emotional drop-through until you reach the Source of who you are.

Continue now by visualising a campfire and inviting whoever popped into your mind as a memory, vision or innate knowing through the emotional drop-through. See yourself as the age you were in your memory with this person. Go into the body of the younger you and look out through their eyes, directly across the campfire, at the other person and express yourself to them. Let all of the unspoken words flow out of you—be honest; say it like it is; get everything off your chest! Speak it aloud; it's powerful for you to hear this with your own ears!

Once you have emptied out, hear their reply and continue the conversation back and forth as if they were right here with you until there's nothing more to say. Your mind doesn't know whether you do this in a visualisation or face-to-face; the chemical changes in your body will be exactly the same, so really be honest with yourself and the other person here.

Now go into their body in your visualisation and 'feel' what it was they were feeling emotionally when they behaved the way they did. What were they feeling or what subconscious programming were they playing out that they projected on to you? Allow yourself to really get a strong experience of their feelings. Often this is when we realise that the way we perceived something to be and the truth of the matter were two completely different scenarios. We see that they were doing the best they could with the resources they had at that time. This is not to say that their behaviour is OK, it's just allowing us to see/feel first-hand the truth, that it was never about us, it was them projecting out their own inner baggage and we had taken that personally and oftentimes made a core belief around that experience.

For example, in another's body we may 'feel' that they were feeling unloved, frightened, confused and distraught, which resulted in them running away, leaving you feeling abandoned and unloved. You may have perceived this as meaning you were unlovable and unworthy, resulting in the creation of a core belief: I don't deserve love, people I love leave me, I'm unlovable etc. You've then begun vibrating this belief out into the world unknowingly and via the Law of Attraction you have drawn to you experiences and people to affirm this belief. But now that you have experienced the truth within their body, you see that this was never the case after all. The truth was that person loved you; they just didn't know how to deal with their own inner turmoil.

Forgiveness often comes easily after allowing ourselves to express the emotions and words that have been held inside for so long and then feeling within the other person's body. If you find at this point you are still unable to forgive, this usually means there's more to say or feel. If you are still unable to forgive authentically, just forgive as much as you can at this time. Any forgiveness will assist your healing.

Take a moment now to give recognition to any negative core beliefs that may have arisen throughout your dialogue or emotional drop-through and write them down...

Now with a new understanding as to how and why this belief was created, make an affirmation to counteract this old programme, affirm this new belief to yourself over and over again every day to reprogramme the mind. Remember, it takes time to change subconscious programming and a negative core belief system that has been running on auto-pilot seven days a week, 24 hours a day oftentimes since birth; yet when we have the self-awareness to see the whole situation for the laughable truth of what it really is, we are automatically empowered with the information needed to take back our sovereignty, our free will to create a belief system based on OUR truth, rather than the beliefs of our parents and ancestors before them or the perception of a younger you.

Via conscious creation in the form of repetitive daily affirmations accompanied by the writing down of our new beliefs, whilst at the same time visualising and feeling emotionally what it would be like to be living from this new programme as if it were here right now, we are able to reprogramme the mind within as little as 30–200 days and via the Law of Attraction subconsciously draw to us the things that were previously inaccessible.

***Healing Dis-ease....** Begin by quietening the mind and feeling into the body. Ask the body to show you the deepest cellular memory that needs healing in order for a certain dis-ease to be healed and then feel into the body, where it is drawing your attention to. It's not always where we might expect, so just be open to where this may be. Now feel into how that area feels emotionally... Continue as above, dropping through the emotional layers, noticing any memories, visions or innate knowledge as to what cellular memory is at the very core. At the campfire, invite those who pop up through the process, empty out wholeheartedly, hear their reply from the level of 'Source', not the ego, and then continue as above with the conversation, feeling into the other person's body until you come to forgiveness.

Remember, getting rid of the emotional baggage by way of expressing the emotions will re-energise you. It's hard work for the body to carry around the burden of stored emotions, it's tiring! True, authentic forgiveness is the key to healing physically and emotionally. For many, this is not the easiest thing to do. I like to remind people that we offer forgiveness to another person in order to assist in our own healing. It's like saying, 'I love myself enough not to allow you to affect my health/healing any longer,' as the truth of the matter is your un-forgiveness is harming you more than the other person.

***For some people this basic processing will be enough, others will need a more in-depth process with a Journey Practitioner. Once again, I highly suggest working with a trained 'Journey' Practitioner if you have experienced very painful or traumatic situations in the past.**

Michelle McKoy Photography

PRACTICE WISHING FOR SELF-KINDNESS DAILY!
LET GO OF THE NEGATIVE; HANG ON TO THE POSITIVE!

The 'THREE INFINITIES' of the Ancient World were
GNOSIS, PRAXIS, INTELECHIS... To Know, To Do, To Be.

When You KNOW something, You can then Do it; When You DO that which you KNOW, You BECOME that which You DO. THERE IS NO END TO THAT WHICH YOU CAN KNOW AND DO AND BECOME! PRACTICE MAKES PERFECT!

Staring at Blossoms and Flowers and Trees or any Plants outdoors in the open air and Sunlight was how the Ancients Practiced 'Wishing for SAFETY, HAPPINESS, HEALTH, and EASE OF WELL-BEING
(No Stress)'.

These were taught as the Foundation for Living a Contented Life of Pleasure and Joy, which they taught is 'THE GREATEST GOOD'!
Daily looking at Plants outdoors and WISHING for these Foundational Qualities is Perfectly Healthy.

Some people are filled with Narcissism, which is characterised by Arrogance. Four Wishes builds a Transformative Power to 'Let Go of the Negative and Hold on to the Positive'.

STONE AND WOOD... When staring at the plant you choose, the ancients taught you should pick up a piece of Wood or Plant Stem and a Stone and hold one in each hand then put your hands over your Sternum, which is the way to 'Tune into your Heart Space'. ♡ Then, Silently or even Vocally, say to yourself, 'Be Safe, Be Happy, Be Healthy, Live with Ease/Peace.' As you do this, Imagine Yourself being Safe, Happy, Healthy, and at Ease. This Practice/Praxis is Creative and its Purpose is to Create Feelings of Kindness towards Yourself!

CowBoy Don Tolman 🤠

I Want Chocolate, I Want Star Wars... and I Want It Now!

...she sobbed, as the exhaustion that had been consistently ignored and pushed down for weeks on end, came flooding to the surface in a tidal wave of tears! With epiphany, I surrendered to the assault taking place within me, the internal tantrum of my Inner Child! I saw clearly how the mental exhaustion of constantly doing and giving, and the total lack of being and receiving, for not just days or weeks on end, but in fact months, had created such an energetic imbalance I was now sitting on the brink of burnout! I had been receiving warnings for weeks, messages from my Higher Self telling me 'body care, body care, rest and retreat, please don't ignore this warning, take notice without delay'.... but did I listen? No! There were things that needed to be done and my 'Pusher Self' was adamant that nobody could do them like I could.... so 'just keep going' she said, 'you will be ok' she said, 'we will stop and rest soon' she said... as she proudly crossed another job off the list with a smile of satisfaction, forcing down the tiredness and apathy that had risen to the surface in a warning from my Soul.

But today the 'Pusher Self' was stopped dead in her tracks, as my 'Inner Child' demanded in no uncertain terms that I love and nurture her and find balance before burn out! The profoundness of her existence had me conversing aloud... 'I'm so sorry, you are right, oh my gosh, I didn't realise!' And as if there was another person in the room, a voice replied, 'It's not fair, what about me, I want chocolate and I want Star Wars and I want it NOW!'

I remember the first time I met my 'Inner Child,' it was years ago during a Voice Dialogue session (based on Jungian psychology). I was absolutely blown away and even a little freaked out when I moved to a different chair and heard the voice of a young girl coming out of me. When my facilitator questioned how old I felt, I peeped 'little' and sat there with hands covering face, peeking out through my fingers, feeling extremely shy and anxious and unsure of whether to giggle or cry! It was one of the most bizarre things I have ever experienced and yet, so, so profound! On this day however, it was a ten-year-old throwing the tantrum, and although still a child energy, she was very strong willed and powerful!

So, here's the thing... we all have different sides of ourselves! Yes, as scary as it sounds, I guess you could say we are all a little bit schizophrenic. ☺ BUT don't panic, there is a difference! The majority of us have awareness of our different sides, or some of them at least! I like to explain it this way... we are eternal Beings (souls) having a human experience. Our body is our vehicle whilst we 'play the game of life' (if we are eternal, this must be a game, right?) So, imagine for a moment that your vehicle is a bus and that all passengers on that bus are the different sides of yourself. These 'selves' take it in turns of driving the bus! Some drive a lot, these are called 'Primary Selves', whilst others hardly get a look in at all! Some are excellent bus drivers and others are very, very scary, just like a learner driver!

Years of experience as a Voice Dialogue facilitator has given me the understanding that whenever a person gets to the point of burnout, breakdown or chronic fatigue etc. it is because one 'self' is driving the bus waaaay too much. What needs to take place in order to restore balance, is for the person to get in touch with an 'opposite self' to the 'bus driver'! For example, in my case on this occasion, my 'Pusher Self' had such a vice grip on the steering wheel, she wasn't giving it up for anyone! In fact, I would say she was driving the bus at least 90% of every day, resulting in mind overdrive to the point of sleep deprivation due to thoughts, ideas, lists, more lists and just a few more lists! Once I was made aware of this however, thanks to my Inner Child's tantrum, and found balance by kicking 'The Pusher' to the back of the bus, buckling my usual 'Primary Self' that knows how to relax, breathe and just BE into the driver's seat, not only did the feelings of sadness, overwhelm and exhaustion disappear, but the inner peace and positivity were restored almost instantly!

Without self-awareness we go through life on auto pilot, playing out the negative core belief programmes passed down generationally or created via perception and installed in the software of our central computer (brain)! Neuroscientists have discovered that the majority of these programmes/beliefs are embedded in the psyche by the time we are just 7 years old! This programming determines how we behave, treat others, what we believe, what we expect and accept, and the lower vibrational emotions that are triggered within us, oftentimes leading to destructive and even detrimental behaviour!

Self-awareness empowers us with choice. Without judgement we have the ability to look at whom we are and make a conscious decision to stay the same, or to instigate change. When we have the ability to access opposites via a process such as Voice Dialogue, change becomes so much quicker and easier. For instance, I have worked with depressed people that discover 'opposite sides' of themselves that do not feel the slightest bit depressed and in fact, have valuable wisdom as to what the person can do to balance, or even be rid of the 'depressed side'. People with chronic anxiety discover a 'self or selves' that are confident and peaceful. 'Control Freaks' are finally able to relax as they discover sides of themselves that feel safe enough to let go of control. 'Inner Critics' lose their power as 'self-loving, nurturing selves' take precedence over the steering wheel!

The time has come with the dawning of this new Age to take responsibility for our thoughts and actions. We have been doing the best we can on autopilot, with the resources we've had available, however, it's time now to step up and take positive action in order to re-programme our minds and let go of ALL lies, fears, illusions and false beliefs, stepping into our truest, most authentic 'selves'... our divine nature... returning home to the truth of whom we really are.

So, my question to you, Beautiful Godlings...WHO'S DRIVING YOUR BUS? ☺

Lynnie

INSIGHT INTO DIS-EASE

THE BODY...

'LET FOOD BE THY MEDICINE AND MEDICINE BE THY FOOD'... Hippocrates
'NATURE IS COMPLEX SO THAT WE DON'T HAVE TO BE'... Don Tolman

Our ancestors knew that there could be but seven disorders or dis-eases of the body simply because there are only seven major body systems. They knew that a SYMPTOM meant a sign or signal of something deeper and when the body gave us a symptom it was time to place focus on the body system and particular organ or body part at the core of that symptom, knowing with certainty that all they had to do in order to bring equilibrium back to the body was to embrace the brilliant intelligence of nature and its Doctrine of Signatures along with the seven principles of health that determine health and longevity. Our ancestors understood that every plant and wholefood created by nature was designed with a geometric presentation that corresponded to the geometric pattern of an organ/body part and to heal a particular organ they should eat the signature food for that organ, along with the other foods that support that particular body system. How cool is that? Nature truly is magnificent! For example, if there was a problem with the heart our ancestors knew that it was time to eat tomatoes and red capsicum along with the other foods that support the circulatory system. They knew that apples were the one food that assisted every single body system and, in fact, it was the job of the SWNWT (lady healers of Egypt) to supply every person in their community with an apple a day and each one of those people knew that it was their job to eat the apple in order to keep the doctor away—this is where the saying 'An apple a day keeps the doctor away' came from!

The SWNWT knew that, in order to be long lived and disease-free, we should eat a Ra food diet, Ra meaning Sun. They knew that by eating a wholefood diet of fruits and vegetables, nuts, seeds and legumes grown in the temperate zone a person was living in, in the season they naturally come forth and drinking/eating the milk, cheese, yoghurts and ferments made from the milks of all of the beasts that were put on Mother Earth, not for us to eat their flesh but to eat the grass grown via the energy of Ra and then provide us with the light/ pure intelligence and nutrition via their milk, the people would be getting the highest nutritional value from those foods and, in fact, the nutritional components would circulate in the blood for one whole year until that particular food came forth again the following year.

The lady healers knew that the body relied on the foods grown in the season in that particular temperate zone to maintain its highest capacity. They understood that foods grown in the summer months have a higher water content, such as melons, stone fruits etc., and that the higher water content actually affected the viscosity of the blood, keeping it thinner in order to keep the body cooler. On the other hand, the foods grown in the winter months, such as root vegetables, lentils and legumes, had the opposite affect due to their lower water content, allowing the blood viscosity to thicken and, in turn, keep the body warmer. The SWNWT knew that by eating wholefoods from Mother Nature's table and drinking pure water from the earth we would have everything we needed for the body to maintain ultimate health.

OK, so I know what you are thinking! **So, how do they get their protein?** Well, I have but one answer to that question... 'How do you think the most muscle-bound animals in the world such as elephants, gorillas and rhinos get their protein?' They are all vegan! The truth is that every plant and wholefood has all of the known proteins found within them in varying degrees. The idea that we need to eat flesh to gain protein is just one example of the mistruths we have been indoctrinated with over the years!

As with the spelling of many words, in later years the word Ra was changed in order to hide its true meaning from the masses (once again, this was when the almighty dollar became more important than the life of a human being). Ra became the word raw and the true meaning, importance and power of the 'sun' was lost forever more. These days, people are so scared to go out in the sun for fear of skin cancer. Our ancestors knew how important the sun was to our health and survival and that a few months each year spent getting a suntan would give our body enough stored vitamin D to last up to three years!

A Ra food diet is a predominately raw diet with the exception of legumes and foods grown under the ground, which can be cooked without losing their nutritional value. Did you know there are still cultures around the world today that live the way nature intended? They are long lived and dis-ease-free, still working in the fields and fathering children in their later years, living well into their 100s, unlike half of our society—sick, tired, overweight and living on medications in their 40s if not younger! It's crazy and ridiculous when the answer is right here and so very simple.

Unless we are living in pristine nature, toxins are everywhere. They are in the food we eat, in the air we breathe and in the water we drink, not to mention all of the processed and takeaway foods and drinks, personal care and cleaning products, etc. Our bodies were not designed to survive on processed foods and drinks. You only have to look at the ingredients of these foods to see a great portion of them are not food at all, they are numbers or, in other words, chemicals! Do you think that is the way nature intended us to eat? No wonder there is so much dis-ease in the world today! Most people are undernourished and full of toxicity, their bodies craving real food in the way of wholefoods and fresh water! From the day we are conceived we start taking in toxins. I recently read a study that confirmed the presence of over 200 different chemicals found in newborn baby placentas these days. How shocking is that? Stored toxins, undigested protein, chemical residues and heavy metals continue to accumulate in the body over our lifetime where they become a thick, sludgy, tar-like substance called plaque. This plaque coats the mucosal lining of the digestive tract and colon and, along with emotional toxicity, is at the core of dis-ease.

OK, SO WHO WANTS TO TALK SHIT? ☺

COLON CLEANSING…

Our ancestors, through observing nature, discovered internal cleansing. Watching the Ibis bird, they discovered that at the completion of eating it will wade out into water, fill its beak from the pond, and then, using its beak, will insert the water where the sun don't shine! Once the colon is filled with water the ibis will then squirt the contents out of its body. This observation resulted in the creation of a douche using leaves and bark to create a waterproof bag and a hollow reed as the tubing. Filling the bag with water then hanging this from a tree, our ancestors would carry out their own inner cleansing. They realised the importance of cleansing the inner body in relation to health and that, in fact, this was even more important than cleansing the outer body. Because of this they practiced a daily salt water flush to achieve the same purging result.

The colon, just like the hands and feet, is covered with reflex points that correspond to every organ and body part. When thick, black and sometimes hard plaque coats a particular area of the colon, not only does this stop absorption of necessary vitamins and minerals but it can also stop the related organ from functioning properly. There are some incredible testimonials from people who have carried out colon cleansing using herbs, enemas and fasting. Some people have regained their sight and hearing; others have miraculously healed dis-ease in their body, whilst others have fallen pregnant when previously they were unable to. One fascinating testimonial I have read was that of a lady who for many years had felt a hard lump in her abdomen. During her 28-day colon cleanse this was released along with the plaque it was embedded in. Intrigued, she fished this out of the toilet bowl and banged it against the side where it burst open into a mass of beautiful colours, discovering that the lump she had felt in her abdomen all of these years was, in fact, an accumulation of the crayons she had eaten as a child. Another testimonial that shows the importance of colon cleansing was that of a man who released a piece of this rope-like plaque and discovered, on investigation, that it was so hard he could not even cut it with a serrated knife! You can only imagine the effect this plaque would have had on the organ related to the area of the colon this had been released from! I myself have done several colon cleanses and one of the 28-day cleanses and I can guarantee that you will feel incredible at the completion of this. Your skin will become translucent, any rashes or acne/pimples will disappear, you will lose at least 10 kilos and more if you have it to lose and will feel so full of energy and vitality. It's a must for ultimate health.

REGULAR INTERNAL CLEANSING-

Now that your healing journey has had a massive kick-start with your colon cleanse, make inner cleansing in the way of enemas or salt water flushing an integral part of your life. Believe me; when you see and smell the filth that comes out of you, you WILL be inspired to continue!

Cowboy Don's Ancient Nutritional Colon Cleanse from the Seminole Indian Tribes of Florida

The chief of the Cherokee Indian tribe, that I taught Self-Care to, asked me to go to the Seminole Indians and teach them Self-Care also. It turned out that the Seminole Indian tribe already knew so much about nature's healing. This colon cleanse has been handed down through the Ages:

Tribal wisdom of a healthy nutritional Colon Cleanse.

The Recipe:
- 1 tsp of powdered Ginger
- 1 tsp of powdered Turmeric
- 2 cups of Warm Water ... stir and mix this up
- Add the mix to 1 quart/litre of fresh Orange juice and squeeze the juice of 1 Lemon into it
- 2 cups of Apple Juice
- 1 tsp of Sea Salt

Drink 1 tall glass of this in the morning first thing

Drink 2 tall glasses at noon

Drink 2 tall glasses at sundown

This isn't a fasting liquids day ... you can eat as well.

FASTING… THE FASTEST WAY TO HEAL THE BODY…

Water Fasting is the best way to maintain optimum health and the fastest way to heal the body of dis-ease, whether minor or major. If you have never water fasted before, a safe way to go into this would be to start with the 'Fast' option of raw foods for a few days, then move into the 'Faster' healing option of juice fasting for seven or more days, then finally the 'Fastest', being water fasting for seven to 10 days or more. Always break your fast with at least one day of eating fruit.

Please note, healing from serious disease is often painful, especially whilst water fasting, as your body is putting every last bit of its energy into breaking down those diseased cells, tumours, etc. If you are very ill, it is recommended to have support during your 'fast' rather fasting alone, and be sure to listen to your body.

Via observing nature and watching the behaviours of sick animals, our ancestors realised there was not a single animal on the face of this earth that would eat whilst sick, or if they did eat, it was simply to cause themselves to vomit up the contents of their stomach.

It was understood that the word FAST meant 'to make strong', and that whilst fasting, the body begins to release fat and gain protein by eating away dis-eased cells, tissues, tumours, etc. Our ancestors knew that just one day of water fasting would clear one whole year of toxicity from the body and that an extended water fast of 40 days would clear a whole lifetime of abuse and toxicity. They understood that there was not a single dis-ease that could outlive the body during water fasting and, therefore, this was the absolute fastest and most powerful remedy for healing dis-ease of any organ or body system. To assist the healing process during fasting, our ancestors knew to embrace the Angels of our Earthly Mother, AFEW—Air, Fire (Sun), Earth and Water. They would fast in nature for up to 40 days in order to gain the freshest of air, the purest of water for drinking and internal cleansing, the energy from the sun and the healing powers of the earth in the form of clay and mud to draw out toxicity and heal the body.

Our ancestors understood that the second fastest way to heal the body was to drink the waters (juices) of fruits and vegetables. Unlike water fasting, some digestion is necessary; therefore, it is a slightly slower way of healing.

They knew that the third fastest way to heal the body was to embrace a raw vegan diet until the body system in a state of dis-ease had restored balance. Whilst still a powerful way to detoxify the body, it is a slower process again, as energy is directed towards digesting for several hours after each meal.

So, there you have it, the FAST, FASTER AND FASTEST ways to heal the human body.

Born Again of The Waters

Each one of us lived in the salt waters of the womb for nine months!

The Ancient Healers of Mother Earth were all Women, and some of their most brilliant words of wisdom, were, 'Fasting on Water is how we can be Reborn into Higher states of Being.'

The King James version of the Bible says Moses fasted 40 days and 40 nights on water. Jesus is said to have been 'Baptized' in order to fulfil the required religious 'ritual' pushed onto the people to 'remove their sins'. Once he was dunked under water, it says, 'He left immediately and went into the woods where He fasted on water for 40 days and 40 nights in order to bring back The New and Living Way.' Even John the Revelator, in the book of John, fasted for 40 days and 40 nights on the Isle of Patmos. When you Fast on Water and even the Waters of Plants, you are being Reborn. It clears your sins away, meaning, dis-comforts, today called dis-eases, which are cleared out of your House/Temple/Library/Museum/Pyramid/TeoCali, all of these meaning Abode, where you Live, today called Your Body.

Fasting clears your mind and brightens your day. Mentally, physically and emotionally you are 'Reborn'. Religious Baptism is a symbolic ritual meaning, 'Fast and be Reborn and Made New'.

While Fasting, be flexible and 'practice focusing on joy and gratitude'. Write down things that are PLEASING to you and that you are THANKFUL for. Do what makes you happy. Take time to 'Smell the Roses'. Walk barefoot in nature. Think and Thank daily. Think of your children, your Mom, Dad, brothers, sisters and friends and thank them for being on Mother Earth and enjoying this lifetime's journey together.

Magus means LIGHT. Magi means those who embrace Light. Magic is the power of Light in the brain. I-magi-nation... Imagination is Everything! While Fasting Imagine what things you want to achieve by Fasting.

The Ancients taught; if you are alive in the Age of Aquarius and you are living a life of joy, kindness, gratitude, fasting and are vegan/vegetarian, you are in your 12th Lifetime on this earth, and you will return to Earth in your 13th Lifetime and join others in truest friendship of Polyamory Families of 13 Men and 13 Women. You will be given, by Lucifer, the knowledge hidden by Satan for your past 12 lifetimes, the Knowledge of Fasting and Plants on the Earth now that arrived on Solar Winds from other Planets in 2012 when all of the planets lined-up on the same side of Father Sun. This only happens once every 26,000 years, this is 13 x 2000 year Ages. Your Body will be a Living Temple of Immortality. No more Dirt Naps! Your Body will become your Space Ship to travel through Space and Time at the Speed of Thought. You and your Family Group will build other worlds and populate them and this is how Human Life has always been throughout eternity.

I found all of this in ancient collections that are now under lock and key, kept from the people by Governing/Religious Ruling Powers.

Cowboy Don

RECIPE *the*
HEALING THE PHYSICAL BODY...

Cowboy Don's Seven Principles of Health

Principle 1 | *Air*

Clean, Fresh, Moving Air Is the Key!

Although it´s easy enough for me to say, 'If you don´t have air, you will die,' it´s actually not just air that you need! It's electrified air that your body can actually use! Moving air is electrified air, the more it moves the more it becomes electrified. Conversely, stagnant air is electrically dead air and, at this point, it becomes useless to the body. There are documented cases of miners underground drilling into a new cavity and within minutes of checking it out, they suffocated. There was air passing in and out of their lungs; however, it was stale air that hadn´t moved since being trapped. You wouldn´t believe the number of people who work in offices without windows and wonder why they feel lethargic, fatigued and demotivated. This is because the air they are breathing is stale, dead, and lifeless.

We Are Electrical Beings By Nature…

We can hook ourselves up to an Electrocardiogram and we will output electricity just like a battery, so it goes without saying that the more electrical our inputs are, the more energy we will have. Air is the greatest source of electricity for human Beings. The more, fresh, moving air we breathe, the more energy we will have and the more our lung tubes will love us. They are getting a clean, fresh breath of Living Air. **Not only can we help our health and energy by ensuring that we immerse ourselves in electrified air, we can use our lungs and breathe in a way that´s for our own best benefit. Deeper, longer, slower breathing has the power to change our emotional state. By not allowing electrified air into the largest part of our lungs (the base), we can only access shallow breathing, which has a tendency to unbalance our emotions.** By using our entire lungs, deep breathing will stabilise feelings of depression, anger, stress, and hyperactivity and clean the plaque that will build up in the largest part of our lungs. Eventually that stuff has to come out! It´s a habit of mine to take five, deep, long, slow, breaths outside in the moving air when I wake in the morning to kick-start my day with the first principle of self-care and true health.

Here are the applications of self-care in relation to Air as I have said above and a couple of extras that are keys to dis-ease free, vibrant and healthy living.

1. Ensure you breathe fresh, moving air every day; the more the better.
2. Breathe deeply during the day. Make it a habit to take five full deep, slow, long breaths outside when you wake in the morning.
3. Keep your windows open in your house, in your office and in your car! Air that moves five meters purifies and electrifies itself.
4. Buy some plants!

Remember: Life is Movement! So, getting outside in the moving electrified air energises your body and cleans your skin and lung tubes! We are electrical Beings —all the trillions of cells that make up our physical bodies. Life is electric! Orgon Means Life—all life has electric properties. The ion channels in cell membranes cause a voltage difference across the membrane of nearly 1/10th of a volt. If you line up 20 neuron cells properly, you get about a 1.5 volt charge—enough to run a small flashlight! We react to electrical sun spots 93 million miles away, just like receivers of energy measurements do. Electric impulses can mend difficult-to-heal bones. Orgonic is the quality of adding life force.

A Glass Of Water Is Like Taking an Internal Shower!

Next to air, water is the substance we need most and give the least thought to. Water is a conductor of electrical current and it has an affinity with air so they electrify one another, which is perfect for our electrical bodies.

We are actually a fluid body. Our bodies are made up of 70% water. Our brain is 93% water and it needs to be rehydrated and refreshed every 24 hours. Our blood is 83% water. Our muscles are up to 75% water. Water is the liquid building block that makes up our body and it needs replacing often. It is the liquid systems (lymphatic, blood and cerebra-spinal) of the body that carry all nutrients to our cells and remove all toxins out of our tubes! It is these two functions that determine our health, energy and vitality. Mucosal cells throughout the body produce mucus in order to capture metabolic waste and toxic residues for body cleaning, protection and healing injuries. When the mucus is dehydrated, it becomes sticky and thick; this is the making of PLAQUE. Not only do we have to ensure that these liquids systems are clear and clean through drinking sufficient clean water, but we lose about 1.4 litres (that´s about six glasses of water) of water per day just through perspiration, respiration and urination. This gives you a starting point to how much clean, fresh water is necessary to stay in a healthy state. Most people suffer (and don´t realise it) from chronic dehydration. As a society we have lost the ability to distinguish thirst from dehydration. Instead of drinking water to cure our dry lips, mouths and throats, we use lip balms, mints and lifeless drinks, all of which add to the dehydration problem.

If you need another indicator to know whether or not you are drinking enough water, then the colour and odour of a person´s urine is the last straw. Urine in a dis-ease-free, healthy person is as clear as water and odourless. The reason for this is because the body is dis-ease-free and it doesn´t need to expel toxins. Here's some reasons to drink more water; if you have a headache, if you have the flu, if you have constipation, if you are chronically fatigued, If you are overweight, If you want youthful skin- a baby´s skin is twice as hydrated as an adult's skin.

As simple as it sounds, drinking enough water every day will clean your tubes, renew your fluid systems and create vitality where other fluids cannot. Here are a couple of key habits that will make a world of difference:

1. Drink a glass of water upon waking.
2. To electrify water the way nature does, pour water through the air—from one glass to another or from a slightly elevated height above the glass.
3. Drink one glass of water regularly during the day until your urine comes clear.
4. Eight glasses of water a day will be just enough for the average person.
5. If you get signs of dehydration, drink water first!

It Heals Everything Else on the Planet, Why Not You?

Sunshine as the third principle of self-care and true health is one of the greatest healers of lifestyle diseases. Our bodies, just like plants and other living organisms on this earth, require sunshine to grow, develop, repair and regenerate.

Contrary to Western medicine, sunlight will not kill you. On a standard Western diet (nutrient deficient), you will burn if you stay in the sunshine for too long, but just like Air and Water, with appropriate use, it is one of the essential parts of living a dis-ease-free and healthy life. As you embrace the seven principles of self-care and true health and you ease your way into sunlight, your skin will adapt and become more accepting of its healing powers and regeneration. By allowing our skin and body to receive the light from the sun, our skin creates a photo-electric response so our body can make vitamin D. This vitamin helps the entire bone structure of the body, the circulatory system, maintains normal heart rhythm and helps every cell in the body regulate its function better. The UV rays that create vitamin D in our body also help to control bacterial and viral overwhelm. Your body stores vitamin D in your liver for three to five years keeping you functioning and healthy every day. Deficiencies in vitamin D are widespread and the results are obvious. Prostate cancer is the number one male disease and with sufficient vitamin D from natural sunlight, very few men will ever experience prostate cancer.

With women, it´s breast cancer and osteoporosis. Both diseases are entirely preventable and sunlight is one of the major and most critical keys to this prevention.

In the same way that the majority of people are dehydrated, most people are mal-illuminated. In today´s modern society we are indoors in our office when the sun is out and we get home when the sun is going down. Not only that, our media teaches us to coat ourselves with sunscreen, which contains toxic chemicals, and to take extreme measures to avoid sunlight. This advice has turned out to be completely wrong. Natural sunlight is absolutely essential for good health and without it you are far more susceptible to cancer, depression, obesity, osteoporosis and many other diseases.

1. Get out in the sun! Get 20–30 minutes a day on as much of your skin's surface as possible.
2. Don´t use sunscreen - Get your sunshine between 9:00 and 11:00 a.m. in the morning or after 2:00 p.m. in the afternoon.
3. Don´t always use sunglasses, they can hurt your vision. Moderate! The sun is amazing for your eyes!

Principle 4 | *Movement*

Exercise Is Energy!
Regular movement or exercise is one of the healthiest and enlivening things you can do. When you walk, that cross-patterning movement strengthens, cleans and electrifies the entire body. Your tubes flex and contract assisting in the process of elimination.

The metabolic process of elimination through movement and perspiration helps cleanse you by 'venting'. **The true meaning of 'pre-venting' is the venting of your tubes of toxins in the body and this 'pre-vents' dis-ease and dis-comfort.** You vent 24 hours a day, and even more so when you move. When you breathe, you are venting and that venting is increased and maximised during exercise. The Immune and Lymphatic systems, which protect our bodies by cleaning our blood and cells of plaque, parasites, viruses, and bacteria are actually only stimulated by movement. Our circulatory system has a heart to pump the blood around the body whereas the only way to get this critical cleaning system online is to move and exercise. Walk, Run, Swim, Bike Ride, Do Yoga, Dance or even Sex works. Just make sure you do something and do it regularly to get your lymphatic system going daily. It can´t work without you!

'We confirm that there is irrefutable evidence of the effectiveness of regular physical activity in the primary and secondary prevention of several chronic diseases (e.g., cardiovascular disease, diabetes, cancer, hypertension, obesity, depression and osteoporosis) and premature death.'
- CANADIAN MEDICAL ASSOCIATION

Life is movement and stagnation, just like in the principles of Air and Water, leads to death. So, take note of my suggestions below:

> It´s all about integrating it into your life. If there´s a certain time of the day when you can do exercise, do it then. It will have massive rewards for the rest of your life. If you can only find the time to walk, walk in the sun for 20 minutes, out in the fresh air, and before you leave take a bottle of water so you can do one of the simplest but healthiest things you can do for yourself. It doesn´t have to be hard, go easy but go regularly. Five minutes is better than no minutes.

Principle 5 | *Wholefoods*

Wholefoods Are the Heal-thiest!
So, you might be asking, 'What are wholefoods?' Wholefoods are wholistic foods. They are complete foods, full of life, energy and electricity. Wholefoods from nature´s table are pure life-force and they assist in all bodily functions and over time and distance can allow the body to reach its highest mental and physical capacities.

Surprisingly, Most of the Healthiest Foods (Wholefoods) Are Familiar Foods... The Healthiest Foods are common ´everyday´ foods. These include the fruits, vegetables, wholegrains, nuts and seeds, as well as nut-seed-vegetable-and grain oils, herbs and spices that are familiar to most people. You don´t need rare superfoods to be healthy! Wholefoods are consumables that have not been highly processed, nor do they contain synthetic, artificial or irradiated ingredients. Wholefoods through their electrical frequency (nutrition) are the only foods that can be picked up by the electrical signal of the body and used for cleaning, healing and repair. Capsules, supplements or drugs as an enhancement to nutrition and health do not work and over time are very toxic. In fact, as they cannot be registered by the body, they clog up the system and if they contain toxic substances (that have side effects), they are actually doing more harm than good. Wholefoods provide all the nutritional requirements of the body and cannot be substituted.

'Supplements have not been found to reduce the risk of cancer and might even add to the problem.'
- NATIONAL INSTITUTE OF HEALTH SCIENCES

'There is always a best way of doing everything.'
- Ralph Waldo Emerson

Wholefoods are the best way to get nutrient density into the human body. Among the thousands of different wholefoods our world provides, each contains most of the nutrients our bodies need. Wholefoods are the Most Nutrient Dense Foods. Nutrient density is a measure of the amount of nutrients a food contains in comparison to the number of calories. Nutritional electrical frequency that the cells can recognise is what´s important, not calories... By eating wholefoods, you´ll get all the essential nutrients that you need for vibrant health, including vitamins, minerals, phytonutrients, essential fatty acids, enzymes, fibre and much more—without the empty calories. Foodless foods and lifeless drinks, which are full of empty calories, eventually lead to dis-ease and you only need to look around in Western society to see it.

'Diet is the greatest single factor in the epidemic of cancer.'
- PHYSICIAN COMMITTEE OF RESPONSIBLE MEDICINE

'Research shows that the majority of diseases we face in this country are preventable, not through new drugs or medical breakthroughs, but through simple lifestyle choices such as diet and exercise.'
- Dr. Leonard Smith, oncologist at UNIVERSITY OF FLORIDA GAINESVILLE

I don´t know how else to tell you, but wholefoods will change your life. They have changed so many lives of my friends, families of friends, clients, families of clients and the ripple effects go on and on, and I want the same for you. I understand that it´s not wise to just drop everything that you know and change. Long-lasting change comes from gradual conditioning. I´m going to share with you the things I know you can get started on now.

1. Look at your diet as it is now and be honest with yourself. Review and study the ingredients of the foods you are putting into your body and start questioning what dis-ease they may be contributing to.
2. Slowly and gradually try new wholefoods and meals and find ones that you love to eat and make them a part of your life.
3. Try shopping at the local market for the freshest alive foods available.
4. And finally, be gentle with yourself because your body will be addicted to so many chemicals that are in the standard Western diet; do it in baby steps.

Principle 6 | *Non Toxic and Loving Relationships*

Unconditional Love Heals the Heart and the Body!
'Self-care' is all about caring. Not just for you but for your loved ones, friends, and family and in fact the rest of the human race. The more you can be caring with others as well as being caring to yourself at the same time the more you create a relationship with others that is in harmony. When you care for others, you give them the opportunity to care for you.

Relationships include those in our personal life, our professional business arenas, socially with friends, with our partners, children, our pets, even with fellow motorists on the road. We are talking about any relationship with another, regardless of the length of time—be it a brief interlude or an association that spans decades. How we interact with others in a non-toxic way is an incredibly important part of our Seven Principles of Health. When you experience a sincere desire of your heart when in the company of another(s), you feel sincere gratitude and love. It is critical that we have loving relationships in our lives. If you honestly believe that just one person loves you, it builds the neuro-immune response in ways that it doesn´t build otherwise. That is how critical the belief that we are loved is to our own health and longevity. If you happen to love that same person back, there is a multiplying factor that comes into play. There is something about mutually shared feelings that enhance the dynamics of the entire spinal cerebral mass and nerves that run through us.

Non-Toxic and Loving Relationships are something we can experience physically through the neuro-chemistry of the brain working our emotional molecules so we experience it on an emotional level and spiritual level. **Toxic Relationships Lead to Stress and Stress Leads to Dis-Ease...** Uncontrollable negative emotions that come from toxic relationships are dangerous and damaging, especially to the neuro chemistry of the brain that develops emotional molecules. An emotional molecule of anger is just as real as a molecule of calcium or magnesium and your body has to deal with it as you feel it. If you feel anger, then it´s you who is hurting yourself even if another is making you feel this way. Do what you can to relate in a caring way to all your relationships even if others don´t want to. You will at least be looking after your health. Being aware and understanding of others who may not be as willing and able to openly discuss or show gratitude and love in relationships helps us develop a greater repertoire of solutions and ideas to offer and assist where we can. Take the time to focus on creating the type of relationships you want for your health.

1. Learn to love yourself more; be acknowledging of what other people could do for you that would make you feel good. Tell them so they can! And do the same for others!
2. Take time out if you feel overwhelmed by negative emotion. In that state we can only react and usually put our pain onto others.
3. And allow yourself to feel love more often with the people you can. They will love you for it.

Principle 7 | *Passion*

Ignite or Reignite Your Passion!
Passion is the driving force of our life. We all love doing the things we love and are passionate about. They make us happy and true happiness can re-enliven the body and give us energy we wouldn´t otherwise have.

Passionate people are healthy people. Those that do what they love are more vibrant and have more energy and are dis-ease-free more than those who aren´t. It is a documented fact that those who don´t have a passion or a will to live after they retire from work die within six months. Those who have a passion for something will stay around to live it. If you know in your heart you haven´t found it yet, be passionate about finding your passion. Not only will you love your life more, but you will be healthier while you are living it.

Passion Gives Us Purpose. Just like every cell in our body has a specific purpose, so do you. When a cell is able to live its purpose, which is to heal, clean and allow you to function at your highest capacities, you feel on top of the world, and when you live your passion and purpose, you allow your cells to as well! It´s a virtuous cycle of happiness and health. Don´t let another day go by before starting this cycle! Passion not only affects you, but it affects everyone around you. Not only will you affect your health but the health of your family and friends as well. And passion is contagious so it will be reflected right back at you. What can I say? There´s no time to lose; the world needs more passionate people:

1. Every day, take the time to become a little clearer on what you like and dislike. You are probably going to like the opposite of what you dislike!
2. When you find things that you are passionate about, do them, or at least set the date!

3. Write down your ideal day and every day work on making your day more like that one.
4. Believe that you can live a passion life. Declare how you want your life to be and affirm it every day. Declare you want a vibrant, healthy, passionate life!
5. Make time every day to take action towards your passion or find your passion because no one is going to get up in the morning and be more dedicated to your life than you are.

'It's Gold! An Apple A Day Keeps The Doctor Away!'

Records in ancient Egypt say, 'All Plants on This Earth Have Gold in Them.' Based on the nature of the plant, they have either Nanoparticle Gold, Colloidal Gold, or even Gold Flakes. ALL apples have high levels of gold.

Anciently, healers were called 'the Tolmans'. By cross-pollinating an apple with a pear, the Tolman's created an apple with the highest healing gold content. This apple is called the Tolman Sweet or Tolman Sweeting. In Ancient biblical writings, this apple was called, 'Adams Apple' and grew in the 'Garden of Eden'... today the Garden of Eden is called New Zealand.

Always eat the core and the seeds! Don't listen to pharma chemistry crap that says the core and seeds are poisonous, it's not true. I have eaten hundreds of apple cores and seeds over the last 60 years and the only effect they cause is Health. This is why the ancient wisdom said, 'An Apple a Day Keeps the Doctor Away!'

Nothing Like A Good OL' Cleanout

Cleaning out the clutter is so good for the Soul. When our home is clean and clutter free, we automatically feel more at peace internally! So, what if there was a way to feel an even deeper cleansing and inner peace? What if 'your body' was your only true house/home, wouldn't you want to keep it clean?

Our ancestors understood that our body was a living temple, the home or abode of our Soul/Spirit, and yet, as with so much of the brilliant ancient wisdom, this truth has long been forgotten. Most of us have no idea who we really are, how powerful we are, the perfect specimens of nature we are! We have no conscious connection with our Spirit, our Living Temple, or the food that sustains us. We defile our bodies with gluttony and the indulgence of toxic foods/drinks, as well as the harbouring of toxic emotions in the form of anger, guilt, shame, hatred etc. that eventually manifest into physical form. For many, there is absolutely no regard for the physical body until we are faced with a serious illness. Only then are we inspired to stop and take notice and make change ... and yet on the healing of this illness, all too quickly, so many go right back to their old ways until next time they are faced with a more serious or chronic dis-ease.

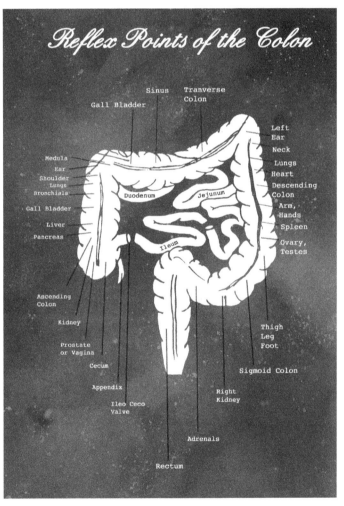

Reflex Points of the Colon

We spend so much time cleansing the outside of our body when, in truth, it's the inside that needs our attention. Studies have concluded that the majority of health problems and dis-ease actually begin in the digestive system. Have you ever had to clean out a blocked drain? Did you notice the slime and muck that coats the sides of the drainpipe? Well, I liken this muck to the toxic plaque that builds up on the walls of the digestive tract and colon, housing a multitude of sins such as chemical residue in the form of pharmaceutical and recreational drugs and alcohol, processed foods and drinks, vaccinations, etc., as well as heavy metals such as mercury and aluminium and the parasites that thrive in these toxic environments, laying up to 10 000 or so eggs every single day. Over our lifetime, this plaque can become thicker and thicker and more and more toxic, until eventually it plays havoc on the body, blocking tubes, inhibiting optimal organ function and supressing nutrition absorption ... eventually creating dis-ease.

As a facilitator of holistic healing retreats, I have come to the conclusion that a clean colon and digestive tract are imperative for optimal organ function and vibrant health and that colon cleansing should be (along with emotional cleansing) the starting point for any healing/health regime. Colonic irrigation and enemas will give you a good flush, and the ancient salt covenant, which entails drinking a litre of salt water each morning, will also purge the digestive tract and colon, yet most often it takes a little more than these healing practices to release the toxic tar like plaque and remove this from the body. Herbs and bentonite clay shakes are brilliant for this, and when you see and smell the toxic waste/plaque being released from your body, you will agree that this stuff is so much better out than in! I remember hearing Cowboy Don speak of a lady with stage 4 cancer discovering two cups of liquid mercury in the plaque released from her body during a colon cleanse! You can only imagine how detrimental this was to her health and how healing it was to remove this toxicity.

PROFOUND STORY IN SUMMARY...

Have you ever read a story that was so profound it actually changed life as you knew it? Well, I have! The book, called **Gaea Speaks, A Mother's Call,** is written by Cowboy Don and based on ancient scrolls, oral traditions and records left by cultures of the past that describe people hearing the earth speak to them. In fact, Indian legend says that corn was actually man-made, created when Gaea (Mother Earth) whispered wisdom into the ear of a young girl, telling her which grasses and grains to touch together in order to bring about this produce. Funnily enough, even to this day it is still called an 'ear of corn'. In this crazy-assed modern world, our heads are so full of meaningless chatter we rarely truly listen to another speak, let alone our Earth Mother! Here's a summary of the story that changed my life and is the basis for much of the ancient wisdom I now embrace on a daily basis...

At the base of a mountain, hundreds of people lay in agonising pain suffering the plague and other diseases. Gaea (Mother Earth) came to them in spirit form and explained the reason they were diseased and dying was because for so long they had impaired their bodies by eating and drinking foodless foods (processed), lifeless coloured drinks, drugs from the poison makers (medicines) and the decay of death (dead bodies of animals, fish and birds) until their bowels had become full of filth, parasites and worms.

She explained that fasting in nature for 7 days and 7 nights along with Mother's Angels of AFEW, Air, Fire (sun), Earth and Water, would clear this filth from their bodies, and if they had defiled their body for a long period of time they should fast for 7 x 7 days and 7 nights, breathing deeply the Angel of Air, bathing in and drinking the Angel of Water and when their body temples were filthier on the inside than the outside they should take a hollow reed grass and a gourd (enema bag) and use the Angel of Water to cleanse internally also. She explained that placing their bodies in the mud of the river would allow the Angel of Earth to take away the pain of aching and deformed limbs and at the completion of the work of the Angels of Air, Water and Earth, they should lay beneath the Angel of Fire and allow the sunshine to purify their bodies.

Gaea explained...'The Greatest Law, the law of our Earthly Mother says, thy shall not kill' (with the exception of preserving life that is innocent). She continued, 'kill neither man nor beast... dead food will kill you, living food will quicken you.' She explained that we should only eat what is in season and of the nature to withstand the heat, frost etc. 'Burned, rotten and frozen foods out of season will do the same to your body,' she taught. Gaea used the example of a farmer sewing cooked, frozen and rotten seed and when autumn came the fields were bare. On the other hand, the farmer who had sewn living seed reaped the rewards of an abundant yield of living fruits. 'Live by the fire of life (the sun) and prepare your foods in this way, eat nothing that a fire stronger than the sun has prepared, as the fire of death (cooking) will kill your food, body and emotions.' 'Eat only from Mother's Table—prepare and eat all the fruits of the trees and the grasses of the fields, the honey from bees and the raw and fermented milk of all the beasts that convert grasses to the Milk of Life.' 'All of these are fed and ripened by the Fire of Life (sun) and are gifts of the Earthly Mother for mental and emotional strength and protection from disease' she taught.

She explained... 'Make your daily bread from grains moistened by the Angel of Water; leave it from morning to evening beneath the Angel of Fire (sun) so that the germ of life will sprout in the grains, nuts and seeds.' 'Crush the grain/seeds to make thin wafers and put back in the sun from dawn until the sun is the highest in the sky, then turn over and leave until sunset so that the Fire of Life gives life to the grains and body.'
She taught that our lack of self-love, through the act of defiling our bodies, caused children 3 to 4 generations onward to suffer in genetic weaknesses, their bodies overcome by death and disease because we did not give them the opportunity of a strong, healthy body.

'Eat just 3 to 4 types of foods from the Table of the Earthly Mother at one time—don't be gluttonous by mixing all sorts together.' 'Cook not, except in times of cold and only things with little water content such as tubers grown under the ground' Gaea taught. She explained that there are foods grown beneath the ground (the basement) that support and enhance the feet to the navel, there are foods grown on the main floor which support and enhance the navel to the throat and there are foods that grow in the upper rooms, which enhance the throat to the crown, these being THE MOST SACRED FOODS OF ALL to the body temple.

'Never eat until fullness,' she explained.' 'Have no more than two meals per day and these should be no less in size than one closed hand and no bigger than two.' 'Eat your first meal when the sun is highest in the sky and second when the sun goes down.' 'Only eat produce in season and locally harvested, don't be deceived into eating foods from countries afar.' 'Eat slowly your first bite, breathe deeply while eating and chew until your food becomes water.' 'Don't eat if you are emotional as this will turn to poison in your body,' she explained.

'On the day of the week you were born, known as Sabbath, have nothing but air, sunshine and water.' 'Commit no whoredom by practicing fidelity to one, or poly-fidelity to a family.' 'Life moves, movement is life, if it is not moving it is dying.' 'Demand logic and reason from all the ideas, philosophy and every coach or teacher—stay free and independent' Gaea educated.

After 7 days and 7 nights of filth and stench leaving their bodies, most people were completely well. One man however, remained in terrible pain. Begging the Earth Mother for help, the people watched in amazement as Gaea took milk from a goat and placed it on the earth in front of him, allowing the Angel of Fire (Sun) to create vapours that rose up into his nose and mouth. The man writhed in pain and fever then fainted as a vile worm the length of his own body came out of his mouth towards the whitish vapours. At the riddance of this parasite, the man instantly became pain free and well.

Eternally grateful to the Earth Mother for teaching them the Laws of Nature and the healing power of her Angels of Air, Fire, Earth and Water, many people returned home, and those that had defiled their bodies for a long period of time stayed on, fasting for 7 x 7 days and nights, purifying their body and emotions.

For the full, original story, see
Gaea Speaks, A Mother's Call
www.thedontolman.com

INSIGHT INTO DIS-EASE

THE SPIRIT...

Quantum science has proven that EVERYTHING in the entire cosmos is energy. The Latin word for air is spirit... We are air-breathing Beings; therefore, we are 'Spirit Beings.'

Within our physical body we have seven major wheel-like, spinning vortex energy centres called chakras that align to the spinal column and the seven major endocrine glands, starting at the base of the spine and finishing at the crown of the head. These chakras are connected to the major glands and organs of our body and body systems. The chakras work by picking up and emanating out vital life force energy called Prana, so it is imperative they stay open and aligned. Each particular chakra resonates to the vibration of a particular colour and sound, just as the colours of wholefoods do!

The chakra system works hand in hand with the emotions and physical body. When we supress our emotions and hold on to un-forgiveness, not only is this exhausting but it affects the chakra that correlates to the organ holding these supressed emotions and, eventually, if not addressed, manifests into physical dis-ease. For example, someone holding anger will often suffer from liver issues, just as a person holding on to grief may suffer from lung or heart conditions. I recently worked with a lady who had suppressed resentment, hatred and anger for most of her 60+ year life. Accessing this emotion caused excruciating pain in her liver, but when the emotion had been released from the cells of her body, so too was the physical pain. Have you ever been into a building and walked out feeling depressed or felt drained after spending time with a particular person? What you are feeling is the emotional molecules picked up from another person by the chakras. If we are aware of this and take a moment to clear the chakras of this unwanted energy, the depressed feeling will disappear. Some people are very sensitive to energy and therefore find it quite difficult going into large shopping centres and similar places.

Every living thing including the earth itself is sustained by the rays of energy (light) that come from the sun; our body utilizes them daily without any conscious awareness on our behalf, another reason why the sun is so crucial to our health and vitality. There are seven different coloured energy light rays and these can be seen in the rainbow—red, orange, yellow, green, blue, indigo and violet. These seven colours are also the colours that resonate at the same vibrational frequency as the chakras. Each colour/vibration affects us differently and therefore it is another important aspect to consider on our healing or preventative journey. You will know yourself that some colours make you feel calm whilst others invigorate and energise. This stimulation is received by light from the sun entering our skin and eyes (get rid of those sunglasses!) and then travelling to the visual cortex of the brain where it stimulates glands such as the pituitary and their hormone secretions, which, in turn, affects our physical and emotional bodies.

Imbalances of our chakra system can be caused by persistent emotional toxicity in the form of negative thoughts and emotions as well as physical chemical toxicity and low-vibrational foods. It is said that an animal at the time of its slaughter retains the low-vibrational emotional molecules of fear and pain and therefore when you eat its flesh, you are receiving these emotional vibrations.

The three lower chakras starting at the base of the spine relate to the physical aspects such as the earth and grounding, whereas the upper chakras relate more to the spiritual aspect of our body/nature.

THE CHAKRA SYSTEM...

Root Chakra is located at the coccyx area of the spine and is associated with the colour **Red.**

Function:	Survival and instincts, gives vitality to the physical body.
Correlating Organs:	Muscular/skeletal system, kidneys, colon, legs, bones and spinal column.
Endocrine Gland:	Adrenals.
Balanced:	Feeling safe and confident.
Imbalanced:	We may suffer from fatigue, depression, obesity, anaemia, cold hands and feet, constipation, sciatic issues and frequent colds.
Day of the Week:	Sunday.
Planet:	Sun.
Archangel:	Michael.
Musical Note:	C.
Western Musical Scale:	Do.
Hum Sound:	Ma-Am-Mam.

Sacral Chakra is located below the navel and above the pubic bone and is the colour **Orange.**

Function:	Procreation, sexuality, vitality and the assimilation of food.
Correlating Organs:	Endocrine/reproductive system, spleen, womb, prostate, genitals and bladder.
Endocrine Gland:	Ovaries and testicles.
Balanced:	Feeling inspired and passionate about people and life.
Imbalanced:	We may suffer from lower back pain, bladder infections, impotence, prostate issues, polarity imbalances, eating disorders, sexuality and sensuality issues.
Day of the Week:	Monday.
Planet:	Moon.
Archangel:	Gabriel.
Musical Note:	D.
Western Musical Scale:	Re.
Hum Sound: M	e-Em-Mam.

is located between the breastbone and the navel and is the colour

Function:	Vitalises the sympathetic nervous system, digestion and the metabolism of emotions.
Correlating Organs:	Digestive/excretory system, pancreas, stomach, adrenals, liver, gallbladder, muscles and the nervous system.
Endocrine Gland:	Neuroendocrine glands of the pancreas.
Balanced:	Strong sense of intention and willpower.
Imbalanced:	We may suffer from diabetes, hepatitis, ulcers, jaundice, digestive problems, hypoglycaemia, constipation, colitis, poor memory, nervousness and other disorders of these glands and organs.
Day of the Week:	Tuesday.
Planet:	Mercury.
Archangel:	Sachiel.
Musical Note:	E.
Western Musical Scale:	Mi.
Hum Sound:	Mi-Im-Mim.

Heart Chakra is located in the centre of the chest and is associated with the colour **Green.**

Function:	To anchor the more physical aspect of us from the spiritual aspect, our Higher Self, serving as a bridge between body and spirit. It energizes the physical body and blood circulation.
Correlating Organs:	Immune system, heart, circulatory system, breasts, arms, hands and lungs.
Endocrine Gland:	Thymus gland.

Balanced:	Good self-control and loving relationships.
Imbalanced:	We may suffer from conditions such as lethargy, lung problems such as asthma, pneumonia and emphysema, high blood pressure or other chest or heart problems.
Day of the Week:	Wednesday.
Planet:	Mars.
Archangel:	Gassiel.
Musical Note:	F.
Western Musical Scale:	Fa.
Hum Sound:	Mo-Om-Mom.

Throat Chakra is located at the throat and is associated with the colour Sky Blue.

Function:	Verbal expression and communication.
Correlating Organs:	Respiratory system, hypothalamus, mouth and throat.
Endocrine Gland:	Thyroid and parathyroid glands.
Balanced:	Great health and communication.
Imbalanced:	We may suffer from conditions such as over or underactive thyroid, flu, swollen glands, fevers, tonsillitis, speech disorders, hyperactivity, hormonal problems and mood-swings, PMS, menopause.
Day of the Week:	Thursday.
Planet:	Jupiter.
Archangel:	amael.
Musical Note:	G.
Western Musical Scale:	So... Hum.
Sound:	Mhu-Hum-Mhun.

Third Eye Chakra is located between the eyebrows and is associated with the colour **Indigo**.

Function:	Intuition and Imagination, vitalises the lower brain (cerebellum), CNS and vision.
Correlating Organs:	Circulatory system, nose, ears and left eye, cerebellum/lower brain.
Endocrine Gland:	pituitary gland.
Balanced:	Intuitively in tune and have great imagination.
Imbalanced:	We may suffer from vision problems, coordination issues, headaches, earaches, migraines, depression, anxiety, paranoia, schizophrenia, sleep disorders and other conditions of the brain.
Day of the Week:	Friday.
Planet:	Venus.
Archangel:	Anael.
Musical Note:	A.
Western Musical Scale:	La.
Hum Sound:	Mu-Um-Mum.

Crown Chakra is located at the crown of the head and is associated with the colour **Violet**.

Function:	Our connection to the Divine and vitalizes the upper brain (cerebrum).
Correlating Organs:	Central nervous system, cerebral cortex, right eye and central nervous system.
Endocrine Gland:	Pineal gland.
Balanced:	Cooperative and a greater awareness of our spiritual origin.
Imbalanced:	We may experience depression, mental illness, confusion, senility, epilepsy, neuralgia, vein and blood vessel problems, rashes and eczema.
Day of the Week:	Saturday.
Planet:	Saturn.
Archangel:	Raphael.
Musical Note:	B.
Western Musical Scale:	Ti.
Sound:	Mwhy-Whym-Myhym.

RECIPE *the*
HEALING THE SPIRIT BODY...

Now that you have a basic awareness of the chakra system and the signs of imbalance within each of these energy vortexes, you can see the importance of maintaining harmony within this energy system. There are several ways to prevent imbalance as well as unblock challenged chakras. Lying in the sun and breath work are two of the most powerful ways to re-energize the body and soul.

Breathwork... We are Spirit Beings and, therefore, flooding the body with oxygen via breath work can be incredibly healing for the mind, body and spirit.

Sunshine... Lie in the sun and expose as much of your body as possible to the rays of light/energy. A healthy dose of sunshine is at least half an hour each day, but at times of depletion you may feel that you need much more; listen to your body!

Visualisation/Meditation... Everything in the cosmos is energy remember; this includes our thoughts and emotions. Intention is incredibly powerful... Whilst lying in the sun, focus on each individual chakra, one at a time, beginning at the base chakra and working your way up to the crown. Place your hands on the area that correlates to that particular chakra in order to receive your own healing vibrations. (Innately, we all have this ability. Think of when you hurt yourself or when your child is hurt, what's the first thing you do without any consideration? You place your hand on it, don't you? This is a natural instinct in all of us and now you know the reason why. See, you are a healer and you didn't even know it!) As you place focus on each chakra, visualise a beautiful golden light moving into it, clearing and re-energising. Send positive, loving affirmations to each individual energy centre as you see it return to a beautiful, balanced state.

- Affirmation for Base Chakra/Colour Red/Coccyx Area... I lovingly accept my body; I am safe; I trust in the process of life.
- Affirmation for Sacral Chakra/Colour Orange/Pubic Area... I embrace my sensuality and sexuality; I am a divine Goddess/God.
- Affirmation for Solar Plexus Chakra/Colour Yellow/Above Navel Area... I am a powerful creator; it is safe to be powerful.
- Affirmation for Heart Chakra/Colour Green/Heart Area... I am love; love conquers all; I feel love and compassion for myself and others.
- Affirmation for Throat Chakra/Colour Blue/Throat Area... I speak my truth with ease and grace.
- Affirmation for Third Eye Chakra/Colour Indigo/Between Eyes... I trust my inner guidance; I lovingly embrace my imagination and intuition.
- Affirmation for Crown Chakra/Colour Purple/Crown of Head... I am a Divine Being; I lovingly embrace my connection to Source.

Crystals/Gemstones- place gemstones of the same colour vibration upon each chakra centre for a few minutes to allow the energy to be absorbed.

Foods- eat foods of the same colour as the chakra that needs balancing in order to receive the energetic vibrations of that colour. To maintain balance of the chakras it's important to eat foods in all seven colours of the rainbow. Make yourself a bowl of salad or fruit salad with all seven of the colour vibrations and mindfully enjoy every single mouthful.

Bush Flower Essence/Aromatherapy- as with each colour, every individual essence or essential oil has its own particular smell/energy vibration that works in harmony with a particular chakra. This is yet another powerful way to regain energetic balance.

Sound- as you have seen, the different colours and smells have varying vibrations and so too does sound. Everything is energy vibrating at different resonances remember, and therefore each chakra has a sound that correlates to that particular colour/energy centre. Using instruments such as the Carillon Singling Bowl, Tibetan Singing Bowls, Gongs, Cymbals, Bells, Tuning Forks, Wind Chimes, Didgeridoos and Drums to create the different sound vibrations can assist in balancing the chakra system. Listen to the music you feel drawn to at any particular time, it will be the music you are requiring energetically.

Colour Therapy- just as the colour of foods affects our energy centres, so to do the colours we wear on our body in the way of clothing, the colours of the walls in our house, the sheets we sleep on, etc. When you feel a particular chakra needs clearing/balancing, use colour therapy to help bring back balance. Sleep on sheets and wear clothing that assist that particular chakra in resonating.

Removing Negative Energy... using a White Sage smudge stick, smoke your auric field and home environment. Whilst doing this, use the power of intention and visualisation to see bright white light filling your home, work environment and the inside and outside of your physical body. Eating wholefoods such as onions and garlic has been used throughout the ages for this purpose also.

THE DARK AND THE LIGHT... This is a topic not openly spoken about, yet, in my opinion, it should be! There is duality in every aspect of life, including the spiritual. When I began my healing work, around 15 years ago, I refused to believe there was a 'dark' side. I can tell you now with 100% certainty that there most definitely is! Within our auric field (energy field) negative energies and entities can attach and reside, causing havoc such as constant fearful thoughts, negative emotions, a very low vibrational feeling and even a run of constant bad luck as the negative vibration attracts to us people and experiences similar in vibration. This is another very important reason for regular clearing/cleansing of our energy centres. I am certainly no expert in this field, but I have friends who work in this area and have had my own first-hand experiences over the past 10 years with the 'dark side'. I know this sounds woo-woo and unbelievable to many, just as it was for me until it was shoved in my face, and therefore I want to share a real-life story with you...

Mother Earth Will Heal You... Air, Fire, Earth and Water... this is the ancient alchemy

Charlotte's Story

Charlotte had been through some very traumatic experiences in her young life and, not knowing how to deal with these, had been enticed by the lure of alcohol and drugs in her early teenage years. (This is said to weaken the auric field, making us susceptible to darker, lower vibrational energies/entities). At 14, she and some friends decided to have a séance during which she was told by a spirit that she would die before her 17th birthday. Of course, this petrified her at the time; and then, putting it out of her mind, she went about her life. With just days to go before her 17th birthday, Charlotte and her boyfriend were texting each other when he began receiving very messed-up, scrambled messages from her. When he questioned her about this, she had no idea what he was talking about; he re-read the messages she had sent him, which had somehow been sabotaged between her pushing the send button and him receiving the message. After the initial non-comprehensive text messages, he received a message that read, 'The majesty said NO, death is awaiting!' Petrified, this is when he rang me; Charlotte was totally oblivious to what was taking place.

The following day, Charlotte's boyfriend compared her mobile phone text register with his own, clearly witnessing the difference in what she had sent and what he had received. Meanwhile, I had managed to make contact with a spiritual healer who I'd heard on the grapevine had helped another friend of mine with a similar, yet somewhat scarier situation. The spiritual healer knew the instant he heard Charlotte's name that she had a 'negative entity' attached to her energy field, informing me that during the séance years earlier, she had had a curse put on her, and as it was nearing her 17th birthday, this was now coming into play. Via the phone, the healer went about his work clearing the 'entity', and at the exact moment this was taking place, Charlotte's body became covered in tingles as a wave of joy flooded over her. For a long time, she had struggled to get out of bed before 11:00 a.m., yet the following morning she reported waking bright and early, feeling vibrant, happy and full of energy, a feeling she had not experienced for a very long time. Inspired, she threw away the anti-depressants prescribed years earlier that she had been unable to ween herself off. Just like that, she stopped taking them and never touched them again! Charlotte's mum was ecstatic, noticing the transformation immediately, commenting how wonderful it was to have her 'old Charlotte' back.

The difference was incredible, and if I hadn't witnessed this with my own eyes, I'm not sure I would have believed it. I think of this experience as such a blessing, a true wake-up call to the importance of clearing/cleansing our energy centres regularly. Unfortunately, I lost touch with the spiritual healer after a while, but one thing he told me that will forever be embedded in my mind was how he visited a mental home one day and discovered that up to 85% of the people admitted had 'negative entities' attached to them. This begs the question in my mind, were/are these people really mentally ill?

––––––––––––––––

I've told you this story not to make you fearful, but in fact the opposite! To empower you by making you aware of how important it is to incorporate the spiritual aspect of ourselves into health and well-being. Cleansing the chakras regularly will ensure a strong, vibrant energy field, free of negative energy and entities, and will assist you in remaining healthy, both emotionally and physically.

Love is

Love is a glistening ocean of a trillion sparkling diamonds as the sun kisses it goodnight and sinks beneath the deep blue

The dew that quenches the thirst of a single blade of grass then rolls off in an abandoned droplet to the parched earth below

Love is the soul of a beautiful Balinese woman, fulfilled by her faith and a handful of rice

The same woman that has everything her heart desires as she holds her child to her breast

Love is the knowledge that freedom sits within our heart, freedom from the anxiety and fear that rules over our Western world

Where the ego dictates, manipulates and punishes in unbearable extremes, stripping its victims of any thread of self-love they may have dared to invest in

Love is the forgiveness of self and others, the doorway to bliss, the unshackling of chains that keep us slaves to our own physicality

Love is the ability to go within, to listen to our heart and soul and have the faith and courage to take steps to follow that guidance

Allow the heart to rule over the ego mind and love will surely be waiting at the end of that beautiful rainbow.

Lynnie

WALKING THE RAINBOW BRIDGE TO FIND 'YOUR BODY' IS THE POT OF GOLD!

HISTORY BEHIND THE RAINBOW BRIDGE ...

Let's just cut to the chase of the message of over 100 ancient scrolls and the saying that 'At the end of the rainbow is a pot of gold'...

Easter was a festival of, 'Spring House Cleaning, for Renewal, Rebirth of one's Body, as well as finding Joy and Pleasure in all things. The Spring Equinox in the northern countries, in today's messed-up solar calendars of measuring time instead of the ancient Lunar measures of the Sun, Moon and Stars (the 'trinity' symbolised by the Shamrock and the Cross) is at mid-point in time on March 20th or 21st, and represents living one's life at the Brightness of the Sun. This was done by performing ordinances (not rituals) of Living Temple Work, today understood as Fasting on Water, or Fasting on the Blood of Jesus, today called Blood of Juices (hence wine as a religious sacrament or Holy Waters), and or **Walking the Rainbow Bridge** by eating the seven colours of the Rainbow from 40 days prior to Easter (today called Christian Lent), which anciently always fell on April 6th. What we know as April 6th (Eastra) was always the end of the 40 days of 'strengthening one's body' in a group celebration of Eastra/Easter or Intimate Pleasures Festival.

East is a word with a history of being one of the four principal coordinates of direction, North, East, West, South (N.E.W.S.). The word News means the four directions and was symbolised by the cross, or + (plus) sign. East originally meant Joy of Light. The Sun, being a star that comes up in the east, was the Eastern Star, later the Eastar, then Easter. Easter celebration was based upon the Lunar Calendar and was 13 days after a Feast of Love Orgy/Orgie celebration, today called St. Patrick's Day, wherein people wore 'blue', meaning 'true blue' or 'Honest and True'. They hunted for and picked the trifoliate plant they called 'seamrog' (later shamrock) because of its three leaves and yellow flower that you could stare at and then project the colour blue onto white rocks or white clouds in the blue sky. Even the monk, (later called St. Patrick) taught the colour of this time of year was yellow. Later Christian groups wore green, for the leaves not the blossom. All of today's Christian Holidays were originally Pagan meaning gardeners or country dwellers) festivals, celebrations of gathering for play and joy and happiness.

Estra was the name of the Norse/Celtic Goddess (feminine power) of Fertility. Today's Easter Egg hunt, was the individual search of a woman looking for a man who had the qualities mentally, physically and emotionally (personality) she wanted her soon-to-be-pregnancy-of-a-child to have. The Easter Bunnies were a symbol of 'Reproductive Energy'. Anciently they saw that bunnies had more sex than any animal they had ever observed. The Goddess Estra (Sexual, Sensual, Pleasure Energy) Celebration Festivals anciently were incredible healing gatherings. Later the Goddess Estra's Fertility celebrations were renamed Easter. The Egg symbolised 'The Return to Life after Death'.

The colours of the eggs meant specific things such as the following:

Red - is probably the oldest symbolic colour, it represents life-giving blood and also passion, vitality, enthusiasm, security, love, joy, and the 'hope of becoming pregnant', to be a mother and a father. It is the light with the longest wavelength.

Orange - is a combination of yellow and red. It is a dynamic colour representing creativity, practicality, playfulness as well as equilibrium or control.

Yellow - symbolised the sun, moon and stars, which they used agriculturally to know when to plant and when to harvest. It is the colour of sunshine itself and represents clarity of thought, wisdom, orderliness, energy and creative genius, as well as fire, joy, cheerfulness, happiness, freshness, hope, positivity, optimism, enlightenment, remembrance, intellect, honour and loyalty. On the other hand, yellow also represents cowardice. People were called yellow bellies because they wouldn't kill animals or people. Yellow protects you from EMF radiation—proven by Richard Tolman and Einstein.

Green - represented 'new to life', safety, 'to move forward'. This is the middle colour of the rainbow and denotes fertility, growth, balance, health and wealth.

Blue - represented blue skies, the 'spirit of life'... today called 'Air'. True Blue meant a 'Pure Heart'. The sky and the wide oceans are blue; hence it has been associated with spirituality and divinity. Spiritually, it signifies the Healing Power of God and represents biblically the Word of God. Blue is the third primary colour and the fifth colour of the rainbow. Blue is calming—it makes us think of good health and the unknown.

Indigo - is mystical and it bridges the gap between finite and infinite. Indigo-coloured gem stones are often used for spiritual attainment, psychic abilities, self-awareness and enhancement of intuition. Indigo is sedating.

Violet - is considered the highest element of spirituality. It can ignite one's imagination and be an inspiration to artists. Dark tones of violet are associated with sorrow. Deeper shades of violet or purple denote high spiritual mastery. It is the last colour of the rainbow and is a mix of red and blue.

White - Signified purity, birth, 'higher light', rejoicing, and virginity.

Many cultures of the past made eggs out of dark chocolate and found flowers that represented the rainbow colours to pick and stick into the eggs. Eating the egg, including flower petals, would deliver the emotional energies of the rainbow spectrum.

In nature, in the northern hemisphere, all plants return in ever-reviving vegetation in the spring. Most of the animals choose this time to get pregnant in order to give birth to their young before winter sets in. All of this was a celebration of Returning to Life ... a renewal.

RAINBOW FOODS

Red Fruits and Vegetables:
Beets, Blood Oranges, Cherries, Cranberries, Guava, Papaya, Pink grapefruit, Pink/Red Grapefruit, Pomegranates, Radicchio,

Radishes, Raspberries, Red Apples, Red Bell Peppers, Red Chili Peppers, Red Grapes, Red Onions, Red Pears, Red Peppers, Red Potatoes, Rhubarb, Strawberries, Tomatoes, and Watermelon.

Yellow and Orange Fruits and Vegetables:
Apricots, Butternut Squash, Cantaloupe, Cape Gooseberries, Carrots, Golden Kiwifruit, Grapefruit, Lemon, Mangoes, Nectarines, Oranges, Papayas, Peaches, Persimmons, Pineapples, Pumpkin, Rutabagas, Sweet Corn, Sweet Potatoes, Tangerines, Yellow Apples, Yellow Beets, Yellow Figs, Yellow Pears, Yellow Peppers, Yellow Potatoes, Yellow Summer Squash, Yellow Tomatoes, Yellow Watermelon, and Yellow Winter Squash.

Green Fruits and Vegetables:
Artichokes, Arugula, Asparagus, Avocados, Broccoflower, Broccoli, Broccoli Rabe, Brussels Sprouts, Celery, Chayote Squash, Chinese Cabbage, Cucumbers, Endive, Green Apples, Green Beans, Green Cabbage, Green Grapes, Green Onion, Green Pears, Green Peppers, Honeydew, Kiwifruit, Leafy Greens, Leeks, Lettuce, Limes, Okra, Peas, Snow Peas, Spinach, Sugar Snap Peas, Watercress, and Zucchini.

Blue and Purple Fruits and Vegetables:
Blackcurrants, Black Salsify, Blackberries, Blueberries, Dried Plums, Eggplant, Elderberries, Grapes, Plums, Pomegranates, Prunes, Purple Belgian Endive, Purple Potatoes, Purple Asparagus, Purple Cabbage, Purple Carrots, Purple Figs, Purple Grapes, Purple Peppers, and Raisins.

White Fruits and Vegetables:
Bananas, Brown Pears, Cauliflower, Dates, Garlic, Ginger, Jerusalem Artichoke, Jicama, Kohlrabi, Mushrooms, Onions, Parsnips, Potatoes, Shallots, Turnips, White Corn, White Nectarines, and White Peaches.

PLANT VITAMINS & MINERALS

Plants- **are the workers of light and life, they activate consciousness, awareness and establish speech and communication of all life form. Plants put out flavour, fragrances, sights, tastes, textures and sounds.**

Vitamin A... apricot, blackberry, logan berry, mango, nectarine, olives, paw paw, peach, pear, rockmelon, beans, broccoli, carrot, celery, chinese spinach, chilli, lettuce, pumpkin, squash, sweet potato, taro, watercress, coriander, dill, rosemary, mint, sage, thyme.

Vitamin B... B6-avocado, B1,2-blackberry, B1,2,3- coconut, B6-custard apple, B5-grapefruit, B6-lemon, B1,2-loganberry, B-pomegranate, B2,3-rosella, B6-broccoflower, B1,2,6,9-capsicum, B1-ginger, B1,2,3-kale, B12-mushroom, B1,2,3-snowpeas, coriander. B12- eggs, fermented dairy, nutrional yeast, seaweed. Eat fruit- in the first 3 feet of small intestine, during digestion, B12 forms. Grains are the highest concentration of B vitamins.

Vitamin C... red and green apples, apricot, cherry, cumquat, custard apple, fig, red and green grapes, grapefruit, honeydew, kiwifruit, lemon, lime, lychee, mandarin, mango, nectarine, orange, passionfruit, paw paw, peach, pear, persimmon, pineapple, pomegranate, raspberry, rockmelon, rosella, strawberry, tamarillo, tangelo, watermelon, starfruit, dragonfruit, rambutan, quince, artichoke, asparagus, beans, broccoflower, broccoli, Brussels sprouts, cabbage, capsicum, cauliflower, celeraic, chinese cabbage, chilli, choco,cucumber, endive, fennel, leek, daikon, okra, onion, parsnip, peas, potato, pumpkin, radish, rhubarb, silverbeet, snowpeas, spinach, sprouts, squash, corn, sweet potato, taro, tomato, turnip, watercress, witlof, zuchini, basil, coriander, parsley, dill, rosemary, mint, sage, thyme.

Vitamin D... mushrooms placed in the sunshine for two or more hours prior to eating.

Vitamin E... almonds, avocado, legumes, sunflowerseeds, safflower and wheatgerm oil, hazelnuts, peanuts, Brazil nuts, olives in salt brine, spinach, papaya, mustard greens, swess chard, blueberries, organic corn, pinenuts, avocados, turnip greens, apricots, papaya, chard, kale, broccoli, spinach, wholegrains, sunflower seeds, coconut and coconut milk/water, oils such as sunflower and wheatgerm oils, artichoke, asparagus,broccoli, capsicum, sweet potato, tomato.

Vitamin K... the best source comes from breast milk colostrum.

High Magnesium... cocao, wholegrains, spinach and dark leafy greens, almonds, quinoa, black beans, cashews, edamame, peanuts, dates, pepitas, sesame seeds, sunflower seeds, flax seeds, Brazil nuts, pumpkin, sunflower, almonds, all seeds, beans, legumes, wild rice, dried fruit, parsley.

High Calcium... broccoli, oranges, rhubarb, tangerines, apricots, kiwifruit, medjool dates, figs, plums, prunes, soybeans, edamame, kale, celery, collard, broccoli, kelp, spinach, leafy greens, loganberry, rosella, dragonfruit, celery, onion, parsley, organic yoghurt, cheeses, milk.

High Zinc... all nuts including almonds and cashews, beans, cheese, chickpeas, eggs, fruit, milk, peanuts, yoghurt.

High Iron... lentils, edamame, beetroot, soybeans, tofu, tempeh, lima beans, quinoa, brown rice, oatmeal, pumpkin, squash, pine, pistachio, sunflower, cashews, un-hulled sesame, spinach, tomatoes, organic tomato sauce, Swiss chard, collard greens, date, loganberry, rosella, leek, lettuce, watercress, parsley, blackstrap molasses, prune juice, and dried prunes, organic dark chocolate, free-range organic eggs, fresh ground peanut butter. (Have a citrus juice with these foods to speed up the iron delivery!)

High Phosphorous... loganberry, dragonfruit, celery, corn, sunflower seeds, chia seeds, sesame seeds, watermelon seeds, flaxseeds, parmesan, goat cheese, nonfat mozzarella, Gruyère and Swiss cheese, pine nuts, almonds, cashews, pistachios, edamame, tofu.

High Antioxidant... organic dark chocolate, blueberries, goji berries, raspberries, strawberries, cranberries, pomegranate, dragonfruit, kale, celery, cherries, leafy greens, red cabbage, beetroot, beans, spinach, sauerkraut , seaweed, avocado, bananas, citurs such as lemon.

High Folic Acid... avocado, strawberry, watermelon, beetroot, broccoflower, cauliflower, chinese spinach, endive, mushroom, okra, parsnip, peas, silverbeet, snowpeas, spinach, corn, sweet potato.
High Potassium... apple red and green, avocado, banana, cherry, custard apple, grapefruit, honeydew, kiwifruit, olives, paw paw, pineapple, plum, pomegranate, quince, capsicum, cauliflower, celery, endive, sweet potato.

High Fibre... red and green apple, apricot, banana, cherry, cumquat, custard apple, date, fig, grapes, grapefruit, kiwifruit, lemon, lychee, mandarin, mango, potassium, passionfruit, paw paw, plum, raspberry, strawberry, tamarillo, tangelo, mangosteen, rambutan, quince, beans, beetroot, cabbage, carrot, celery, chinese cabbage, Chinese spinach, choco, cucumber, eggplant, garlic, ginger, kale, leek, diakon, okra, parsnip, peas, potato, pumpkin, rhubarb, silverbeet, snowpeas, spinach, witlof, sprouts, corn, sweet potato.

High Bromelain... pineapple, banana, Brazil nuts. (Lower cortisol levels by eating foods high in bromelain daily—one cup of pineapple, ½ cup Brazil nuts and one or two bananas.)

High Niacin... mushroom, onion, watercress.

Good Source Riboflavin... mushroom, watercress.

Good Source Thiamine... artichoke, peas, watercress.

Good Source Sodium... celery.

Good Source Pectin... apples, peaches, oranges, tomatoes, grapefruit, apricots and pith of capsicum.

TO LOWER CORTISOL LEVELS... Daily one cup of pineapple, ½ cup Brazil nuts and one or two bananas

NATURES CHELATOR TO RID EXCESS IRON: all colours of cabbage including fermented cabbage and sauerkraut.

PLANTS/FOODS THAT KILL VIRUSES- onions, garlic, apple cider vinegar, honey.

Plants, Plants, Glorious Plants...
Fruit- to enliven... Vegetable- to strengthen... Nut- nux or light... Seeds- source of all that is Grains- fuel of grasses which fruit is united with its seed as food.

BEGIN HEALING FROM DIS-EASE AND DIS-COMFORT TODAY 'NATURE'S WAY'

BODY... Discover the signature foods that, during digestion, target their corresponding anatomical site, supporting the healing of that body organ/part whilst assisting and enhancing the body as a whole. Use wholefoods to assist in the building of positive emotions and the releasing of stored negative emotional molecules AND discover Cowboy Don Tolman's healing protocols for each particular dis-ease or dis-comfort for all body systems.

MIND... Discover the likely negative core belief and/or emotional blockages at the core of physical dis-ease.

SPIRIT... Discover the energy centre (chakra) that is in need of balancing/cleansing.

BE YOUR OWN HEALER... HOW TO USE THIS BOOK...

After reading the information at the front of the book, turn to the particular organ of concern or dis-ease in the Body System/ Epicure section...

1. Look at the Signature Food and other foods that enhance and support the healing of the particular organ and body system and begin to base your diet around these foods. Remember, all whole foods are beneficial to every single cell, system and organ of the body, so it's not about cutting out, but instead, making sure to include the healing foods for that particular organ/system and especially the Signature Foods. Use 'The Recipe' to heal the physical body in conjunction with this. If dealing with a particular dis-ease, take note of Don's step by step epicure.

2. Look at the emotional (psychosomatic) reasons that are most often at the core of physical dis-ease of the particular organ. Ring any bells? What feelings are rising to the surface as you contemplate this? Allow yourself to fully feel the emotions and continue by carrying out 'The Recipe' for emotional healing in order to get to the core memory/experience and subconscious belief causing dis-ease of the particular organ. Remember, forgiveness brings closure, which brings true, authentic healing.

3. Look at the chakra energy centre that relates to this particular organ and use 'The Recipe' for healing the spirit to clear the blocked or negative energy, allowing flow and balance to return.

4. Carry out 'The Recipe' for healing body, mind and spirit for several weeks or months in order to allow the body time to heal and re-generate.

WE WISH YOU THE MOST POWERFUL, LIFE TRANSFORMATIONAL HEALING JOURNEY AHEAD. YOUR BODY IS A POWERFUL HEALER AND YOU DESERVE ULTIMATE HEALTH AND VITALITY!

Don & Lynnie xx

JUST ONE MORE THING BEFORE WE GET STARTED...

Our ancestors believed that the first meal of the day should be eaten when the sun is highest in the sky! The word 'breakfast' actually means break-fast and fasting is exactly what we begin to do at the completion of our evening meal. We abstain from eating food for the duration of the night, meaning, essentially, that we are fasting. This is why amazing healing takes place during the night. Our ancestors also believed that the final meal of the day should be eaten as the sun goes down and this meal was called sups, meaning soups or breads dipped in good quality oils infused with different herbs to assist the body systems. In comparison to the late night dinners so many Westerners indulge in, rolling away from the table so full they can hardly move, this is a huge contrast. It's pretty obvious which meal would digest quicker and easier, leaving more time for the body to direct its energy toward healing.

My philosophy is, 'listen to your body and feed it what it's asking for.' Generally, I don't eat until around 11am, when the sun is almost highest in the sky. I love to start my day hydrating the body by drinking a litre or more of pure water. By eating my last meal no later than 6pm and first meal at 11am, I am actually fasting for 17hrs and, by doing this, assisting my body greatly to stay healthy and vibrant. I don't believe in set breakfast, lunch and dinner foods. To me this is just another way we have been indoctrinated. Eat what you feel like and if you don't feel hungry, don't eat! No, you won't die and, yes, you might feel tired, dizzy, lethargic and shaky if you skip a meal, but this is not because you are starving, you are simply feeling the powerful effects of detoxification.

That said, the meals in this book are for when your body desires them. If you feel like eating muesli for dinner or a bowl of Brussels sprouts for breakfast, go for it I say! And who ever told us we couldn't eat chocolate for breakfast? 😊

Ra Healing Food Testimonials

I was invited to attend the ReWake Retreat in Ubud, Bali. I have been vegan for 3 years, but in those few days I have never felt so much healing from within, as I ate the home-made food morning, noon and night. Lyn created medicine for my body with simple yet powerful fruits and vegetables, spices, plants and most of all, love. You certainly do feel amazing. Plus, each mouth full was heaven. I have worked alongside many retreat chefs and I can recommend Lyn at the highest levels of Retreats. She works in flow of the retreat and also has a gift in many ways, to help create a perfect environment for the hosts of these retreats. All in all, she is amazing and the words that spring to mind are, 'let medicine be thy food, let food be thy medicine' and she lives up to those words and more...
- Mark Bajerski (Founder of Pure Energy Healing Worldwide)

The food Lynnie Nichols prepared at the retreat in Bali was out of this world. Her meals where like a Picasso painting full of colour, energy and an amazing combination of tastes. I rejoiced at every sitting. I felt the meals where more than just filling my stomach they were also healing my mind and body...
- John Richards

Hi guys, my name is Tyler Tolman. I love going up to North Bali, it is such a beautiful space. I go up there especially to fast and whenever I've done this, after breaking the fast on the beautiful fruits and juices, there has never been any good food spots. Until NOW. Warung Ra is a god send and has some of the best food on the whole island. Lyn has done a spectacular job of training and her food will blow your mind. The only way to describe it is ORGASMIC!! And super healthy at the same time which most of you know is hard to find. I love this gem in North Bali. If you get the chance, check it out. 🙏 🧇

DISCLAIMER...

Cowboy Epicures & Ra Healing Food Recipes ☺

Disclaimer; the following healing protocols are a summary of what Don would do personally in each particular circumstance. Don Tolman claims no formal health credentials; therefore, we must tell you that the content provided is for informational purposes only and not intended to be a substitute for professional medical advice, diagnosis or treatment and you should therefore check with your doctor before following any of the guidance provided in the contents of this book! Should you choose to follow the information provided, we take no responsibility.

If water fasting for the first time, a slow approach is recommended, working up to the duration suggested. Please use your own discretion and/or seek advice when getting off medications.

Michelle McKoy Photography

The CENTRAL NERVOUS SYSTEM

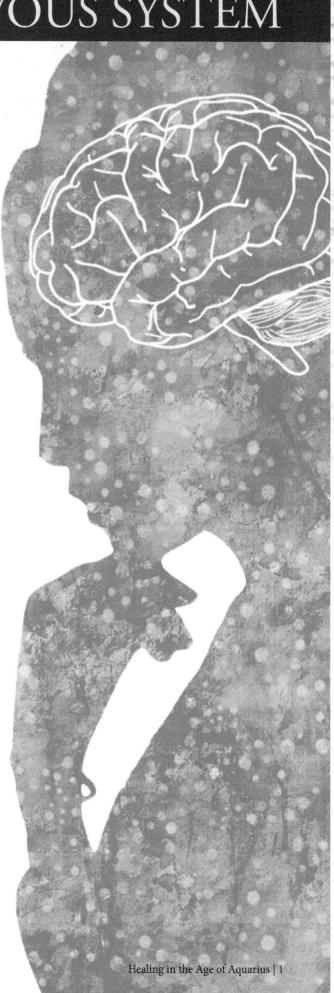

Consists of... brain, cerebrum, cerebellum, brain stem, eyes, ears, nose, spinal cord and nerves.

Chakra- Crown (violet) /Endocrine Gland and Function... Pineal Gland produces and regulates the production of melatonin, which regulates circadian rhythms (sleep patterns).

Holds Emotional Molecules of contentment and serenity, depression, dread and apathy.

Foods That Support This System Are... apples, almonds, blueberries, broccoli, Brussels sprouts, cabbage, rockmelon, cauliflower, ginger, lettuce, pine nuts, walnuts, watermelon.

Support the Emotional/Physical Healing of This System with... YELLOW and PURPLE foods.

Yellow wholefoods help to release nerve diseases and emotions of despair and helplessness.

Purple wholefoods assist us within this system to feel balanced whilst promoting imagination and creativity.

***NUGGET... *The word berry originates from the Latin word vaccinium, which is where the word vaccine comes from. Berries are Nature's vaccines and every spring our ancestors would vaccinate themselves by pigging out on berries!*

BRAIN

BODY *FOODS THAT HEAL* ---	MIND *POSSIBLE EMOTIONAL CAUSE* ---	SPIRIT *IMBALANCED CHAKRA* ---
SIGNATURE FOODS... walnuts, almonds, head foods such as cabbage, Brussels sprouts, broccoli, lettuce and cauliflower	Are you refusing to change an outdated belief system/ programming? Is your mind filled with negative, fearful or stressful thoughts?	Crown Chakra- **colour Violet** and Third Eye Chakra- **colour Indigo**

***NUGGETS... *B-RAIN, meant 'House of Pure Waters'. When we drink Nature's pure waters, we are healing our brain.*

*** Did you know that watermelon has the same chemistry, fluidity and dynamics as the hydranium fluid of the brain? Watermelon is 93% water and the brain is 93% water, making it the perfect signature.

CENTRAL NERVOUS SYSTEM
WALDORF CUPS

Ingredients: 1 cup walnuts, whole or chopped, ¼ cup pine nuts, 2 green apples diced, 1 stick of celery sliced, lettuce leaves left intact for serving

LEMON DRESSING; (see recipe under Dressings in back of book)

CASHEW MAYONNAISE; (see recipe under Dressings in back of book)

Method: Toss all ingredients together in a bowl with some lemon dressing. Spoon the waldorf filling into the lettuce leaf cups, add a spoonful of cashew mayonnaise and serve. (serves 2)

EAR

BODY	MIND	SPIRIT
FOODS THAT HEAL	***POSSIBLE EMOTIONAL CAUSE***	***IMBALANCED CHAKRA***
---	---	---
SIGNATURE FOODS... plums, prunes, mushroom	Is there something you don't want to hear or maybe you are feeling unheard? Are you holding on to anger, blame, guilt or frustration?	Crown Chakra- **colour Violet** and Third Eye Chakra- **colour Indigo**

***NUGGET... To restore hearing, do a 14–21-day water fast. Ear candle daily - two candles per ear. Use extra extra virgin olive oil (in a glass bottle, not plastic) and, using a glass eyedropper, put ¾ drops in the problem ear, keeping this in with a cotton ball; leave this all day then clean out with a cotton bud at night. Do this for three to fou days. Go into the fresh air, pinch the nose and mouth shut and blow to pop the ears. Do a colon cleanse with bentonite clay, herbs etc. to remove plaque... Nerves from the ears run down the throat and body and attach to the transverse colon; therefore, plaque on this area of the colon can diminish and create hearing loss.

CENTRAL NERVOUS SYSTEM
GINGER MUSHROOMS WITH BROCCOLI

Ingredients: Organic button mushrooms brushed and sliced, 1–2 cups broccoli chopped into small pieces, 2 inches of ginger diced, 1 clove garlic diced, 2 tbs coconut oil for cooking, organic olive oil, sea salt and pepper for seasoning

Method: Fry all ingredients together in coconut oil for a few minutes until heated, but still crunchy. Add a good dose of sea salt and olive oil and serve immediately. (serves 2)

EYE

BODY *FOODS THAT HEAL*	MIND *POSSIBLE EMOTIONAL CAUSE*	SPIRIT *IMBALANCED CHAKRA*
---	---	---
SIGNATURE FOODS... carrot, kiwi fruit, parsnip	What are you not wanting to see— past, present or future? Are you feeling stuck or fearful of the future?	Right Eye... Crown Chakra- **colour Violet** Left Eye... Third Eye Chakra- **colour Indigo** and Crown Chakra- **colour Violet**

CENTRAL NERVOUS SYSTEM
HONEYED CARROT SPIRALS

Ingredients: 2 large carrots spiralized, ¼ cup olive oil, a sprinkle of turmeric, 2 tsp pure honey

Method: To prepare the dressing, combine the olive oil, turmeric and honey together in a glass jar and shake well.

Toss the carrot noodles and dressing together in a serving bowl. (serves 2)

COWBOY DON'S VISION RESTORATION

Part 1 ...

Vision training is designed to both relax and strengthen eye muscles. It is effective in reducing high degrees of refractive errors in near-sightedness, far-sightedness, astigmatism, cataracts, glaucoma and aging vision, including spots and 'dead cell' floaters.

There are colours, music and sounds, foods, herbs, light frequencies, and eye muscle exercises that keep and restore clarity of vision. Best of all, it's simple and not expensive nor 'invasive' to the human body or the eyes.

FIRST, AND MOST CRITICAL, IS: YOU HAVE TO STOP WEARING GLASSES OR CONTACTS!

The only EXCEPTION is if you are doing something that could be dangerous or even life threatening, such as driving if your eyesight is that bad. Otherwise, you have to take them off and get over the 'habit' of using them. THEY ARE A CRUTCH! They weaken your vision over time so you go back pay for eye tests, and then you pay for a stronger lens set. If you put your arm in a sling because of a broken arm, that's great, for four to six weeks. If you leave the sling on longer and don't go through the pain and discomfort of using it again, the muscles atrophy and get weaker and weaker the longer you don't use your arm. **IT'S THE SAME WITH YOUR EYES!**

Eye Exercises...

With a routine of daily eye exercises for just one month, I believe most people can see a dramatic vision improvement. It all boils down to relieving near-point stress and using your eyes the way they were meant to be used! Glasses and contacts don't allow for nature to work.

Just so you know, this approach has worked for thousands who previously suffered from blurry vision. It's no fluke—eye exercises, sunshine, and foods work for a wide range of people who suffer from the common complaint of refractive errors and other eye problems.

A lot of young people develop vision problems while growing up because they spend too much time indoors, at school, or watching TV in the daytime or reading books and doing hours of homework indoors, or looking at computer screens with no long-distance visual break time. All too often they are focusing within a close-range 'bubble' and fail to strengthen their distance vision.

Fortunately, it's not too late to turn back the clock. Eye exercises retrain your eyes to be more flexible and accommodate better to your surroundings. This means they work for the four main vision disorders: near-sightedness, far-sightedness, astigmatism and aging vision; these with sunshine and foods that target the eyes repair other visual problems.

The problem with glasses:

Years of experience have probably already demonstrated to you the sickening truth: over time, eyeglasses make your vision worse. And for those who thrive on studies, read this scientific trial... Dr Earl Smith of the University of Houston College of Optometry fitted corrective lenses on monkeys with healthy vision. (Monkeys have near identical visual systems to humans.) Within weeks, the monkeys adapted to the lenses. Those wearing minus lenses (prescribed for near-sightedness) became nearsighted. Those wearing plus lenses (prescribed for far-sightedness) became farsighted. And the same thing happened with glasses designed for astigmatism.

The exact same natural reaction is likely to be happening with your own eyesight; so here it is again—the first step to improving your vision naturally is to stop wearing your glasses. The only exception is when you can't physically see what you need to or when it would be dangerous (when driving) like I mentioned before. If this seems impossible because your eyesight is so bad, you can wear a weaker pair of glasses for now because it will still encourage your eyes to work harder on their own without relying on overly strong prescription lenses.

The First of Three Exercises:

1. The Three Cups:

Step 1
Relax and adjust your chair so that you are 12 to 24 inches from the computer monitor at eye level. If the image is not perfectly clear to you, that's alright, as long as you can make out the image roughly.

Step 2
Hold a pen vertically between the two circles approximately one inch from the screen. The top of the pen should be at the same level as the image.

Step 3
Focus on the top of the pen as you slowly bring it toward your face. As you bring the pen closer to your face you will notice the two circles gradually merge to become three circles. When the three circles are all the same shape and proportion, stop moving the pen. It may be a little blurry to start with, but the image will sharpen when you get used to focusing this way.

Step 4
Try to shift your focus from the pen to the centre circle. This may be difficult and could take a few days to master. (If you have trouble doing this, refer to the troubleshooting tips below.)

Step 5
Once you can focus on the centre circle, move your pen away while maintaining your focus. Try to see the centre circle as clearly as possible. As you increase your focus you will notice that the centre circle becomes three-dimensional. It will look as if you are peering down into a Styrofoam cup.

Step 6
Your final goal is to look at the two circles and create the three circles (with the centre one appearing three dimensional) without using your pen at all. Once you can easily achieve this, proceed to step 2.

2. The 13-Knot Rope:

Get a rope or string about the thickness of the end of your little finger. Measure the rope in 13 lengths of your arm from elbow to longest (middle) finger. Tie a knot in the rope at both ends and at every length going up the rope that is the distance of the elbow to middle finger. In other words, you'll have 13 knots when finished.

Troubleshooting this cost-free eye exercise of vision return...

Tip #1
If you have trouble creating the third circle... Move closer or farther away from the monitor. Also, your eyes may have become tired very quickly, so look away for 30 seconds.

Tip #2
If you see four circles... Bring the pen closer to your face and keep your eyes focused on it. This should transform the four circles into three. Another option is to move a few inches farther away from the monitor.

Tip #3
If you cannot focus on the centre circle or if you can see the centre circle but have trouble focusing on it without the pen, be assured that this is normal when you're first performing this eye exercise. Focus on the top of the pen; then slowly look over it at the centre circle. Keep going back and forth between the two until you are able to focus on the centre circle without the pen.

Online you will find other free eye exercises that aim to relax and strengthen the eyes. Make a daily commitment to vision training; in this way, habit brings the result.

Pin or nail one end of the knot into a tree, wall or whatever and get a chair to sit in comfortably; move the chair out away from the pinned/nailed/tied to a tree/wall; knot and lift the rope/string to the end of your nose; hold the string/rope tight and straight. Now look at the next knot out and focus on it until it is as clear as you can get it. Look out to the next knot and do the same. Continue this next knot viewing and focusing till you get to the knot in the tree/wall.

Now look into the distant sky for a bird, cloud, airplane or just the sky itself for one minute; then, starting at the tree/wall knot, focus as clearly as you can get it and work your way back to the closest knot one arm length out from your nose.

3. All Things Under the Sun/Son… Even Vision

Morning and evening SUNGAZING is critical to total eye sight restoration. Fire is an ancient acronym that originally meant Fuel Ignited Releases Energy. The bio-photons of sunlight heal the brain, nervous system, eyesight, endocrine function and support all 10,000 trillion cells of the body in their functional capacities. Make sungazing a habit for Life, Health, and Happiness.

Testimonials

---

*'Cowboy Don, when I began this routine, I could only perform The Three Cups from 12 inches away.
After 30 days of practice, I could perform this exercise from eight feet away!
That is a considerable improvement in focus, thanks Cowboy.'*

'Are you sick of wearing glasses all the time and frustrated that your eyeglass prescription gets stronger year after year? I knew the feeling (until I met the Cowboy). I was diagnosed with near-sightedness (myopia) at age 10 within days of getting a vaccine and struggled with blurry eyesight right into adulthood. I also developed astigmatism. Then, three years ago, I was told by Cowboy Don about simple eye exercises that could allow me to see clearly, naturally for the first time in years. The secret was learning better vision habits like not wearing my contacts, getting off the meds that made my eyes even worse and following the simple daily eye exercises, then eating the foods that support vision. Within three days of doing the new routine, I could read the titles of books on the bookshelf across the room. My eyesight was improving—and fast!'

NERVES

BODY *FOODS THAT HEAL*	MIND *POSSIBLE EMOTIONAL CAUSE*	SPIRIT *IMBALANCED CHAKRA*
---	---	---
SIGNATURE FOODS... fava beans, fennel, butter, poppy seeds, ginger, avocado, walnuts	Are you blocking verbal or emotional communication? Are you experiencing feelings of distrust, anxiety, fear, guilt or shame? Are you feeling like it's all work and no play?	Crown Chakra- **colour Violet** and Third Eye Chakra- **colour Indigo**

CENTRAL NERVOUS SYSTEM
FAVA BEAN AND FENNEL SALAD

Ingredients: 1 cup fava beans (option; use fava bean tempeh), 1 cup fennel, sprinkle of poppy seeds, 1tsp fresh finely diced ginger, 1 avocado cut into chunky pieces, 1 cup walnuts, juice and zest of 1 lemon, ½ cup torn mint, ¼ cup cold pressed virgin olive oil, 1 tsp raw honey, nature made salt

Method: Blanch the raw fava beans in hot water for a few minutes then pop into iced water. If using tempeh; fry in coconut oil until golden then cut into 2cm pieces. Chop the fennel into thin slices and place in a serving bowl with all other ingredients. Sprinkle with poppy seeds and serve. (serves 2)

SPINAL COLUMN

BODY	MIND	SPIRIT
FOODS THAT HEAL	**POSSIBLE EMOTIONAL CAUSE**	**IMBALANCED CHAKRA**
SIGNATURE FOODS... apples, almonds, blueberries, broccoli, Brussels sprouts, cabbage, rockmelon, cauliflower, ginger, lettuce, pine nuts, walnuts, watermelon, basmati	Are you feeling unsupported and unloved? Are you worrying about money? Are you feeling stuck in guilt and shame of the past?	Crown Chakra- **colour Violet**

***TESTIMONIAL-** *HEALING A BROKEN SPINE. Two weeks after shattering her lumbar vertebrae, Jennifer was told that, in order to save function, the doctors needed to cut function by severing her spinal cord. This rendered her a 'T12-complete paraplegic', meaning, no chance of ever walking again. The medical approach to her condition was about 32 pills every day. In a wheelchair, in constant pain, and at around 68lb, she commenced Don's healing protocol, beginning with a 7 day water fast then moving into a 2 month diet of Pulse, liquid aloe vera (Joule of Thor), and blended berries. Jennifer began to put on weight and build muscle, then step by step she healed completely. Jennifer is now healthy and vibrant, walking and running leg brace free! See Jennifer's video testimonial here https://youtu.be/rXdt9UhBuBw*

CENTRAL NERVOUS SYSTEM
BRAINFOOD COLESLAW

Ingredients: ½ small green cabbage shredded, ½ small head of broccoli diced finely, ½ small cauliflower diced finely, ½ cups pine nuts, 1 cup walnuts left whole or chopped, 1 green apple diced finely- including seeds and skin

CASHEW MAYONNAISE; (see recipe under Dressings in back of book)

Method: Place all ingredients together in a salad bowl. Dress with a generous dose of mayonnaise so that it's nice and creamy. (serves 4)

DIS-EASES/DISORDERS OF
The CENTRAL NERVOUS SYSTEM

ADDICTION TO SUBSTANCE

WHAT IS IT?... Addiction is when the intake of a particular substance or activity becomes habitual and necessary to that person. For example, drug addiction, cigarette addiction, alcohol addiction.

BODY – EPICURE

- Get off all medication and supplements- herbs in the form of powders or teas are okay. You may have 72 hours of feeling toxicities leave the bloodstream.
- **Fastest...** Water fast for 7-10 days **OR...**
- Cabala juice fast if possible 7–14 days; if not, combine this with a raw, vegan, wholefoods diet.
- Snack on liquorice and macadamia nuts together.
- Reset the flora/fauna of the gut by eating and drinking fermented foods such as sauerkraut, green olives in brine, keffir, natural organic yoghurt, tempeh, kombucha, etc.
- Suck on Himalayan rock salt.
- Fresh air- windows open and or a fan gently blowing day and night.
- Hydration- 1 litre of water per 22 kilos of bodyweight every day.
- Do a colon cleanse to remove residual substance toxicity and toxic plaque.

- Do daily self-administered colonics via an enema douche bag (available **www.lynnienichols.com/shop**)
- If possible- sungazing morning and evenings in 13-second intervals; look at the sun until it reaches a 10-degree arc, or a clenched fist sitting on horizon as sun comes up, stop at top of fist. At night, start gazing as sun hits top of fist until it's gone.
- Develop the darkest suntan you can by covering your body in Divine Body Butter or coconut oil and then exposing at least 70% of your body to the sun for one hour every day (30 mins each side).
- **ESSENTIAL OIL...** peppermint, geranium, grapefruit, lemon, tea tree.
- (Divine, Congest Ease, Colon Cleanses, Ra 24ct See Salt, Himalayan rock salt, essential oil of peppermint and Joule of Thor available USA **www.thedontolman.com/store** and Australia **www.lynnienichols.com/shop**)

BODY	MIND	SPIRIT
FOODS THAT HEAL	*POSSIBLE EMOTIONAL CAUSE*	*IMBALANCED CHAKRA*
---	---	---
SIGNATURE FOODS... apples, almonds, blueberries, broccoli, Brussels sprouts, cabbage, rockmelon, cauliflower, ginger, lettuce, pine nuts, walnuts, watermelon	• What from the past are you blocking from your reality/ not wanting to see or feel? • What don't you like about yourself and are unsure how to change?	Crown Chakra- **colour Violet** and Third Eye Chakra- **colour Indigo**

CENTRAL NERVOUS SYSTEM
MACADAMIA & LIQUORICE SNACK

Ingredients: 1 cup of macadamia nuts, 1 cup of organic liquorice

Method: Chop the liquorice into bite-sized pieces and place both ingredients into a jar or sealable bag in order to carry with you and snack on throughout the day

ALLERGIES / ALLERGIC REACTION

***WHAT IS IT?...** **Allergic reaction** is when the body's immune system, which is responsible for defending the body against toxins and harmful bacteria, reacts to substances that typically don't pose a threat to the body, known as allergens. A strong reaction to foods can mean that there is an extreme deficiency to certain nutritional components in that food. The reaction is the body desperately trying to get and assimilate what it is in dire need of. Introducing minute then small amounts of the allergy foods back into the body will heal the allergy.

***BODY – EPICURE*

- Get off all medication and supplements- herbs in the form of powders or teas are okay.
- Water fast for 14–20 days to get rid of the allergens; then follow this with 14 days on Pulse or a vegetarian diet that includes organic free-range omelette with eggs, cheese and veggies.
- Do a self-administered colonic, enema, to remove the allergen from the body (enema douche travel kit available **www.lynnienichols.com/shop**)
- Suck on Himalayan rock salt.
- Reset the flora/fauna of the gut by eating and drinking fermented foods such as sauerkraut, green olives in brine, keffir, natural organic yoghurt, tempeh, kombucha, etc.
- Hydration- 1 litre of water per 22 kilos of bodyweight every day.
- If possible- sungazing morning and evenings in 13-second intervals; look at the sun until it reaches a 10-degree arc, or a clenched fist sitting on horizon as sun comes up, stop at top of fist. At night, start gazing as sun hits top of fist until it's gone.
- Develop the darkest suntan you can by covering your body in Divine Body Butter or coconut oil and then exposing at least 70% of your body to the sun for one hour every day (30 mins each side).
- RE- INTRODUCING ALLERGY FOODS... For 1 week... lick the lips and then rub the food on the lips; wait for the lips to dry then lick again. Wash the mouth out with water and drink a glass of water. Next... for 1 week... lightly scrape the food on the teeth, lick the granuals, insalivate, rinse the mouth with water and spit out. Next... for 1 week... do the same again but, this time, drink the water. Next...for 1 week, taste a tiny piece of the food and swallow this followed by a big glass of water.
- **CHILDREN...** Rub their chest, back and feet with Congest Ease. Waft peppermint oil under the nose and keep air moving day and night. Cut a red onion in half and put into the room night and day. Get them to lick some Himalayan rock salt and drink lots of water.
- **ESSENTIAL OIL...** peppermint, lavender, tea tree, lemon, sandalwood, eucalyptus.
- (Divine, Congest Ease, Ra 24ct See Salt, Himalayan rock salt, essential oil of peppermint and Joule of Thor available USA **www.thedontolman.com/store** and Australia **www.lynnienichols.com/shop**)

BODY *FOODS THAT HEAL*	MIND *POSSIBLE EMOTIONAL CAUSE*	SPIRIT *IMBALANCED CHAKRA*
---	---	---
SIGNATURE FOODS... apples, almonds, blueberries, broccoli, Brussels sprouts, cabbage, rockmelon, cauliflower, ginger, lettuce, pine nuts, walnuts, watermelon	• Is someone or something annoying you or are you annoying yourself? • Are you having difficulty creating boundaries and therefore giving away your own power?	Crown Chakra- **colour Violet** and Third Eye Chakra- **colour Indigo**

CENTRAL NERVOUS SYSTEM
BRAINFOOD SMOOTHIE BOWL

Ingredients: 1 cup of blueberries, 1 cup rockmelon, 1–2 banana, 1 cup walnuts, 1 cup watermelon, ¼ cup of olive oil.

Method: Place all ingredients together in a blender and mix on high until smooth and creamy. Pour into a shallow bowl and decorate with nut granola, banana, blueberries and diced rockmelon. (serves 2)

ALZHEIMER'S DISEASE (AD) / PRIMARY DEMENTIA

***WHAT IS IT?...** **Alzheimer's disease/primary dementia** is a neurodegenerative disease caused by severe brain dehydration and plaque that has become thick in order to contain heavy metals stored at the base of the brain, such as mercury, lead and aluminium. This results in a loss of mental function due to the deterioration of brain tissue and can cause behavioural changes such as mental disorientation, abusive and violent behaviour, loss of memory and cognitive decline.

***BODY – EPICURE*

- Get off all medication and supplements- herbs in the form of powders or teas are okay. You may have 72 hours of feeling toxicities leave the bloodstream.
- **Fastest...** Water fast for 7–10 days **OR...**
- Cabala juice fast if possible 7–14 days; if not, combine this with a raw, vegan, wholefoods diet.
- Fresh air- fan gently blowing in the direction of the face constantly.
- Hydration- one glass of water every hour for at least eight hours of the day (crucial).
- Diet of raw fruit and vegetables... snack on macadamia, hazelnuts, pecans, walnuts, almonds and berries, especially blueberries ... eat three apples per day, including the seeds and core! Pepitas improve blood flow to the brain- eat 2 cups per day to improve memory. Eat rosemary for memory.
- Have daily a berry, asparaus smoothie, consisting of two cups berries and 12 stalks of asparagus (can add a banana to sweeten) plus water to desired consistency. Drink within 30 minutes of making it. Can eat the foods instead if preferred.
- Suck on Himalayan rock salt.

- Massage peppermint oil into the temples and back of neck and waft under the nose regularly.
- If possible- sungazing morning and evenings in 13-second intervals; look at the sun until it reaches a 10-degree arc, or a clenched fist sitting on horizon as sun comes up, stop at top of fist. At night, start gazing as sun hits top of fist until it's gone.
- Develop the darkest suntan you can by covering your body in Divine Body Butter or coconut oil and then exposing at least 70% of your body to the sun for one hour every day (30 mins each side).
- Have 1 cup of lemon juice every day, can mix with pure water.
- 1 shotglass of Joule of Thor every day.
- Stay away from all foods/drinks with aspartame.
- **ESSENTIAL OIL...** peppermint, frankincense, cypress, ylang ylang, basil, ginger, cedarwood.
- (Divine, essential oil of peppermint, Himalayan rock salt and Joule of Thor available in the USA **www.thedontolman.com/store** and Australia **www.lynnienichols.com/shop**)

BODY *FOODS THAT HEAL*	MIND *POSSIBLE EMOTIONAL CAUSE*	SPIRIT *IMBALANCED CHAKRA*
---	---	---
SIGNATURE FOODS... apples, almonds, blueberries, broccoli, Brussels sprouts, cabbage, rockmelon, cauliflower, ginger, lettuce, pine nuts, walnuts, watermelon	- Are you feeling hopeless, overwhelmed and unable to deal with life/ not wanting to be here? - Are you feeling angry, lost and confused?	Crown Chakra- **colour Violet**

***NOTE...** *Exposure to aluminium and mercury have been recognised as definitive markers of Alzheimer's Disease. Aluminium fluoride... eliminate ALL sources of aluminium, including cookware, utensils, foil, anti-perspirant deodorants, liquids packaged in aluminium-lined cartons etc. The amalgam silver filling, still used by some dentists, has been by far the biggest culprit of mercury poisoning with fish/seafood now coming a close second due to big corporations dumping their toxic waste into the ocean; therefore, all fish, including fish oils and seafood, should be eliminated.*

***NUGGET...** *Malic acid rich fruits bind aluminium. Pectins are soluble fibres in apples that cross the blood /brain barrier and clear out heavy toxic metals. Combine eating apples with enough water to replenish the hydronium fluids and you'll get it done. Organic CBD oil is also very helpful.*

***TESTIMONIAL...** *An 82-year-old woman suffering from dementia so severe she had to be kept in hospital for her own safety recovered after changing her diet. Sylvia was so bad she couldn't even recognise her own son, and at one stage she phoned the police accusing the nurse who was caring for her of kidnap. A diet comprised of high amounts of blueberries, walnuts, broccoli, kale, spinach, sunflower seeds, green tea, oats, sweet potatoes and organic dark chocolate was the key to her recovery.*

CENTRAL NERVOUS SYSTEM
ALUMINIUM ELIMIN8 SMOOTHIE

Ingredients: 2 cups of grapes, 1 apple, 1 cup strawberries, 1 cup water (extra water for desired consistency)

Method: Put ingredients together in a blender and mix well. Drink within half hr of making it (serves 1)

Note: If preferred, you can eat these ingredients each day rather than having as a smoothie... The wisdom here applies not only to Alzheimer's Disease but to all neuro-degenerative diseases including Parkinson's Disease, Multiple Sclerosis (MS), Amyotrophic Lateral Sclerosis (ALS) (also known as Motor Neurone Disease (MND) and Lou Gehrig's disease), Huntington's Chorea, Asthenia, and all forms of Dementia.

ANEURYSM-BRAIN

***WHAT IS IT?...** **A cerebral aneurysm** is where an artery supplying blood to the brain bulges and sometimes ruptures, releasing blood into the skull, which may cause a stroke.

***BODY – EPICURE*

- Get off all medication and supplements- herbs in the form of powders or teas are OK, but no pills or capsules!
- **Fastest...** Water fast for 7–10 days, or cabala juice fast 14–28 days **OR...**
- Hydration- one glass of water every hour for at least eight hours of the day or 1 litre per 22 kilos of bodyweight.
- Diet of raw fruit and vegetables... lots of apples– including the core; snack on walnuts, macadamia, hazelnuts, pecans, almonds and blueberries.
- Eat blueberry Pulse, which targets the brain.
- 1 shotglass of Joule of Thor every day.
- Sungazing morning and evenings in 13-second intervals; look at the sun until it reaches a 10-degree arc, or a clenched fist sitting on horizon as sun comes up, stop at top of fist. At night, start gazing as sun hits top of fist until it's gone.
- Develop the darkest suntan you can by covering your body in Divine Body Butter or coconut oil and then exposing at least 70% of your body to the sun for one hour every day (30 mins each side).
- **ESSENTIAL OIL...** peppermint, frankincense, cypress, ylang ylang, basil, ginger, cedarwood.
- (Divine, blueberry Pulse, essential oil of peppermint and Joule of Thor available in the USA **www.thedontolman.com/store** and Australia **www.lynnienichols.com/shop**)

BODY *FOODS THAT HEAL*	MIND *POSSIBLE EMOTIONAL CAUSE*	SPIRIT *IMBALANCED CHAKRA*
---	---	---
SIGNATURE FOODS... apples, almonds, blueberries, broccoli, Brussels sprouts, cabbage, rockmelon, cauliflower, ginger, lettuce, pine nuts, walnuts, watermelon	• Is the central computer overloaded with pressure and stress? • Are you refusing to make change and release outdated patterns/programming/behaviours? • Are you stubbornly refusing to release what's stressing you?	Crown Chakra- **colour Violet**

***NOTE...** You can protect the brain and avoid a brain aneurysm by targeting with nutitional components such as organic apples—including the core/seeds, peanut butter (get it ground in front of you so you know it's from a good source), organic dried apricots and raisins.*

***NUGGET...** Apples contain pectin, which is the only fibre that is able to cross the blood-brain barrier and remove toxins, including heavy metals, from the brain. Apple seeds have plant synthesised arsenic, which is blood thinning and highly beneficial to the body, unlike man-made arsenic, which is rat poison and deadly for humans.*

CENTRAL NERVOUS SYSTEM
RAW PEANUT & APRICOT BRAIN BALLS

Ingredients: ½ cup organic dried apple, ½ cup organic sulphite free dried apricots, ½ cup raisins, ½ cup walnuts, 1 cup organic peanuts, dessicated coconut

Method: Place the nuts together in a food processor on high until chopped to breadcrumb consistency; add chopped dried apple, apricots and raisins. Blend again on medium speed until mixed well. It should be slightly sticky in order to hold together so, if needed, add a tiny bit of water. Roll into balls and coat with coconut. Refrigerate.
Makes 8–10 balls

ANXIETY (SOCIAL ANXIETY)

***WHAT IS IT?...** **Social anxiety** is when a person feels extreme nervousness, fear, or worry relating to the unknown and unexpected. This anxiety is exaggerated by being in public or group situations and may cause panic attacks over the thought of being made the centre of attention or being judged or embarrassed, thus resulting in a constant nervous fight-or-flight mode, which creates adrenal fatigue.

***BODY – EPICURE*

- Get off all medication and supplements- herbs in the form of powders or teas are OK, but no pills or capsules!
- **Fastest...** Water fast for 7–10 days, or cabala juice fast 14–28 days **OR...**
- Do a 14-day cabala juice fast then become a fruitarian, including nuts and seeds for 30 days.
- Eat at least two cups of orange and yellow foods combined, every day. For example, pineapple and orange together. Also surround yourself with these colours, i.e. your clothing, bed linen, paintings on walls, etc.
- Go nuts on nuts- two handfuls every day, especially almonds as these target the amygdala, which is the part of the brain responsible for the emotional chemistry.
- Eat dark organic chocolate for it's 'feel-good' properties.
- Walking daily, several times if possible; this is essential as it lifts the neurochemistry of the brain and releases endorphins.
- Sungazing morning and evenings in 13-second intervals; look at the sun until it reaches a 10-degree arc, or a clenched fist sitting on horizon as sun comes up, stop at top of fist. At night, start gazing as sun hits top of fist until it's gone.
- Develop the darkest suntan you can by covering your body in Divine Body Butter or coconut oil and then exposing at least 70% of your body to the sun for one hour every day (30 mins each side).
- Laughter truly is the best therapy, so watch funny videos, join a laughter therapy group, be with people who make you laugh and feel good, and stay away from those who do the opposite!
- Take up meditation/yoga.
- Make the home environment a sanctuary ... light and bright, warm, cozy, uplifting music, etc.
- **ESSENTIAL OIL...** peppermint, bergamot, valerian, jasmine, holy basil, chamomile, orange, lemon.
- (Divine, essential oils of peppermint, orange and lemon available in the USA www.thedontolman.com/store and Australia www.lynnienichols.com/shop)

BODY	MIND	SPIRIT
FOODS THAT HEAL	***POSSIBLE EMOTIONAL CAUSE***	***IMBALANCED CHAKRA***
---	---	---
SIGNATURE FOODS... apples, almonds, blueberries, broccoli, Brussels sprouts, cabbage, rockmelon, cauliflower, ginger, lettuce, pine nuts, walnuts, watermelon	• Are you neglecting yourself? • Are you unable to trust in the process of life? • Are you feeling stuck, unable to make a decision for fear of the worst?	Crown Chakra- **colour Violet**

***NOTE...** *Cacao and the hops in organic unfiltered beer are part of the Cannabis family... The delta 9 cannabinoids target the emotions and make you feel happy. Eat raw, unprocessed chocolate for breakfast, lunch and dinner! This is good and healthy!*

***NUGGET...** *Our ancestors understood that the foods growing highest from the ground were the most healing and sacred to the living temple. These foods are fruits, which include nuts and seeds! The word fruit means 'that which comes from a five-pointed star' and 'to add splendour'.*

*** TESTIMONIAL...** *Here is an excerpt from a memoir I am currently writing ... it will give you a little insight into living with social anxiety. Thanks to The Journey emotional healing, Voice Dialogue, exercise, meditation, detoxifying the body via water fasting and colon cleansing, along with living a clean, vegetarian, chemical-free life, I am now free of this condition! (Lyn)*

'...I loved the family-oriented social life we experienced and, for me, accompanying this was the extra benefit that alcohol provided in numbing the persistent anxiety, the anxiety that was so incredibly powerful and at times held me prisoner in my own home. I felt excited at the prospect of doing something positive and empowering for my body (yoga) and hoped that, by some miracle, this might be the key to taming the monster that thrived within my mind.

'I thought about the hours I'd spent creating strategies in order to feel safe enough to do the simple everyday tasks such as grocery shopping, paying bills and taking the kids to school, how I'd used the breath to psyche myself into leaving the safety of my home, even when it was to do something as pleasurable as meeting a girlfriend for coffee. Over time, with constant scrutiny and analysis, I had gained a sense that the core of this anxiety was the fear of the unexpected and fear of the unknown, creating a constant state of fight-or-flight mode in my body, and when the unexpected did occur, catching me off guard, and this especially related to bumping into someone I knew down the street, I'd be instantly overwhelmed with anxiety, sending me into a state of panic and embarrassment resulting in sweaty palms, going bright red and my heart racing uncontrollably. If the other person spoke to me, I'd reply with short, sharp answers in order to excuse myself as quickly as possible and get the hell out of there! The amount of times I'd reacted ridiculously by turning around on the spot and walking in the other direction after seeing someone I knew in the distance, or by pretending I hadn't seen them at all then making myself inconspicuous and dodging them throughout the aisles, I could not tell you. I thought about the occasions when the anxiety was particularly overwhelming and I'd left the store without completing my shopping in order to avoid someone, returning to the safety of my own home where I would berate myself, feeling embarrassed, depressed and disgusted with my behaviour. I'm sure at times I must have been thought of as rude or snobby, yet if only they knew!

'The whole thing was crazy and I knew just how ridiculous it was, yet I had no control over any of it. In my desperate attempt to seek answers to a behaviour I tried my best to hide from the world I discovered that other family members knew all too well the experiences I described, suggesting that this issue/illness had been passed down generationally, but still no answers as to why.

' I thought about how I'd found reprieve in a bourbon bottle and other alcoholic beverages, loving the emotional freedom they provided right back as far as my teenage years and thanked God I was blessed with a strong will, ensuring this never became my daily reality unlike those with a lesser will, lured by drugs and alcohol and their promise of emotional freedom from the relentless and often torturous stories of the mind, only to find themselves in the grip of an even more sabotaging and soul-destroying evil. There was no doubt about it; I'd been kept small, terrified of unexpectedly finding myself the centre of attention, which only emphasised my need to be on guard, plotting and planning, ready to make an immaculate departure if deemed necessary. And yet bizarrely, just like Jeckyl and Hyde, I had another side that was blissfully married with a beautiful little family and gorgeous friends; I was happy and positive, excited and ambitious, an inspiration to those around me—yet nonetheless, looming in the background like a monster in the dark, just waiting, delighting in the opportunity to inject its poisonous thoughts and emotions, ridding its victim of any shred of self-love she may have dared to invest in was this!

'I'd found comfort in knowing that I could wholeheartedly relax in the safety of my own home and on holidays with my parents and loving family until one day I realised that even there the monster could get to me, denying me of any hope of reprieve. I remember that day as clearly as it was yesterday, forcing me to do the unthinkable and go against everything I believed in, the path I'd defied wholeheartedly since Jess's eczema, yet here I was, at the mercy of the doctor, begging for anti-anxiety medication. I'm not proud to say, and yet at the same time not ashamed to say, that I happily popped one of those little pills each day for over twelve months of my life and loved every minute of the freedom it provided me. As with all medications, though, I knew it was just a suppressant and was most likely doing me more harm than good with negative side-effects such as profuse sweating, extreme thirst, heart palpitations and involuntary muscle jerking spasms. I felt bad for my body and, as much as I loved the emotional freedom, I knew it was time to get real, time to find a cure rather than using a toxic poison for temporary relief. I stopped taking the Effexor cold turkey, resulting in me spending the next three days of my life in bed, sicker than I'd ever been before, giving me a whole new perspective and compassion for drug addicts coming off heroin or other hard drugs cold turkey.'

CENTRAL NERVOUS SYSTEM
CHOCOLATE COATED FRUIT SKEWERS

Ingredients: Fresh peeled orange, pineapple and banana, ¾ cup organic cacao, ½ cup coconut oil, ½ cup almond butter, 2 tbsp raw honey.

Method: In a mixing bowl place the cacao, coconut oil, almond butter and honey and mix well. Cut the orange and pineapple into 2 cm cubes. Slice the banana into 1 cm thick rounds. Make up your skewers by alternating the three fruits and then coating with the dark chocolate mix. Place on banana leaf or a tray lightly greased with coconut oil and refrigerate for 30 mins or until the chocolate is set.

ATTENTION DEFICIT HYPERACTIVITY DISORDER (ADHD)

***WHAT IS IT?...** **ADHD** is a brain disorder affecting both children and adults, which may cause hyperactivity and lack of concentration along with a lack of control when it comes to impulses. What's needed is a reconstruction of the electrical frequencies of the brain, the seratonin and dopamine.

***BODY – EPICURE*

- Get off all medication and supplements- herbs in the form of powders or teas are OK, but no pills or capsules!
- Eat a diet of PULSE for 30 days whilst snacking on nuts... This is the brain regenerative meal of the ancient world.
- OR... Eat a vegetarian diet with plenty of fruit, good salt and eggs for B vitamins, especially niacin B3 that converts into so many things for the cognitive process of the brain.
- Go nuts on raw salted walnuts, macadamia, peanuts, pecans and especially almonds as they target the amygdala, the area of the brain responsible for the emotions.
- Eat avocado filled with organic coldpressed olive oil, a squeeze of lemon and some good sea salt or Himalayan rock salt.
- Hydrate with pure water... 1 litre per 22 kilos of bodyweight every day.
- Sungazing morning and evenings in 13-second intervals; look at the sun until it reaches a 10-degree arc, or a clenched fist sitting on horizon as sun comes up, stop at top of fist. At night, start gazing as sun hits top of fist until it's gone.
- Develop the darkest suntan you can by covering your body in Divine Body Butter or coconut oil and then exposing at least 70% of your body to the sun for one hour every day (30 mins each side).
- **ESSENTIAL OIL...** peppermint, lavender, vetiver.
- (Divine, essential oil of peppermint, Ra 24ct See Salt, Himalayan rock salt available in the USA **www.thedontolman.com/store** and Australia **www.lynnienichols.com/shop**)

BODY	MIND	SPIRIT
FOODS THAT HEAL	*POSSIBLE EMOTIONAL CAUSE*	*IMBALANCED CHAKRA*
---	---	---
SIGNATURE FOODS... apples, almonds, blueberries, broccoli, Brussels sprouts, cabbage, rockmelon, cauliflower, ginger, lettuce, pine nuts, walnuts, watermelon	• Are you feeling fearful, controlled, pressured?	Crown Chakra- **colour Violet**

***NOTE...** NEVER have refined sugars of any kind or chemical sweeteners such as aspartame, which is in so many soda drinks and processed foods! Ritalin is a mixture of drugs such as heroine and cocaine. As the children get older, a drug called Adderall is prescribed, which is a higher dosage of these drugs... Investigative studies show that, by this point, 90% of these children are drug addicts.*

***NUGGET...** The word peppermint means 'lively mentally' (pepper - lively, mint - mental). Our ancestors understood the beneficial healing properties of peppermint when it came to dis-ease of the brain and CNS.*

CENTRAL NERVOUS SYSTEM
BLUEBERRY PULSE

Ingredients: Fruit, nuts and seeds including blueberries

Method: (available in the USA **www.thedontolman.com/store** and Australia **www.lynnienichols.com/shop**) Eat a diet of PULSE for 30 days whilst snacking on nuts... This is the brain regenerative meal of the ancient world.

AUTISM / ASPERGER'S (Autism Spectrum Disorder...ASD)

***WHAT IS IT?...** **Autism** is the name given to a wide spectrum of developmental disabilities caused by a brain disorder/abnormality characterised by varying degrees of difficulty in non-verbal and verbal communication skills and emotional and social interaction. People with ASD are often resistant to change and those with the level of autism known as Asperger's are often seen as eccentric.

***BODY – EPICURE*

- Get off all medication and supplements.
- Most critical is clean air, pure water and regular exercise to restore and maintain mental function.
- Get a pet for your child for bonding and love; this activates centres of the brain that stimulate the functional capacity that's been damaged, which is what causes autism in the first place. This powreful release of inner emotions will help the child to be social and less self absorbed, and can be a trigger to restructure a functional capacity.
- If you can find a natural hot spring, use the clay and rub this all over the child's body then allow this to dry completely in the sun before rubbing off in the hot spring water. Alternatively, use a 50/50 mixture of bentonite clay and diamotaceous clay. Fill the bathtub with very warm water, mix in one or two cups of the clay mix and let the child soak in this for 15–20 minutes, leaving only their head and face out. This is a chelation process that will remove heavy metals from the body.
- Get nano bentonite clay and add this to organic juice and drink (may experience detox symptoms of fatigue, nausea, diarrhoea, flu symptoms, hperactivity and more as heavy metals are removed from the brain and body).
- Develop a suntan by covering the body in Divine Body Butter or coconut oil and then exposing at least 70% of the body to the sun for one hour every day (30 mins each side).
- Drink raw organic cow's milk.
- Eat keffir, organic yoghurt and other fermented foods and drinks for probiotics.
- Eat a raw diet of organic fresh fruit (especially apples two or three per day if possible), vegetables, nuts, seeds and grains. Eat blueberry Pulse, which targets the brain.
- Have daily a berry, asparaus smoothie, consisting of two cups berries and 12 stalks of asparagus (can add a banana to sweeten) plus water to desired consistency. Drink within 45 minutes of making it. Can eat the foods instead if preferred.
- Listening to relaxing music can also be helpful.
- **ESSENTIAL OIL...** lavender, vetiver, frankincense, sandalwood, chamomile, bergamot, ylang ylang, cannabis.
- (Divine, essential oil of lavender and blueberry Pulse available in the USA www.thedontolman.com/store and Australia www.lynnienichols.com/shop)

BODY FOODS THAT HEAL	MIND POSSIBLE EMOTIONAL CAUSE	SPIRIT IMBALANCED CHAKRA
---	---	---
SIGNATURE FOODS... apples, almonds, blueberries, broccoli, Brussels sprouts, cabbage, rockmelon, cauliflower, ginger, lettuce, pine nuts, walnuts, watermelon		Crown Chakra- **colour Violet** and Third Eye Chakra- **colour Indigo**

***NOTE...** What's needed is to get rid of toxicity that causes functional brain disorders. Particles of bentonite clay have negative iron chelation which pulls heavy metals out of the brain, as does the pectin in apples and the white part of the inner capsicum.

***NUGGET...** Autism was originally called Asperger's disease. Autism means 'self-absorbed'.

CENTRAL NERVOUS SYSTEM
BLUEBERRY SMOOTHIE

Ingredients: 1 cup blueberries, 1 green and 1 yellow organic apple with skins and cores, 1 cup organic natural yoghurt, 1 cup raw organic cows milk, 5 or more pitted medjool dates for sweetening

Method: Place all ingredients together in a blender on high and process until a smooth, creamy consistency. (serves 2)

BRAIN TUMOUR

***WHAT IS IT?...** **A brain tumour** is a cancerous or non-cancerous growth of cells in the brain that often grows at an abnormal rate.

***BODY – EPICURE*

- Get off all medication and supplements- herbs in the form of powders or teas are OK, but no pills or capsules!
- Do the five-week 35% food-grade hydrogen peroxide protocol combined with a cabala juice fast for 14–28 days; if needed, can have raw vegan food also.
- Sungazing morning and evenings in 13-second intervals; look at the sun until it reaches a 10-degree arc, or a clenched fist sitting on horizon as sun comes up, stop at top of fist. At night, start gazing as sun hits top of fist until it's gone.
- Rub peppermint oil in the palm of your hand until warm... breathe in through nose and out through mouth. Do this for 30–45 seconds two or three times each day.
- Develop the darkest suntan you can by covering your body in Divine Body Butter or coconut oil and then exposing at least 70% of your body to the sun for one hour every day (30 mins each side).
- Have 1 cup of lemon juice every day, can mix with pure water.
- Eat and juice a locally grown, fresh, raw organic vegan diet for highest nutritional force, making sure that every day you eat raw wholefoods of all seven colours of the rainbow—red, orange, yellow, blue, green, indigo/violet and white. Especially beneficial are locally grown organic broccoli, cauliflower and asparagus (when in season).
- Snack on nuts—walnuts, almonds and macadamias. Eat dried apricots and other dried fruits as these remove plaque and give the brain energy.
- Suck on rock salt every day.
- Drink one litre per 22 kilos bodyweight of pure water, every day.
- Have daily a berry, asparaus smoothie, consisting of two cups berries and 12 stalks of asparagus (can add a banana to sweeten) plus water to desired consistency. Drink within 30 mins of making it. Can eat the foods instead if preferred.
- Herbal and epsom salt water baths for 20 minutes every day.
- Get three small juggling bags/balls and practice juggling daily—this creates neuroplasticity in the cells to redevelop lost function.
- **ESSENTIAL OIL...** peppermint, frankincense, thyme, myrrh, turmeric, clary sage, cannabis.
- (Divine, Himalayan rock salt, Ra 24ct See Salt, essential oil of peppermint, 35% food-grade hydrogen peroxide available in the USA **www.thedontolman.com/store** and Australia **www.lynnienichols.com/shop**)

BODY *FOODS THAT HEAL*	MIND *POSSIBLE EMOTIONAL CAUSE*	SPIRIT *IMBALANCED CHAKRA*
---	---	---
SIGNATURE FOODS... apples, almonds, blueberries, broccoli, Brussels sprouts, cabbage, rockmelon, cauliflower, ginger, lettuce, pine nuts, walnuts, watermelon	• Are you being stubborn/refusing to change old beliefs/programming? • Are you refusing to make necessary changes in order to be happy and peaceful? • Is the central computer constantly on overdrive/overloaded? • Are you unwilling to forgive yourself and/or others?	Crown Chakra- **colour Violet** and Third Eye Chakra- **colour Indigo**

***NOTE...** *Hydrogen peroxide is simply water with one extra oxygen atom. When absorbed by the body, it releases the extra atom into the blood, flooding the blood with oxygen and killing off cancer cells, viruses and other pathogens that cannot survivie in a highly oxygenated environment.*

***NUGGET...** *Good nature-made salt is the energy electrolyte of all cells of the body and assists in avoiding brain damage.*

CENTRAL NERVOUS SYSTEM
RAINBOW SALAD

Ingredients: 1 cup slithered almonds lightly toasted, ½ cup blueberries, 1 small head of broccoli grated, ¼ red cabbage finely shredded, 1 small head of cauliflower grated, 1 large carrot coarsely grated, 1 small beetroot coarsely grated, 1 yellow capsicum finely sliced, 1 large tomato diced, 1 cm ginger peeled and finely diced, 3 cups of mixed lettuce, ½ cup pine nuts, 3 stalks of fresh locally grown asparagus cut into 1cm pieces, 1 cup walnuts chopped
HERB DRESSING; **(see recipe under Dressings in back of book)**

Method: Toss all ingredients together in a large salad bowl. Dress with herb dressing and serve

BIPOLAR / MANIC DEPRESSIVE ILLNESS... DEPRESSION

***WHAT IS IT?...** **Bipolar disorder**, previously known as manic-depressive illness, is characterised by extremes in behaviour and energy, from manic to depressive.

Depression is an illness that affects the way a person feels emotionally, causing a low feeling of sadness and despondency for long periods of time, often for no apparent reason.

***BODY – EPICURE*

- Get off all medication and supplements- herbs in the form of powders or teas are ok, but no pills or capsules!
- **Fastest...** Water fast for 7–10 days, or cabala juice fast 14–28 days **OR...**
- Eat at least two cups of orange and yellow foods combined every day, for example pineapple and orange together. Also surround yourself with these colours, i.e. your clothing, bed linen, paintings on walls, etc.
- Go nuts on nuts- two handfuls every day, especially almonds as these target the amygdala, which is the part of the brain responsible for the emotional chemistry.
- Eat dark organic chocolate for it's 'feel-good' properties.
- Walking daily, several times if possible, this is essential as it lifts the neurochemistry of the brain and releases endorphins.
- Sungazing morning and evenings in 13-second intervals; look at the sun until it reaches a 10-degree arc or a clenched fist sitting on horizon as sun comes up, stop at top of fist. At night, start gazing as sun hits top of fist until it's gone.
- Develop the darkest suntan you can by covering your body in Divine Body Butter or coconut oil and then exposing at least 70% of your body to the sun for one hour every day (30 mins each side).
- Laughter truly is the best therapy, so watch funny videos, join a laughter therapy group, be with people who make you laugh and feel good, and stay away from those that do the opposite!
- Take up meditation/yoga.
- Make the home environment a sanctuary ... light and bright, warm, cozy, uplifting music, etc.
- Add 1 drop each of essential oils of lemon and orange to water and drink throughout the day. Diffuse to breathe in through the nose also.
- At night, spray lavender onto your pillow and rub a little bit on the temples and back of the neck to help promote sound sleep.
- **When coming off antidepressants;** practice sungazing daily, do a 28 day cabala juice fast, drink 1L water per 22kilos of bodyweight each day, exercise daily, go nuts on nuts-especially brazil an almonds, eat foods of the blue/indigo/violet spectrum-especially blueberries, eat mushroom soup with lots of garlic, eat good organic dark chocolate, eat daily; a mix of pineapple and orange.
- **ESSENTIAL OIL...** lemon, orange, lavender, frankincense, chamomile, cedarwood, peppermint.
- (Divine and essential oil of peppermint, lavender, lemon and orange available in the USA **www. thedontolman.com/store** and Australia **www. lynnienichols.com/shop**)

BODY	MIND	SPIRIT
FOODS THAT HEAL	**POSSIBLE EMOTIONAL CAUSE**	**IMBALANCED CHAKRA**
---	---	---
SIGNATURE FOODS... apples, almonds, blueberries, broccoli, Brussels sprouts, cabbage, rockmelon, cauliflower, ginger, lettuce, pine nuts, walnuts, watermelon	• Are you feeling hopeless, helpless, lost, a failure, a deep sense of disappointment? • Are you feeling angry and unforgiving towards yourself or guilty about feeling angry towards someone else? • Are you feeling un-needed/alone?	Crown Chakra- **colour Violet** and Third Eye Chakra- **colour Indigo**

***NOTE... *Our ancestors knew that in times of mental fatigue or emotional imbalance, it was time to 'go nuts'! They knew that pigging out on nuts would restore mental alertness and neurological imbalance. The walnut looks like a brain, it has a left and right hemisphere and upper and lower cerebellum just like the brain, and studies have proven that walnuts are brilliant for the brain! An almond looks like the amygdala, the area of the brain at the foundation of our emotions, and guess what; almonds have proven to be the perfect signature food, enhancing and negating our positive and negative emotions.*

***NUGGET... *The simple gesture of smiling releases endorphins, which are the feel-good hormones! This is why laughter therapy is so powerful and gives true meaning to the saying, 'Fake it till you make it.'*

CENTRAL NERVOUS SYSTEM
HAPPINESS RECIPE

Ingredients: $^1/_3$ cup freshly squeezed orange juice, $^1/_3$ cup strawberries, $^1/_3$ cup raspberries, ½ cup blueberries, 1 cup ice

Method: Blend all ingredients together into a slushie... The coldness will send it straight to the brain for instant results

CENTRAL NERVOUS SYSTEM
FEEL-GOOD SMOOTHIE BOWL

Ingredients: 1 orange, 2 bananas, 2 mango, 1 small pineapple, ½ rock melon, 1 cup of coconut cream.

Granola; ½ cup almonds, ½ cup walnuts, ¼ cup hazelnuts and ⅛ cup pine nuts, ½ cup diced dried apricots, ¼ cup raisins and ⅛ cup cacao nibs, ¼ cup dried shredded coconut

Method: Chop all ingredients, leaving a little of the banana, mango and pineapple to garnish the smoothie bowl. Place the rest in the blender on high speed until thick and creamy. Pour into a shallow bowl and garnish with granola and the remainder of the fruit

Granola; Chop nuts and cacao nibs and place in a jar. Add raisins, coconut and finely diced dried apricots. Keep in a jar in the fridge

CARPEL TUNNEL SYNDROME

WHAT IS IT?... **Carpel tunnel** is a tingling and numb sensation in the hand and arm caused by pressure or compression of the medial nerve that runs the length of the arm and passes through a passage in the wrist called the carpel tunnel. It's thought to be caused by repetitive movements.

BODY – EPICURE

- Get off all medication and supplements- herbs in the form of powders or teas are OK, but no pills or capsules! No antibacterial soaps and wipes!
- **Fastest...** Water fast for 10 days then cabala for 10 days and then 28 days on fruit, nuts and seeds or cherry Pulse **OR...**
- Cabala juice fast for 28–40 days.
- Eat two or three cups of organic cherries each day – these can be fresh, dried or frozen – or eat cherry Pulse.
- Eat and juice a locally grown, fresh, raw organic fruit diet for 90 days.
- Salt- have plenty of good, nature-made salt in the diet and suck on Himalayan rock salt the size of the last segment of your little finger each day.
- Take one teaspoon of Concentrated Boron Solution (7mg) twice daily with meals.
- Take hot water salt baths with one cup epsom salts and one cup bicarb soda first thing in the morning, and again at night if necessary, and then massage with essential oils, Healing Chrysm and Golden ReLeaf.
- Soak in the ocean.
- Use healing clay- mix with hot water to make a thick mud consistency then put the hands into the clay and soak for 10 minutes; follow this by massaging with Healing Chrysm.
- Carry a soft rubber ball and squeeze this throughout the day.
- Sunshine- lie in the sun to assist the liver and neuroendorine glands to stimulate strength to the muscles.
- **ESSENTIAL OIL...** peppermint, eucalyptus, lavender, rosemary.
- (Divine, Cherry Pulse, Mango Pulse, Healing Chrysm, Golden ReLeaf, Ra 24ct See Salt, Himalayan rock salt, essential oils of peppermint, eucalyptus available in the USA **www.thedontolman.com/store** and Australia **www.lynnienichols.com/shop**)

BODY *FOODS THAT HEAL*	MIND *POSSIBLE EMOTIONAL CAUSE*	SPIRIT *IMBALANCED CHAKRA*
---	---	---
SIGNATURE FOODS... apples, asparagus, beans, lentils, legumes, bean sprouts, cashews, eggs, chickpeas, oats, rye, sprouts, spelt, spinach, soybeans, tomatoes, tubers	• Are you feeling angry and bitter that life isn't fair?	Crown Chakra- **colour Violet** / Heart Chakra- colour Green

TESTIMONIAL... *For 6 years, an attendee at my retreat, following carpel tunnel operations, had lived with just 10 degree movement in each wrist. Via a Journey emotional healing process, she was able to determine the blocked cellular memories at the core of the energy blockages in these areas. Much to both of our surprise and absolute delight, the following morning, as she was explaining to the Yoga Teacher that she couldn't do downward dog, she began screaming and crying! Overnight, she had regained full movement in both wrists! This is the power of dealing with the core of dis-ease and not just the symptom! Lyn*

CENTRAL NERVOUS SYSTEM
CONCENTRATED BORON/BORAX SOLUTION

Ingredients: 1 level teaspoon boron/borax, 1 litre of water

Method: Dissolve the borax/boron in one litre of water to make a concentrated solution.

CATARACT / GLAUCOMA

***WHAT IS IT?...* **A cataract** is where the eye's natural lens, which lies behind the pupil and iris, becomes cloudy due to a blockage in the eye's drainage system that prevents light entering the eye sufficiently. This is the most common cause of blindness in the world.

Glaucoma is a condition where the optic nerve, which links the eye to the brain, is damaged due to a blockage in the eye's drainage system, which causes pressure in the eyeball. This is the second leading cause of blindness in the world.

***BODY – EPICURE*

- Get off all medication and supplements- herbs in the form of powders or teas are OK, but no pills or capsules!
- **Fastest...** Water fast for 7–10 days **OR...**
- 21–28-day cabala juice fast whilst snacking on blueberry Pulse, which targets the brain and eyes.
- Do a colon cleanse to remove toxicity/plaque from the colon.
- CARROTS, CARROTS AND MORE CARROTS... Eat two or three medium-sized carrots every day as the sun goes down. Also have carrot juice and a diet rich in all other orange foods for their cartenoids, which heal the eyes.
- Drink one litre of pure water per 22 kilos bodyweight every day.
- Sungazing morning and evenings in 13-second intervals; look at the sun until it reaches a 10-degree arc, or a clenched fist sitting on horizon as sun comes up, stop at top of fist. At night, start gazing as sun hits top of fist until it's gone.
- Use Eyebright herbal tea ... get a glass cup, put a little tea in it then put the cup over the eye and tip up so the tea goes all through the eye; roll eyes around in the tea to help clear infection/blockage.
- Gently warm some organic honey; then, with eyedropper, place two or three drops in each eye before bed.
- **ESSENTIAL OIL...** carrot, frankincense, helichrysm, cypress.
- (Pulse and colon cleanses available at available in the USA **www.thedontolman.com/store** and Australia **www.lynnienichols.com/shop**)

BODY *FOODS THAT HEAL*	MIND *POSSIBLE EMOTIONAL CAUSE*	SPIRIT *IMBALANCED CHAKRA*
---	---	---
SIGNATURE FOODS... apples, almonds, blueberries, broccoli, Brussels sprouts, cabbage, rockmelon, cauliflower, ginger, lettuce, pine nuts, walnuts, watermelon	• Are you disappointed in life/not liking what you see ahead? • Are you afraid of what you see in your future?	Crown Chakra- **colour Violet** and Third Eye Chakra- **colour Indigo**

***NOTE...* *The residues of pharmaceutical eye drops block the drainage channels of the lens of the eye and the back of the eye, causing cataracts and glaucoma... This is the number one cause of both!*

***NUGGET...* *When you cut a carrot, it looks like a pupil and radiating lines. Studies now show that eating one medium-sized carrot every day for seven days increases the blood supply into the eyes by 25%. Visual problems can be remissed in as little as 60 days by eating carrots and doing eye exercises.*

CENTRAL NERVOUS SYSTEM
CARAMALISED SWEET POTATO WITH HONEY CARROTS

Ingredients: 2 large orange sweet potatoes, ½ cup coconut oil, 2 large carrots, juice of 1 orange, 1 tbsp honey, ½ cup olive oil, ½ tsp nature made salt

Method: Cut the sweet potato into 1 cm-thick slices and season with salt. Bake in a moderate oven with the coconut oil until caramelised. Scrub the skins of the organic carrots and then cut with a spiralizer. Make a dressing of olive oil, salt, orange juice and honey and marinate the spirals for a few minutes. Place 1–2 slices of the hot caramelised sweet potato on a serving plate, top with the honeyed carrots and serve. (serves 2)

CEREBRAL PALSY

WHAT IS IT?... Cerebral palsy refers to disorders of the brain, typically caused before or during birth, affecting muscle coordination and causing other disabilities.

BODY – EPICURE

- Get off all medication and supplements- herbs in the form of powders or teas are OK, but no pills or capsules!
- Eat blueberry Pulse, which targets the brain.
- Eat one or two apples every day—especially yellow.
- Drink one litre of pure water per 22 kilos bodyweight every day.
- Magnesium... Have herbal and epsom salt water baths for 20 minutes every day. Also take pure magnesium mixed with water or fresh juice.
- Eat high-magnesium foods such as wholegrains, spinach and dark leafy greens, almonds, quinoa, cashews, edamame, peanuts, dates, pepitas, sesame seeds, sunflower seeds, flax seeds, Brazil nuts, beans including blackbeans, legumes, wild rice, dried fruit, and cocao.
- Sungazing morning and evenings in 13-second intervals; look at the sun until it reaches a 10-degree arc, or a clenched fist sitting on horizon as sun comes up, stop at top of fist. At night, start gazing as sun hits top of fist until it's gone.
- Develop the darkest suntan you can by covering your body in Divine Body Butter or coconut oil and then exposing at least 70% of your body to the sun for one hour every day (30 mins each side).
- Bring back functioning by taking dominant side and do exercises with both sides... Take beanbags and juggle, kick with both feet, become ambidextrous.
- **ESSENTIAL OIL...** peppermint, frankincense.
- (Divine, essential oil of peppermint available at available in the USA **www.thedontolman.com/store** and Australia **www.lynnienichols.com/shop**)

BODY *FOODS THAT HEAL*	MIND *POSSIBLE EMOTIONAL CAUSE*	SPIRIT *IMBALANCED CHAKRA*
---	---	---
SIGNATURE FOODS... apples, almonds, blueberries, broccoli, Brussels sprouts, cabbage, rockmelon, cauliflower, ginger, lettuce, pine nuts, walnuts, watermelon	• Are your thoughts paralysing you, literally?	Crown Chakra- **colour Violet** /Third Eye Chakra- **colour Indigo**

CENTRAL NERVOUS SYSTEM
MAGNESIUM BOOSTER BALLS

Ingredients: ¼ cup almonds, ¼ cup cashews, ¼ cup peanuts, ½ cup brazil nuts, ⅛ cup pepitas, ⅛ cup sunflower seeds, 1 tsp flax seeds, ¾ cup organic cocao powder, 1 ½ cups pitted medjool dates, ¼ cup sesame seeds

Method: Place the nuts in a blender and mix on high until chopped finely. Add the pepitas and flax seeds, dates and cocao and blend again until the mixture forms a ball in the processor or feels moist enough to stick together in balls (if it feels a little dry, add a few drops of water). Roll into balls and coat with sesame seeds. Keep in airtight container in the fridge

Makes 10 balls

Magnesium Booster Balls and Lemon Balls

CHRONIC FATIGUE SYNDROME (CFS)/MYALGIC ENCEPHALOMYELITIS(ME)/ SYSTEMIC EXERTION INTOLERANCE DISEASE (SEID)

WHAT IS IT?... **Chronic fatigue syndrome** is a condition characterised by prolonged periods of extreme tiredness and/or fatigue with no underlying medical conditon that persists regardless of the amount of rest a person has.

BODY – EPICURE

- Get off all medication and supplements- herbs in the form of powders or teas are OK, but no pills or capsules!
- **Fastest...** Water fast for 7–14 days **OR...**
- Cabala Fast for 30–40 days or water fast combined with eating blueberry Pulse for 30 days.
- Become fruitarian, including nuts and seeds for 30–90 days.
- Do the five-week 35% food-grade hydrogen peroxide protocol combined with a cabala juice fast for 14–28 days. If needed, can have raw vegan food also.
- Sungazing morning and evenings in 13-second intervals; look at the sun until it reaches a 10-degree arc, or a clenched fist sitting on horizon as sun comes up, stop at top of fist. At night, start gazing as sun hits top of fist until it's gone.
- Develop the darkest suntan you can by covering your body in Divine Body Butter or coconut oil and then exposing at least 70% of your body to the sun for one hour every day (30 mins each side).
- Walk for 30–45 minutes, twice a day if possible, to oxygenate the blood and lift the neurochemistry of the brain by releasing endorphins.
- Eat and juice a locally grown, fresh, raw organic vegan diet for highest nutritional force, making sure that every day you eat raw wholefoods of all seven colours of the rainbow—red, orange, yellow, blue, green, indigo/violet and white. Especially beneficial are locally grown organic broccoli, cauliflower and asparagus (when in season).
- Snack on nuts—walnuts, almonds and macadamias. Eat dried apricots and other dried fruits as these remove plaque and give the brain energy.
- Suck on Himalayan rock salt every day.
- Drink one litre per 22 kilos bodyweight of pure water every day.
- Eat at least two cups of orange and yellow foods combined every day, for example pineapple and orange together. Also surround yourself with these colours, i.e. your clothing, bed linen, paintings on walls, etc. This will help lift the emotional state, which will in turn help the physical body.
- Rub peppermint oil in the palm of your hand until warm; breathe in and blow out, put hands back over nose and inhale. Do this for 30–45 seconds two or three times each day. Massage a drop of peppermint oil into the temples and back of neck.
- Laughter truly is the best therapy, so watch funny videos, join a laughter therapy group, be with people who make you laugh and feel good, and stay away from those who do the opposite!
- Take up meditation/yoga.
- **ESSENTIAL OIL...** peppermint, rosemary, lemon.
- (Divine, 34% food-grade hydrogen peroxide, Himalayan rock salt, essential oil of peppermint available in the USA **www.thedontolman.com/store** and Australia **www.lynnienichols.com/shop**)

BODY *FOODS THAT HEAL*	MIND *POSSIBLE EMOTIONAL CAUSE*	SPIRIT *IMBALANCED CHAKRA*
---	---	---
SIGNATURE FOODS... apples, almonds, blueberries, broccoli, Brussels sprouts, cabbage, rockmelon, cauliflower, ginger, lettuce, pine nuts, walnuts, watermelon	- Are you feeling stuck or stubborn, unable or unwilling to change, just wanting to give up? - Are you feeling like a victim, 'it's not fair' mentality? - Are you subconsciously gaining something from being ill, i.e. attention, love, monetary assistance? (secondary gains) - Are you giving your power away to others by just settling with what is?	Crown Chakra- **colour Violet** /Third Eye Chakra- **colour Indigo**

***NOTE...** In a pre-1900s dictionary, you will find the original meaning of FRUIT to be: 'to add splendour and light...food that comes from a star pattern.' When you cut open an apple, the seeds are in a five-pointed star. The green parts of the stems of tomatoes, strawberries, blueberries, etc. are all five-pointed stars. Nuts are fruits, they grown on fruit trees. Seeds are the fruits of grasses.*

***NUGGET... *The 'Ancients' knew that each 24-hour day should be made up of eight hours of sleep, eight hours of passion/work and eight hours of family time, and that living this way would ensure a beautiful balanced life.*

CENTRAL NERVOUS SYSTEM
FATIGUE BOWL WITH BLUEBERRY CASHEW CREAM

Ingredients: 1 yellow, 1 green and 1 red apple including skin and seeds, 1/2 rockmelon, 1/2 cup chopped walnuts, 1/2 cup chopped almonds

CASHEW CREAM; **(see recipe in back of book, then add ¼ cup blueberries)**

Method: Chop the apples and rockmelon into 1–2 cm square pieces. Place in a bowl and drizzle with cashew cream. Garnish with the chopped almond/walnut mix and serve.

CHRONIC PAIN SYNDROME (CPS)

WHAT IS IT?... **Chronic pain syndrome** is the term given to an acute pain or injury that lasts longer than six months.

BODY – EPICURE

- Get off all medication and supplements- herbs in the form of powders or teas are OK, but no pills or capsules!
- **Fastest...** Water fast for 14 days **OR...**
- A mono diet of water and blueberry Pulse.
- Cabala juice fast for 30–40 days... Do the five-week 35% food-grade hydrogen peroxide protocol combined with a cabala juice fast. If needed, can have raw vegan food also.
- Pig out on cherries.
- Eat and juice a locally grown, fresh, raw organic vegan diet for highest nutritional force, making sure that every day you eat raw wholefoods of all seven colours of the rainbow—red, orange, yellow, blue, green, indigo/violet and white.
- Suck on rock salt every day.
- Drink one litre per 22 kilos bodyweight of pure water, every day or one glass every hour on the hour for at least 10 hours of the day.
- Have daily a berry, asparaus smoothie, consisting of two cups berries and 12 stalks of asparagus (can add a banana to sweeten) plus water to desired consistency.

Drink within 45 minutes of making it. Can eat the foods instead if preferred.
- Take hot water salt baths with one cup epsom salts and one cup bicarb soda first thing in the morning, and again at night if necessary, and then massage with essential oils, Healing Chrysm and Golden ReLeaf.
- Sungazing morning and evenings in 13-second intervals; look at the sun until it reaches a 10-degree arc or a clenched fist sitting on horizon as sun comes up, stop at top of fist. At night, start gazing as sun hits top of fist until it's gone.
- Develop the darkest suntan you can by covering your body in Divine Body Butter or coconut oil and then exposing at least 70% of your body to the sun for one hour every day (30 mins each side).
- **ESSENTIAL OIL...** lavender, peppermint, eucalyptus, sandalwood.
- (Blueberry Pulse, Divine, 35% food-grade hydrogen peroxide, essential oil of lavender available in the USA **www.thedontolman.com/store** and Australia **www.lynnienichols.com/shop**)

BODY *FOODS THAT HEAL*	**MIND** *POSSIBLE EMOTIONAL CAUSE*	**SPIRIT** *IMBALANCED CHAKRA*
---	---	---
SIGNATURE FOODS... apples, almonds, blueberries, broccoli, Brussels sprouts, cabbage, rockmelon, cauliflower, ginger, lettuce, pine nuts, walnuts, watermelon	• Are you feeling guilty/unable to forgive yourself? • On some level, do you believe you should be punished?	Crown Chakra- **colour Violet** /Third Eye Chakra- **colour Indigo**

***NUGGET... *Pain is a mechanism of the autogenic self-healing system that drives the cells that heal and repair the trauma or problem in the body—don't stay on pain pills for more than seven days.*

CENTRAL NERVOUS SYSTEM
CHERRY RIPE CHOCOLATE SLAB

Ingredients: ¾ cup almonds, ¼ cup walnuts, 1 cup chopped dried cherries, 1 cup dessicated coconut, ¾ cup cacao powder, 2 tbsp honey, ½ cup almond butter, ²/₃ cup coconut oil, pinch of Himalayan salt

Method: Place the almonds and walnuts in a processor and blend until nuts are breadcrumb texture. Remove and place in a mixing bowl. Add to nut mix the cherries, coconut, cacao powder, honey, almond butter, salt and coconut oil. Mix well. Pour the chocolate onto a greased tray and refrigerate for an hour before cutting into squares.

CONJUNCTIVITIS/PINKEYE

WHAT IS IT?... **Conjunctivitis** is infection/inflammation of the mucous membrane that lines the inner eyelid and the whites of the eyeballs, called the conjunctiva.

BODY – EPICURE

- Flush the eyes with salt water several times per day and then place two drops of colloidal silver in each eye before bed.
- Can also warm some raw honey and put one to three drops in each eye to clear infection.
- Eat blueberry Pulse to target the central nervous system.
- Suck on rock salt every day.

- Drink one litre per 22 kilos bodyweight of pure water, every day or one glass every hour on the hour for at least 10 hours of the day.
- **ESSENTIAL OIL...** carrot, frankincense, helichrysum, cypress.
- (Blueberry Pulse, Divine, Natures Silver Bullet (colloidal silver) available in the USA www.thedontolman.com/store and Australia **www.lynnienichols.com/shop**)

BODY *FOODS THAT HEAL*	MIND *POSSIBLE EMOTIONAL CAUSE*	SPIRIT *IMBALANCED CHAKRA*
---	---	---
SIGNATURE FOODS... apples, almonds, blueberries, broccoli, Brussels sprouts, cabbage, rockmelon, cauliflower, ginger, lettuce, pine nuts, walnuts, watermelon	• Are you feeling angry or frustrated? • Are you only seeing the negative in life?	Crown Chakra- **colour Violet** /Third Eye Chakra- **colour Indigo**

***NOTE...** For fungal invasion/eye infection- melt organic honey and drop two or three drops in each eye before bed.

*** **TESTIMONIAL...** For several days my teenage daughter had complained about sore, irritated eyes. They looked OK to me, so I didn't take much notice until one morning she woke up with very bad conjunctivitis. I took her to the chemist to see if there was something semi-natural we could put in her eyes, only to be told that the conjunctivitis was extreme and therefore she would need to go to the doctor for antibiotics. I pursuaded my daughter to give me 24 hrs trying colloidal silver, which I'd used previously and found to be amazing. Sure enough, two drops of colloidal silver in each eye, and the following day all signs of the conjunctivitis were completely gone and did not return! Lyn

CENTRAL NERVOUS SYSTEM
CARROT AND BLUEBERRY JUICE

Ingredients: 4 large carrots, 1 cup blueberries, 1 tbsp honey

Method: Juice the carrots and blueberries and pour into a serving glass. Add the honey and serve

CUSHING'S DISEASE/SYNDROME

WHAT IS IT?... **Cushing's disease** occurs when too much of the the hormone responsible for cortisol production called ACTH is produced, caused by a tumour on the pituitary gland. The high levels of ACTH then signal the adrenal glands to produce high levels of cortisol. Cushing's disease is the most common form of Cushing's syndrome.

BODY – EPICURE

- Get off all medication and supplements- herbs in the form of powders or teas are OK, but no pills or capsules!
- **Fastest...** Water fast for 7–10 days **OR...**
- A mono diet of water and blueberry Pulse.
- Cabala juice fast for 30–40 days.
- Lower cortisol levels by eating foods high in bromelain daily—one cup of pineapple, ½ cup Brazil nuts and one or two bananas.
- Eat and juice a locally grown, fresh, raw organic vegan diet for highest nutritional force, making sure that every day you eat raw wholefoods of all seven colours of the rainbow—red, orange, yellow, blue, green, indigo/violet and white. Especially beneficial are locally grown organic broccoli, cauliflower and asparagus (when in season).
- Have daily a berry, asparaus smoothie, consisting of two cups berries and 12 stalks of asparagus (can add a banana to sweeten) plus water to desired consistency. Drink within 30 mins of making it. Can eat the foods instead if preferred.
- Snack on almonds, walnuts, pecans, macadamias, pinenuts, potato, sweet potato and carrots.
- **ESSENTIAL OIL...** frankincense, peppermint.
- (Blueberry Pulse available, essential oil of peppermint available in the USA **www.thedontolman.com/store** and Australia **www.lynnienichols.com/shop**)

BODY *FOODS THAT HEAL*	MIND *POSSIBLE EMOTIONAL CAUSE*	SPIRIT *IMBALANCED CHAKRA*
---	---	---
SIGNATURE FOODS... apples, almonds, blueberries, broccoli, Brussels sprouts, cabbage, rockmelon, cauliflower, ginger, lettuce, pine nuts, walnuts, watermelon	• Are you feeling overpowered or a loss of your own power? • Are you feeling mentally overwhelmed/too many negative thoughts about your own ideas?	Crown Chakra- **colour Violet** /Third Eye Chakra- **colour Indigo**

***NOTE... *In case of a seizure, take a brown paper bag and breathe into the bag for one to three minutes to rebalance the gasses going into the brain. Eat high calcium foods, especially spinach and other dark leafy greens, to correct this.*

***NUGGET... *The highest source of bromelain is found in pineapple.*

CENTRAL NERVOUS SYSTEM
PINEAPPLE MOUSSE

Ingredients: 1 large pineapple including core, 1 cup Brazil nuts soaked in the fridge overnight then skins removed, 1 cup cashews soaked in the fridge for 2 hrs or more, 2 large bananas

Method: Place all ingredients in a blender and process until a thick, smooth creamy mousse consistency. Serve in a cocktail glass garnished with a slice of pineapple

EPILEPSY/TEMPORAL LOBE EPILEPSY

WHAT IS IT?... **Epilepsy** is a neurological disorder resulting in seizures, sensory distortion, convulsions and even loss of consciousness, caused by an imbalance of gases in the brain, which can be caused by a shortage of blood calcium.

Temporal lobe epilepsy is the most common form of epilepsy, originating in the temporal lobe of the brain, with seizures lasting around one to two minutes.

BODY – EPICURE

- Get off all medication and supplements- herbs in the form of powders or teas are OK, but no pills or capsules!
- Drink two or three cups of rosemary tea every day.
- Eat lots of high calcium foods including all green foods, especially dark leafy greens, oranges, rhubarb, tangerines, apricots, kiwifruit, medjool dates, figs, plums, prunes, soybeans, edamame, kale, celery, collard, broccoli, kelp, spinach, and leafy greens.

KIDS...

- Take a brown paper bag squeezed at the top, put over the nose and get the child to breathe into the bag for three to five minutes to balance the brain gases and overwhelm; this stops the seizure.
- Smoothies or green drinks, can add organic honey, almonds, organic yoghurts/kefir.
- **ESSENTIAL OIL...** orange, lavender, lemongrass.
- (Essential oil of orange available in the USA **www.thedontolman.com/store** and Australia **www.lynnienichols.com/shop**)

BODY *FOODS THAT HEAL*	MIND *POSSIBLE EMOTIONAL CAUSE*	SPIRIT *IMBALANCED CHAKRA*
---	---	---
SIGNATURE FOODS... apples, almonds, blueberries, broccoli, Brussels sprouts, cabbage, rockmelon, cauliflower, ginger, lettuce, pine nuts, walnuts, watermelon	• Are you feeling criticised/attacked, or are you rejecting and criticising yourself? • Are you feling neglected/ mistreated?	Crown Chakra- **colour Violet**

***NOTE...** Eating/drinking green foods, especially dark leafy greens, is the best way to increase blood calcium levels.*

CENTRAL NERVOUS SYSTEM
CALCIUM BOOSTER SMOOTHIE

Ingredients: 2 cups of dark leafy greens including kale, collard and spinach, 2 large oranges peeled and de-seeded, 5 medjool dates pitted, ½ cup water, either 1–2 large bananas or 1 cup organic natural yoghurt or vegan option, coconut yoghurt

Method: Chop all ingredients and place in a blender with the water on high speed until mixed to a smooth consistency. Add more water until desired consistency. (serves 1)

INSOMNIA

WHAT IS IT?... **Insomnia** is a sleep disorder where people regularly have trouble falling asleep or wake during the night and cannot get back to sleep.

BODY – EPICURE

- Get off all medication and supplements- herbs in the form of powders or teas are OK, but no pills or capsules!
- **Fastest...** Water fast for 7–10 days **OR...**
- 21–28-day cabala juice fast whilst snacking on nuts and berries or blueberry Pulse.
- Do a colon cleanse to remove toxicity/plaque.
- Drink one glass of water every hour on the hour for 10 hours of each day for 30 days.
- Ensure you have a routine sleep pattern every night and resist napping during the day. Mix 1 tsp of lavender oil with a cup of water and spray on the pillow and bed, can also massage some of this on temples and the back of the neck just before bed.
- Eat and juice a locally grown, fresh, raw organic vegan diet.
- Have your evening meal at least two hours before bed and drink a mug of warm raw, organic cow's milk or a warm nut milk mixed with raw organic honey just before bed.
- Eat dark organic chocolate or drink one or two unfiltered organic wheat beers an hour or so before bed.
- Drink cammomile tea an hour or so before bed.
- Sungazing morning and evenings in 13-second intervals; look at the sun until it reaches a 10-degree arc, or a clenched fist sitting on horizon as sun comes up, stop at top of fist. At night, start gazing as sun hits top of fist until it's gone.
- Develop the darkest suntan you can by covering your body in Divine Body Butter or coconut oil and then exposing at least 70% of your body to the sun for one hour every day, 30 mins each side.
- Exercise five days a week, walk 30–45 minutes morning and night if possible.
- Take up meditation and practice this just before you go to bed.
- **ESSENTIAL OIL...** lavender, chamomile.
- (Blueberry Pulseavailable, Divine, colon cleanses, essential oil of lavender available in the USA **www.thedontolman.com/store** and Australia **www.lynnienichols.com/shop**)

BODY *FOODS THAT HEAL*	MIND *POSSIBLE EMOTIONAL CAUSE*	SPIRIT *IMBALANCED CHAKRA*
---	---	---
SIGNATURE FOODS... apples, almonds, blueberries, broccoli, Brussels sprouts, cabbage, rockmelon, cauliflower, ginger, lettuce, pine nuts, walnuts, watermelon	• Are you feeling guilty/not good enough/a failure? • Is fear of the future constantly on your mind? • Are you holding unforgiveness toward people from your past?	Crown Chakra- **colour Violet**

CENTRAL NERVOUS SYSTEM
WARM CHOCOLATE NUTMILK DRINK

Ingredients: ½ cup cashews, ½ cup almonds, ½ litre water, 1 tsp honey, 1 tsp organic cacao powder

Method: Place the cashews, almonds and water into a high-speed blender and process to a smooth liquid. Pour the liquid into a nutmilk bag and squeeze, capturing the milk in a bowl. Place a cup of nutmilk in a saucepan with the cacao powder and warm gently. Remove from the stove and add the honey

(The nut pulp can be used to make chocolate or raw balls)

MACULAR DEGENERATION

WHAT IS IT?... **Macular degeneration** is where the central portion of the retina, called the macula, deteriorates, causing progressive loss of vision.

BODY – EPICURE

- Get off all medication and supplements- herbs in the form of powders or teas are OK, but no pills or capsules!
- **Fastest...** Water fast for 7–10 days **OR...**
- 21–28-day cabala juice fast whilst snacking on blueberry Pulse, which targets the brain and eyes.
- Do a colon cleanse to remove toxicity/plaque from the colon.
- CARROTS, CARROTS AND MORE CARROTS... Eat two or three medium-sized carrots every day as the sun goes down. Also have carrot juice and a diet rich in all other orange foods for their cartenoids, which heal the eyes.
- Drink one litre of pure water per 22 kilos bodyweight every day.

- Sungazing morning and evenings in 13-second intervals; look at the sun until it reaches a 10-degree arc, or a clenched fist sitting on horizon as sun comes up, stop at top of fist. At night, start gazing as sun hits top of fist until it's gone.
- Use Eyebright herbal tea ... Get a glass cup, put a little tea in it then put the cup over the eye and tip up so the tea goes all through the eye. Roll eyes around in the tea to help clear infection/blockage.
- **ESSENTIAL OIL...** carrot, frankincense, helichrysum, cypress.
- (Blueberry Pulse available, Divine, colon cleanses available in the USA **www.thedontolman.com/store** and Australia **www.lynnienichols.com/shop**)

BODY *FOODS THAT HEAL*	MIND *POSSIBLE EMOTIONAL CAUSE*	SPIRIT *IMBALANCED CHAKRA*
---	---	---
SIGNATURE FOODS... apples, almonds, blueberries, broccoli, Brussels sprouts, cabbage, rockmelon, cauliflower, ginger, lettuce, pine nuts, walnuts, watermelon	• Are you afraid of what the future holds, or not liking what you see in the past? • Is your view of the future scary or unclear?	Crown Chakra- **colour Violet** / Third Eye Chakra- **colour Indigo**

***NUGGET... *We receive biophotons of light via the sun so NO sunglasses and NO pharmacy eyedrops!*

CENTRAL NERVOUS SYSTEM
SUNDOWNER SALAD

Ingredients: 1 large carrot, 2 oranges peeled and deseeded, 1 large sweet potato, ½ cup of slithered almonds, ½ cup coconut oil, sea salt

Method: Peel and dice the sweet potato into 2 cm cubes then toss in a bowl with some coconut oil to coat well. Place on an oven tray, sprinkle with sea salt and bake until caramelised. Set aside to cool. Peel the carrot and slice into matchsticks with a mandolin or grate coarsely. Peel and deseed the oranges and cut into 2 cm cubes. Lightly toast the slithered almonds in a dry pan. Mix all ingredients together and drizzle with orange dressing just before serving

ORANGE DRESSING; **(see recipe under Dressings in back of book)**

Serves 1

MENINGITIS/MENINGOCOCCAL DISEASE

WHAT IS IT?... **Meningitis/meningococcal disease** is a disease caused by inflammation of the meninges, which are the delicate membranes covering the brain and spinal cord, resulting in intense headaches, fever, stiff muscles, light sensitivity and, in some cases, death.

BODY – EPICURE

- Get off all medication and supplements- herbs in the form of powders or teas are OK, but no pills or capsules!
- Water fast for 7–10 days **OR...**
- Do a five-week 35% food-grade, hydrogen peroxide protocol whilst cabala juice fasting... You can also have raw vegan foods if necessary.
- Drink 1 cup of pure lemon juice with honey every day (can add water).
- Suck on rock salt every day.
- Drink one litre per 22 kilos bodyweight of pure water every day.
- Have daily a berry, asparaus smoothie, consisting of two cups berries and 12 stalks of asparagus (can add a banana to sweeten) plus water to desired consistency. Drink within 30 mins of making it. Can eat the foods instead if preferred.
- Do a colon cleanse with bentonite clay, herbs etc. to remove chemical toxicity/plaque.
- CHILDREN... Drink three or four cups of hot lemon juice with water and honey each day.
- Have daily a berry, asparaus smoothie, consisting of two cups berries and 12 stalks of asparagus (can add a banana to sweeten) plus water to desired consistency. Drink within 45 minutes of making it. Can eat the foods instead if preferred.
- Eat a diet consisting of lots of good nature-made salt, apples and blueberries, along with all other foods that support the cleansing and healing of the CNS.
- **ESSENTIAL OIL...** frankincense, lavender, lemon.
- (Blueberry Pulse, Divine, colon cleanses, 35% food-grade hydrogen peroxide, Himalayan rock salt, Ra 24ct See Salt, essential oil of lemon available in the USA **www.thedontolman.com/store** and Australia **www. lynnienichols.com/shop**)

BODY *FOODS THAT HEAL*	MIND *POSSIBLE EMOTIONAL CAUSE*	SPIRIT *IMBALANCED CHAKRA*
---	---	---
SIGNATURE FOODS... apples, almonds, blueberries, broccoli, Brussels sprouts, cabbage, rockmelon, cauliflower, ginger, lettuce, pine nuts, walnuts, watermelon	• Are you unable to accept new ideas due to feeling you know everything? • Are you feeling scared and attached? • Are you feeling restricted, supressed, exhausted and unable to cope with life?	Crown Chakra- **colour Violet**

***NOTE... *Viruses cannot live in the presence of honey or the anions of lemon.*

CENTRAL NERVOUS SYSTEM
CLEANSING SALAD

Ingredients: ½ small green cabbage, ½ small red cabbage, ½ cos lettuce, 1 green apple with skin and seeds, 1 cup blueberries, ½ cup pine nuts, 1 tsp ginger

DRESSING; juice of 2 lemons, ½ tsp sea salt, 1 tbsp honey, 1 cup cold pressed virgin olive oil

Method: Finely shred the cabbage and lettuce and place in a salad bowl. Dice the ginger—add to lettuce mix. Slice the apple into matchsticks with a mandolin and add, along with the pine nuts and blueberries. Blend the dressing ingredients together, mix into the salad and serve.

MIDDLE EAR INFECTION

WHAT IS IT?... **Middle ear infection** is when a virus or bacteria causes the area behind the eardrum to become infected, causing pus, redness, inflammation, pain and possible fever.

BODY – EPICURE

- Get off all medication and supplements- herbs in the form of powders or teas are OK, but no pills or capsules!
- Firstly, cleanse the inner ear with 3% food-grade hydrogen peroxide (can make this by mixing one part 35% food-grade hydrogen peroxide with 11 parts water … i.e. 11 tbsp water to 1 tbsp 35% food-grade h2o2). Place three or four drops of 3% hydrogen peroxide in one ear, let it fizz and bubble for three or four minutes then twist up a tissue the size of a cigarette and push into the ear to clear all of the dirt etc. from the ear. Roll over and do the same to the opposite ear. Do this twice for each ear. The next day, use two ear candles per ear to cleanse the inner ear. In the morning, put three or four drops of warm olive oil or safflower oil in each ear. Keep this in with a cotton ball throughout the day. In the evening, get a cotton bud and clear the oil out of the ear. Do this daily for three or four days.
- You can also put two drops of colloidal silver in the ear, keeping it there overnight with a cotton ball.
- You can roast some onion and squeeze two drops of warm onion juice into the ear, allowing the onion fumes to also go into the ear; keep this in overnight with a cotton ball.
- Do a liver/gall bladder cleanse to clear toxicity by mixing one litre of grapefruit juice and one cup of olive oil together. Drink this just before you go to bed at night. Try not to get up after doing this except if needing to go to the toilet. Typically the next day you will pass gallstones.
- Do an intestinal cleanse as the nerve flux from the ears connects to the transverse colon; therefore, removing the toxic plaque by stripping the mucosal lining will be highly beneficial.
- Snack on fresh ginger.
- Suck on Himalayan rock salt throughout the day.
- Place one or two drops of peppermint oil in the mouth, swish and swallow.
- Sniff a mix of peppermint oil/tea tree oil and water into the nose, allow this to run into the throat and swallow or use Breathe-EZ nasal spray.
- **ESSENTIAL OIL...** peppermint, tea tree, oregano, basil, garlic.
- (Breathe-EZ, Divine, colon cleanses, Nature's Silver Bullet colloidal silver, Himalayan rock salt, 35% food-grade hydrogen peroxide, essential oil of peppermint and tea tree available in the USA **www.thedontolman. com/store** and Australia **www.lynnienichols.com/ shop**)

BODY *FOODS THAT HEAL*	**MIND** *POSSIBLE EMOTIONAL CAUSE*	**SPIRIT** *IMBALANCED CHAKRA*
---	---	---
SIGNATURE FOODS... apples, almonds, blueberries, broccoli, Brussels sprouts, cabbage, rockmelon, cauliflower, ginger, lettuce, pine nuts, walnuts, watermelon	• Are you feeling like no one is listening? • Are you angry and not wanting to hear?	Crown Chakra- **colour Violet** / Third Eye Chakra- **colour Indigo**

CENTRAL NERVOUS SYSTEM
ANCIENT DEAFNESS REMEDY

Ingredients: 1 tbsp honey, 1 tbsp cinnamon, hot water

Method: In a mug of hot water add the cinnamon and honey. Drink one cup in the morning and one cup in the afternoon daily for three to six months

MIGRAINE HEADACHE

WHAT IS IT?... **A migraine** is a severe and painful headache that can last for hours, even days, typically affecting one side of the head and often accompanied by nausea, sensitivity to light and sound and sometimes even numbness/ mild temporary paralysis.

BODY – EPICURE

- Get off all medication and supplements- herbs in the form of powders or teas are okay, but no pills or capsules!
- **Fastest...** Water fast for 7–10 days **OR...**
- 21–28-day cabala juice fast whilst snacking on blueberry Pulse, which targets the brain and eyes.
- Do a colon cleanse to remove toxicity/plaque from the colon.
- Become a fruitarian—all fruits, nuts and seeds.
- Drink one glass of water every hour throughout the day for 7–14 days.
- Suck on Himalayan rock salt and have salt in your diet.
- Every 20 minutes during the day get up and walk away from what you are doing, i.e. your computer, and do long-distance viewing for three minutes.
- Sungazing morning and evenings in 13-second intervals; look at the sun until it reaches a 10-degree arc, or a clenched fist sitting on horizon as sun comes up, stop at top of fist.
- At night, start gazing as sun hits top of fist until it's gone.
- If you have a migraine, get someone to push the palm of their hand down on your forehead while their other hand pushes and squeezes the back of your head intensely for 30 seconds, then release immediately. This pressure and constriction opens and dialates the blood flow to the brain.
- **ESSENTIAL OIL...** lavender, peppermint, rosemary, chamomile.
- (Blueberry Pulse, Himalayan rock salt, Ra See Salt, essential oil of lavender available in the USA **www. thedontolman.com/store** and Australia **www. lynnienichols.com/shop**)

BODY *FOODS THAT HEAL*	MIND *POSSIBLE EMOTIONAL CAUSE*	SPIRIT *IMBALANCED CHAKRA*
---	---	---
SIGNATURE FOODS... apples, almonds, blueberries, broccoli, Brussels sprouts, cabbage, rockmelon, cauliflower, ginger, lettuce, pine nuts, walnuts, watermelon	• Are you neglecting to communicate your needs to others? • Are you allowing others to control you and resenting that? • Are you lacking in self-love and acceptance and placing pressure on yourself by having to be perfect? • Are you holding on to fears around sexuality?	Crown Chakra- **colour Violet** / Third Eye Chakra- **colour Indigo**

CENTRAL NERVOUS SYSTEM
RAW BLUEBERRY CHEESECAKE

Ingredients: Base: ½ cup almonds, ½ cup walnuts, ½ cup coarsely shredded coconut, 1 cup deseeded medjool dates, 1 cup cacao nibs, 1 tsp vanilla paste

Filling; 2 cups cashews soaked for 2hrs. in water, 1 cup blueberries, ⅛ cup apple cider vinegar, ½ cup water, ¾ cup organic virgin cold pressed coconut oil, 2 ½ tbsp honey, 1 cup pitted medjool dates

Method: Base... place the almonds, walnuts and shredded coconut into a food processer and mix on high speed until breadcrumb texture. Add the dates, cacao nibs and vanilla paste and process again until the mixture forms a ball in the processor or sticks together when you squeeze some between your fingers. If it feels a bit dry, add a drizzle of coconut oil or water and mix again. When ready, press into a lightly greased spring-form cake tin and refrigerate

Filling: Place the deseeded dates in a blender with ¾ cup water, ¾ cup coconut oil, 2 tbsp honey, the ACV and blueberries and let sit for half an hour before blending on high speed until creamy. Drain the cashews and add to the blueberry mix. Process on high speed to a very smooth, creamy consistency. Pour filling onto the base and set overnight in the fridge or freezer

Decorate with fresh blueberries when serving.

MILD TRAUMATIC BRAIN INJURY (MTBI)

WHAT IS IT?... **Mild traumatic brain injury** is the result of impact or force to the head, which causes a brief state of disorientation, confusion or loss of consciousness, resulting in symptoms such as headaches, fatigue, lack of concentration and dizziness for up to one year afterward.

BODY – EPICURE

- Get off all medication and supplements- herbs in the form of powders or teas are okay, but no pills or capsules, especially fish oils.
- **Fastest...** Water fast for 7–10 days **OR...**
- 21–28-day cabala juice fast whilst snacking on blueberry Pulse, which targets the brain.
- Eat and juice a locally grown, fresh, raw organic vegan diet for highest nutritional force.
- Eat lots of pectin—apples, peaches, oranges, tomatoes, grapefruit and apricots, i.e. two or three apples every day.
- Eat lots of carrots, potatoes and all other tubers.
- Drink one glass of water every hour throughout the day for 7–14 days.
- Have one cup of lemon juice every day, can mix with pure water.

- Sungazing morning and evenings in 13-second intervals; look at the sun until it reaches a 10-degree arc, or a clenched fist sitting on horizon as sun comes up, stop at top of fist. At night, start gazing as sun hits top of fist until it's gone.
- Sniff essential oil of peppermint at regular intervals.
- Develop the darkest suntan you can by covering your body in Divine Body Butter or coconut oil and then exposing at least 70% of your body to the sun for one hour every day (30 mins each side).
- **ESSENTIAL OIL...** peppermint, frankincense, orange.
- (Divine, Blueberry Pulse, essential oil of peppermint, orange available in the USA **www.thedontolman.com/store** and Australia **www.lynnienichols.com/shop**)

BODY *FOODS THAT HEAL*	MIND *POSSIBLE EMOTIONAL CAUSE*	SPIRIT *IMBALANCED CHAKRA*
---	---	---
SIGNATURE FOODS... apples, almonds, blueberries, broccoli, Brussels sprouts, cabbage, rockmelon, cauliflower, ginger, lettuce, pine nuts, walnuts, watermelon	• The brain symbolises the central computer, so... • Are you refusing to change beliefs and outdated programming? • Are you being stubborn? • Are you feeling a sense of emotional overwhelm/overload?	Crown Chakra- **colour Violet** / Third Eye Chakra- **colour Indigo**

NUGGET... *Carrots, potatoes and all other tubers grown under the ground are 'house cleaners' and get to the very foundation of the human body's ability to cleanse and heal itself.*

Pectin crosses the blood/brain barrier and pulls out the heavy metals such as lead and mercury, which have become stored at the base of the brain.

CENTRAL NERVOUS SYSTEM
PECTIN PIGOUT

Ingredients: 2 red, 2 green and 2 yellow apples, 5 peaches, 3 oranges, 2 ruby-red grapefruit, 2 cups dried preservative-free apricots

ORANGE CASHEW CREAM; 1 drop orange essential oil, ½ cup fresh squeezed orange juice, 1 cup cashews, 1 tbsp honey

Method: Dice the apples with skins and cores into 2 cm cubes, peel the peaches and cut the flesh into slices, peel and deseed the oranges and grapefruit and cut into 2 cm cubes, cut the dried apricots into thin slices. Mix together in a serving bowl.

Cashew Cream; Soak the cashews in water for 2 hours. Strain and place in a blender with the orange juice, honey and orange oil. Mix on high speed until very smooth and creamy. Dollop this onto the fruit salad and serve. (serves 4)

MULTIPLE SCLEROSIS (MS)

WHAT IS IT?... **Multiple sclerosis** is a disease that affects the nerve cells in the brain, spinal cord and optic nerve in the eyes. Symptoms may include impairment to muscular coordination and balance, vision and speech, and may create numbness and severe fatigue.

BODY – EPICURE

- Get off all medication and supplements- herbs in the form of powders or teas are okay, but no pills or capsules!
- **Fastest...** Water fast for 7–10 days **OR...**
- 21–28-day cabala juice fast whilst snacking on blueberry Pulse, which targets the brain. Do the five-week 35% food-grade hydrogen peroxide protocol at the same time.
- Do a colon cleanse to remove toxicity from the body.
- Have one cup of lemon juice every day, can mix with pure water.
- Eat and juice a locally grown, fresh, raw organic vegan diet for highest nutritional force, making sure that every day you eat raw wholefoods of all seven colours of the rainbow—red, orange, yellow, blue, green, indigo/violet and white. Especially beneficial are locally grown organic broccoli, cauliflower and asparagus (when in season).
- Snack on nuts—walnuts, almonds and macadamias. Eat dried apricots and other dried fruits as these remove plaque and give the brain energy.
- Suck on rock salt every day.
- Drink one litre per 22 kilos bodyweight of pure water every day.
- Have daily a berry, asparaus smoothie, consisting of two cups berries and 12 stalks of asparagus (can add a banana to sweeten) plus water to desired consistency. Drink within 45 minutes of making it. Can eat the foods instead if preferred.

- Magnesium... Have herbal and epsom salt water baths for 20 minutes every day. Also take pure magnesium mixed with water or fresh juice.
- Eat high-magnesium foods such as wholegrains, spinach and dark leafy greens, almonds, quinoa, cashews, edamame, peanuts, dates, pepitas, sesame seeds, sunflower seeds, flax seeds, Brazil nuts, beans including blackbeans, legumes, wild rice, dried fruit, and cacao.
- Sungazing morning and evenings in 13-second intervals; look at the sun until it reaches a 10-degree arc, or a clenched fist sitting on horizon as sun comes up, stop at top of fist. At night, start gazing as sun hits top of fist until it's gone.
- Develop the darkest suntan you can by covering your body in Divine Body Butter or coconut oil and then exposing at least 70% of your body to the sun for one hour every day (30 mins each side).
- Get three small juggling bags/balls and practice juggling daily—this creates neuroplasticity in the cells to redevelop lost function.
- **ESSENTIAL OIL...** peppermint, frankincense, orange.
- (Blueberry Pulse, Divine, colon cleanses, 35% food-grade hydrogen peroxide, Himalayan rock salt, Ra 24ct Gold See Salt, essential oil of peppermint and orange available in the USA **www.thedontolman.com/store** and Australia **www.lynnienichols.com/shop**)

BODY *FOODS THAT HEAL*	MIND *POSSIBLE EMOTIONAL CAUSE*	SPIRIT *IMBALANCED CHAKRA*
---	---	---
SIGNATURE FOODS... apples, almonds, blueberries, broccoli, Brussels sprouts, cabbage, rockmelon, cauliflower, ginger, lettuce, pine nuts, walnuts, watermelon	• Are you being inflexible, stubborn, hard on yourself and others? • Are you constantly worried about what others think?	Crown Chakra- **colour Violet** / Third Eye Chakra- **colour Indigo**

***NUGGET... *Chemicals in personal care products, cleaning products etc. lead to damage of the nervous system. Your skin is the largest organ of the body, and what you put on it gets absorbed into the body.*

CENTRAL NERVOUS SYSTEM
RAINBOW CAULIFLOWER RICE

Ingredients: 1 large head of cauliflower, 2 large carrots, ⅛ purple cabbage, 4 stalks asparagus, 1 cm turmeric, 1 tbsp ginger, 1 cup mushrooms, 2 large cloves garic, 2 stalks of spring onion, 1 large chilli, 1 medium red and yellow capsicum with seeds, sea salt, pepper, 1 large brown onion, ¼ cup coconut oil for frying

Method: Place the cauliflower in a processor on high speed until rice size. Slice the carrots into matchsticks with a mandolin, finely shred the purple cabbage and capsicums, chop the asparagus and shallots into small pieces, finely dice the garlic, onion, turmeric, ginger, and chilli. Peel the mushrooms and finely slice

Heat coconut oil in a frypan and fry the onion and garlic until golden. Add all other ingredients and continue to fry for 2 minutes, turn off the heat. Pop a lid on the frypan and leave to steam for 5 minutes. Add salt and pepper to taste then serve. (serves 4)

NARCOLEPSY

WHAT IS IT?... **Narcolepsy** is neurological condition that is characterised by sudden, uncontrollable episodes of falling asleep throughout the day during any type of activiity.

BODY – EPICURE

- Get off all medication and supplements- herbs in the form of powders or teas are okay, but no pills or capsules!
- **Fastest...** Water fast for 7–10 days **OR...**
- 21–28-day cabala juice fast whilst snacking on nuts and berries, or blueberry Pulse.
- Do a colon cleanse to remove toxicity from the body.
- Drink one glass of water every hour on the hour for 10 hours of each day for 30 days.
- Ensure you have a routine sleep pattern every night, approx. eight hours' sleep.
- Eat and juice a locally grown, fresh, raw organic vegan diet for highest nutritional force, making sure that every day you eat raw wholefoods of all seven colours of the rainbow—red, orange, yellow, blue, green, indigo/violet and white.
- Sungazing morning and evenings in 13-second intervals; look at the sun until it reaches a 10-degree arc, or a clenched fist sitting on horizon as sun comes up, stop at top of fist. At night, start gazing as sun hits top of fist until it's gone.
- Develop the darkest suntan you can by covering your body in Divine Body Butter or coconut oil and then exposing at least 70% of your body to the sun for one hour every day (30 mins each side).
- Walk five days a week for 30–45 minutes, and every 20 minutes during the day get up and walk away from what you are doing, i.e. your computer, and do long-distance viewing for three minutes.
- **ESSENTIAL OIL...** peppermint, orange, spearmint, rosemary, lemon.
- (Blueberry Pulse, Divine, colon cleanses, 35% food-grade hydrogen peroxide, Himalayan rock salt, Ra Sea Salt, essential oil of peppermint and orange available in the USA **www.thedontolman.com/store** and Australia **www.lynnienichols.com/shop**)

BODY *FOODS THAT HEAL*	MIND *POSSIBLE EMOTIONAL CAUSE*	SPIRIT *IMBALANCED CHAKRA*
---	---	---
SIGNATURE FOODS... apples, almonds, blueberries, broccoli, Brussels sprouts, cabbage, rockmelon, cauliflower, ginger, lettuce, pine nuts, walnuts, watermelon	• Are you feeling like life's just too hard, you want to get away from it all? • Are you feeling like you'd rather not be in this world? • Are you feeling fearful of the future?	Crown Chakra- **colour Violet**

CENTRAL NERVOUS SYSTEM
PEPPERMINT & ORANGE BRAIN ENERGISER BALLS

Ingredients: 1 cup cacao, ½ cup almonds, ½ cup walnuts, 1 cup medjool dates, 2 drops of pure essential oil of peppermint, 2 drops of pure essential oil of orange, dessicated coconut

Method: Place all ingredients except the essential oils together in a food processor and mix on high until the ingredients clump together in a ball. Break the mixture in half, add peppermint oil to one half and orange oil to the remainder. Take dessert spoon full and roll into balls. Finish by rolling in coconut and refrigerate. Makes approx. 8–10 balls

PARKINSON'S DISEASE

WHAT IS IT?... **Parkinson's** is a progressive neurodegenerative disease associated with a deficiency of dopamine, which is the neurotransmitter than normally signals the part of the brain in charge of movement. The lack of dopamine causes a loss of muscle function, rigidity, slowness of movement and tremors.

Two of the main contributors to this condition are aspartame (and other chemical sweeteners) and a buildup of heavy metals, such as mercury, at the base of the brain.

BODY – EPICURE

- Get off all medication and supplements- herbs in the form of powders or teas are okay, but no pills or capsules, and absolutely NO artificial sweeteners or refined sugars!
- **Fastest...** Water fast for 7–10 days **OR...**
- 21–28-day cabala juice fast whilst snacking on blueberry Pulse, which targets the brain. Do the five-week 35% food-grade hydrogen peroxide protocol at the same time.
- Do a colon cleanse to remove toxicity from the body.
- Have one cup of lemon juice every day, can mix with pure water.
- Eat and juice a locally grown, fresh, raw organic vegan diet for highest nutritional force, making sure that every day you eat raw wholefoods of all seven colours of the rainbow—red, orange, yellow, blue, green, indigo/violet and white. Especially beneficial are locally grown organic carrots, apples, broccoli, cauliflower and asparagus (when in season).
- Snack on nuts—walnuts, almonds and macadamias. Eat dried apricots and other dried fruits as these remove plaque and give the brain energy.
- One shotglass of Joule of Thor every day, along with plenty of 24ct gold salt in the diet.
- Drink one litre per 22 kilos bodyweight of pure water every day.
- Have daily a berry, asparaus smoothie, consisting of two cups berries and 12 stalks of asparagus (can add a banana to sweeten) plus water to desired consistency. Drink within 30 mins of making it. Can eat the foods instead if preferred.
- Eat high-magnesium foods such as wholegrains, spinach and dark leafy greens, organic dark chocolate/cacao, almonds, quinoa, cashews, edamame, peanuts, dates, pepitas, sesame seeds, sunflower seeds, flax seeds, Brazil nuts, beans including blackbeans, legumes, wild rice, and dried fruit.
- Magnesium... Have herbal and epsom salt water baths for 20 minutes every day. Also take pure magnesium mixed with water or fresh juice.
- Develop the darkest suntan you can by covering your body in Divine Body Butter or coconut oil and then exposing at least 70% of your body to the sun for one hour every day (30 mins each side).
- Sungazing morning and evenings in 13-second intervals; look at the sun until it reaches a 10-degree arc, or a clenched fist sitting on horizon as sun comes up, stop at top of fist. At night, start gazing as sun hits top of fist until it's gone.
- Get three small juggling bags/balls and practice juggling daily.
- **ESSENTIAL OIL...** peppermint, frankincense, orange, helichrysm, lavender, rose.
- (Blueberry Pulse, Divine, colon cleanses, 35% food-grade hydrogen peroxide, Himalayan rock salt, Ra Sea Salt, essential oil of peppermint and orange, Joule of Thor available in the USA **www.thedontolman.com/store** and Australia **www.lynnienichols.com/shop**)

BODY *FOODS THAT HEAL*	MIND *POSSIBLE EMOTIONAL CAUSE*	SPIRIT *IMBALANCED CHAKRA*
---	---	---
SIGNATURE FOODS... apples, almonds, blueberries, broccoli, Brussels sprouts, cabbage, rockmelon, cauliflower, ginger, lettuce, pine nuts, walnuts, watermelon	• Are your thoughts paralysing you? • Are you needing to control everyone/everything? • Are you stuck in fear or guilt and unable to trust in the process of life?	Crown Chakra- **colour Violet**

***NOTE... *Refined sugars and artificial sweeteners are detrimental to the brain. Aspartame is made by placing white sugar crystals and chlorine in stainless steel vats where it's then stirred and heated until the liquid evaporates. What remains is aspartame.*

***NUGGET... *Juggling daily—the hand, eye, brain involvement activates the neuroplasticity of the brain to activate the neurochemistry and redevelop lost bodily/muscle function.*

CENTRAL NERVOUS SYSTEM
TOXIN-CLEARING STIR-FRY

Ingredients: 1 medium cauliflower, 1 large broccoli, 12 stalks of asparagus, 3 spring onions, 2 inches of ginger, 2 large cloves of garlic, ¼ cup coconut oil, 1 tsp sea salt , ⅛ cup tamari

Method: Cut the cauliflower and broccoli into small pieces. Chop the asparagus and spring onions into 2 cm lengths. Finely dice the ginger and garlic. Heat the coconut oil in a frypan, add the vegetables and gently stir-fry for a few minutes leaving them a little crunchy. Add salt and tamari to taste. Serve immediately

PERIPHERAL NEUROPATHY

WHAT IS IT?... **Peripheral neuropathy** is a condition where the peripheral nerves (that carry messages to and from the brain) connecting the brain and spinal cord to the internal organs, muscles and skin become damaged or diseased. This damage causes pain, weakness and numbness within the body.

BODY – EPICURE

- Get off all medication and supplements- herbs in the form of powders or teas are okay, but no pills or capsules, and absolutely NO artificial sweeteners or refined sugars!
- **Fastest...** Water fast for 7–10 days **OR...**
- 21–28-day cabala juice fast whilst snacking on blueberry Pulse, which targets the brain. Do the five-week 35% food-grade hydrogen peroxide protocol at the same time.
- Do a colon cleanse to remove toxicity from the body.
- Drink one litre per 22 kilos bodyweight of pure water every day and have one cup of lemon juice every day, can mix with water.
- Have daily a berry, asparaus smoothie, consisting of two cups berries and 12 stalks of asparagus (can add a banana to sweeten) plus water to desired consistency. Drink within 30 mins of making it. Can eat the foods instead if preferred.
- Eat a locally grown, fresh, raw organic vegan diet that is made up of 50–60% yellow and orange foods; 40-50% raw wholefoods of all seven colours of the rainbow— red, orange, yellow, blue, green, indigo/violet and white. Especially beneficial are locally grown organic carrots, apples, broccoli, cauliflower and asparagus (when in season).
- One shotglass of Joule of Thor every day, along with plenty of 24ct gold salt in the diet.
- Snack on nuts—walnuts, almonds and macadamias. Eat dried apricots and other dried fruits as these remove plaque and give the brain energy.
- Suck on rock salt every day.
- Eat high-magnesium foods such as wholegrains, spinach and dark leafy greens, almonds, quinoa, cashews, edamame, peanuts, dates, pepitas, sesame seeds, sunflower seeds, flax seeds, Brazil nuts, beans including blackbeans, legumes, wild rice, dried fruit, and cacao.
- Magnesium... Have herbal and epsom salt water baths for 20 minutes every day. Also take pure magnesium mixed with water or fresh juice.
- Sungazing morning and evenings in 13-second intervals; look at the sun until it reaches a 10-degree arc, or a clenched fist sitting on horizon as sun comes up, stop at top of fist. At night, start gazing as sun hits top of fist until it's gone.
- Develop the darkest suntan you can by covering your body in Divine Body Butter or coconut oil and then exposing at least 70% of your body to the sun for one hour every day (30 mins each side).
- Get three small juggling bags/balls and practice juggling daily.
- **ESSENTIAL OIL...** peppermint, frankincense, orange, geranium, helichrysum, lavender, chamomile.
- (Blueberry Pulse, Divine, colon cleanses, 35% food-grade hydrogen peroxide, Himalayan rock salt, Ra Sea Salt, essential oil of peppermint and orange, Joule of Thor available in the USA **www.thedontolman.com/store** and Australia **www.lynnienichols.com/shop**)

BODY *FOODS THAT HEAL*	MIND *POSSIBLE EMOTIONAL CAUSE*	SPIRIT *IMBALANCED CHAKRA*
---	---	---
SIGNATURE FOODS... apples, almonds, blueberries, broccoli, Brussels sprouts, cabbage, rockmelon, cauliflower, ginger, lettuce, pine nuts, walnuts, watermelon	• Are your thoughts, guilt and unforgiveness paralysing you? • Are you needing to control everyone/everything? • Are you stuck in fear, unable to trust in the process of life?	Crown Chakra- **colour Violet**

***NOTE... *Yellow and orange foods offer the highest frequency to the nerve centres.*

***NUGGET... *Dietary gold such as Joule of Thor and 24ct Ra Sea Salt gets the electrical spark back and increases the capillary infusion of blood, which brings in nutrients to the nerve centres and muscles.*

CENTRAL NERVOUS SYSTEM
BRAIN SNACK

Ingredients: Walnuts, almonds, macadamias, dried apricots chopped, raisins, dried figs chopped, Ra See Salt

Method: Place all ingredients together in a container and sprinkle with Ra salt. Snack on this during the day to energize the brain and clear toxicity

SCIATICA

WHAT IS IT?... **Sciatica** is pain that begins in the lower back, extending through the hip area and outer side of the leg, due to compression of the sciatic nerve, which is the largest nerve in the body, with its roots at the lumbar spinal cord, extending through the buttocks and to the lower limbs.

BODY – EPICURE

- Lie flat on the floor, on your stomach, with your arms out, hands flat on the floor. Get someone to push their thumbs as hard as they can into the indentations at the base of the spine, above the buttocks; hold for 30 seconds and release immediately so the nerve flux can flow again.
- Lie flat on the floor on your back, head on a pillow, bend at the knees and rest the feet on a chair. Pull the front legs of the chair towards you until all tension on the spine goes away. Stay there and relax for 20 minutes at a time.
- Use Healing Chrysm and essential oils topically.
- **ESSENTIAL OIL...** ginger, peppermint, rosemary, lavender.
- (Healing Chrysm available in the USA **www.thedontolman.com/store** and Australia **www.lynnienichols.com/shop**)

BODY *FOODS THAT HEAL*	MIND *POSSIBLE EMOTIONAL CAUSE*	SPIRIT *IMBALANCED CHAKRA*
---	---	---
SIGNATURE FOODS... apples, almonds, blueberries, broccoli, Brussels sprouts, cabbage, rockmelon, cauliflower, ginger, lettuce, pine nuts, walnuts, watermelon	• Are you neglecting yourself and all that you desire? • Are you rejecting yourself, supressing your greatness? • Are you feeling fearful about the future?	Crown Chakra- **colour Violet** / Base Chakra- **colour Red**

***NUGGET...** Anciently it was believed that the herb helichrysum represented the nerves and healing of the nerves. 'Heli' means 'sun'.*

CENTRAL NERVOUS SYSTEM
NERVE FRUIT CRUNCH

Ingredients: 2 apples, ½ cup slithered almonds, 1 cup blueberries, little bit fresh ginger, ½ cup walnuts

CASHEW CREAM; (see recipe in back of book)

Method: Grate the apples with core and place in a bowl. Toast the slithered almonds until golden brown and add to the apple, along with the blueberries and chopped walnuts. Finely dice the ginger and add. Mix all ingredients together and serve with cashew cream. (serves 1)

TINNITUS

WHAT IS IT?... **Tinnitus** is a loud humming/ringing in the ears that can not be heard externally.

BODY – EPICURE

- Get off all medication and supplements- herbs in the form of powders or teas are okay, but no pills or capsules!
- Firstly, cleanse the inner ear with 3% food-grade hydrogen peroxide (can make this by mixing one part 35% food-grade hydrogen peroxide with 11 parts water ... i.e. 11 tbsp water to 1 tbsp 35% food-grade h2o2). Place three or four drops of 3% hydrogen peroxide in one ear, let it fizz and bubble for three or four minutes then twist up a tissue the size of a cigarette and push into the ear to clear all of the dirt etc. from the ear. Roll over and do the same to the opposite ear. Do this twice for each ear THEN the next day, use two ear candles per ear to cleanse the inner ear. In the morning, put three or four drops of warm olive oil or safflower oil in each ear. Keep this in with a cotton ball throughout the day. In the evening, get a cotton bud and clear the oil out of the ear. Do this daily for three or four days.
- You can also put two drops of colloidal silver in the ear, keeping it there over night with a cotton ball.
- You can roast some onion and squeeze two drops of warm onion juice into the ear, allowing the onion fumes to also go into the ear, keep this in overnight with a cotton ball.
- Do a liver/gall bladder cleanse to clear toxicity by mixing one litre of grapefruit juice and 1 cup of olive oil together. Drink this just before you go to bed at night. Try not to get up after doing this except if needing to go to the toilet. Typically the next day you will pass gallstones.
- Do an intestinal cleanse as the nerve flux from the ears connects to the transverse colon; therefore, removing the toxic plaque by stripping the mucosal lining will be highly beneficial.
- Snack on fresh ginger
- Suck on Himalayan rock salt throughout the day.
- Place one or two drops of peppermint oil in the mouth, swish and swallow.
- Sniff a mix of peppermint oil/tea tree oil and water into the nose, allow this to run into the throat and swallow or use Breathe-EZ nasal spray.
- Do ear candling.
- **ESSENTIAL OIL...** peppermint, tea tree, helichrysum, onion.
- (Breathe-EZ, Divine, colon cleanses, Nature's Silver Bullet colloidal silver, Himalayan rock salt, 35% food-grade hydrogen peroxide, essential oil of peppermint and tea tree available in the USA **www.thedontolman.com/store** and Australia **www.lynnienichols.com/shop**)

BODY *FOODS THAT HEAL*	MIND *POSSIBLE EMOTIONAL CAUSE*	SPIRIT *IMBALANCED CHAKRA*
---	---	---
SIGNATURE FOODS... apples, almonds, blueberries, broccoli, Brussels sprouts, cabbage, rockmelon, cauliflower, ginger, lettuce, pine nuts, walnuts, watermelon	• Are you feeling unheard, nobody is listening to you? • Are you not wanting to hear what others have to say?	Crown Chakra- **colour Violet** / Third Eye Chakra- **colour Indigo**

CENTRAL NERVOUS SYSTEM
PRUNE & MUSHROOM CAULIFLOWER RICE

Ingredients: 2 cups mixed mushrooms, ½ cup pitted prunes, 1 large red onion, 1 medium head of cauliflower, 1-2 tsp sea salt, 2 large cloves garlic, 1tsp fresh ginger, pepper, ⅛ cup coconut oil

Method: Use a coarse grater to grate the cauliflower into rice-size texture. Take the skin and stems off the mushrooms then slice; cut the onions into wedges; finely dice the garlic and ginger. In coconut oil, fry the mushrooms, onion, garlic and ginger for a few minutes until onion softens. Add the cauliflower and fry for a further 2 minutes. Turn off the heat, pop a lid on and allow to steam for a further 5 minutes. Add the finely sliced prunes, pepper and extra salt if desired

To serve, place the cauliflower rice in a small bowl and press down firmly so that the rice is compact and sticks together; turn the bowl over onto a serving plate and then remove the bowl, leaving the rice bowl in tact. Garnish with sliced prune and parsley. (serves 2)

VERTIGO/EAR PROBLEMS

WHAT IS IT?... **Vertigo** is a sensation of spinning or moving when you are actually still, causing loss of balance. This can be due to a problem with the inner ear, brain or nerve pathway in the spinal column.

BODY – EPICURE

- Get off all medication and supplements- herbs in the form of powders or teas are okay, but no pills or capsules!
- Firstly, cleanse the inner ear with 3% food-grade hydrogen peroxide (can make this by mixing one part 35% food-grade hydrogen peroxide with 11 parts water ... i.e. 11 tbsp water to 1 tbsp 35% food-grade h2o2). Place three or four drops of 3% hydrogen peroxide in one ear, let it fizz and bubble for three or four minutes then twist up a tissue the size of a cigarette and push into the ear to clear all of the dirt etc. from the ear. Roll over and do the same to the opposite ear. Do this twice for each ear THEN the next day, use two ear candles per ear to cleanse the inner ear. In the morning, put three or four drops of warm olive oil or safflower oil in each ear. Keep this in with a cotton ball throughout the day. In the evening, get a cotton bud and clear the oil out of the ear. Do this daily for three or four days.
- You can also put two drops of colloidal silver in the ear, keeping it there over night with a cotton ball.
- You can roast some onion and squeeze two drops of warm onion juice into the ear, allowing the onion fumes to also go into the ear, keep this in overnight with a cotton ball.
- Do a liver/gall bladder cleanse to clear toxicity by mixing one litre of grapefruit juice and one cup of olive oil together. Drink this just before you go to bed at night. Try not to get up after doing this except if needing to go to the toilet. Typically the next day you will pass gallstones.
- Do an intestinal cleanse as the nerve flux from the ears connects to the transverse colon; therefore, removing the toxic plaque by stripping the mucosal lining will be highly beneficial.
- Snack on fresh ginger.
- Suck on Himalayan rock salt throughout the day.
- Place one or two drops of peppermint oil in the mouth, swish and swallow.
- Sniff a mix of peppermint oil/tea tree oil and water into the nose, allow this to run into the throat and swallow or use Breathe-EZ nasal spray.
- Do ear candling.
- **ESSENTIAL OIL...** peppermint, tea tree, helichrysum, onion.
- (Breathe-EZ, Divine, colon cleanses, Nature's Silver Bullet colloidal silver, Himalayan rock salt, 35% food-grade hydrogen peroxide, essential oil of peppermint and tea tree available in the USA **www.thedontolman.com/store** and Australia **www.lynnienichols.com/shop**)

BODY *FOODS THAT HEAL*	MIND *POSSIBLE EMOTIONAL CAUSE*	SPIRIT *IMBALANCED CHAKRA*
---	---	---
SIGNATURE FOODS... apples, almonds, blueberries, broccoli, Brussels sprouts, cabbage, rockmelon, cauliflower, ginger, lettuce, pine nuts, walnuts, watermelon	• Are you feeling scattered and unable to focus? • Are you feeling as though you are going around in circles? • Is there something you are not wanting to see?	Crown Chakra- **colour Violet** / Third Eye Chakra- **colour Indigo**

CENTRAL NERVOUS SYSTEM
PLUM & BLUEBERRY SOFT SERVE ICECREAM

Ingredients: 2 cups walnuts chopped, 2 cups deseeded plums, 2 cups blueberries, 4 large bananas

Method: Cut the banana and plums into blueberry size pieces, mix all of the fruit together and freeze overnight. To make the ice cream, just before serving, put through a champion juicer. Gently mix the chopped walnuts through the ice cream and serve immediately. (serves 2)

More On NEURO DEGENERATIVE DESEASES: Parkinson's, MS, MD, ALS

Things that contribute to the deterioration of brain and nerve function, known as neurological dysfunctions:

- Poisoning by heavy metals and toxins such as pesticides, herbicides, insecticides and fungicides and artificial food additives and preservatives.

- Excessive oxidative stress, causing inflammation in the brain.

- Long-term use of OTC drugs, recreational drugs, prescription medications and antibiotics all lead to eventual memory loss if a person doesn't detox.

- Prolonged stress causes gut damage, and most, if not all diseases start in the gut.

- Excessive iron intake from iron supplements, which is typically ground up micro particles of rusted-out iron, in the attempt to remedy low blood pressure.

- Diabetes insulin, excessive consumption of white refined pharma sugars and artificial sweeteners.

- Various nutrient deficiencies.

How to reverse Parkinson's Disease and other Neuro Degenerative Diseases naturally:

New studies are proving that our gut is our 'second brain' and has thousands more neurotransmitters than the brain itself. The deterioration of gut health is linked to the deterioration of brain health. Understanding these facts will help you to reverse the damage and create an environment in which your intelligent body can heal by itself.

Detoxification:

When you STOP putting harmful chemicals and crap food and drinks into your body, detoxification STARTS. In your own environment, analyse for yourself your exposure to heavy metals, pesticides, herbicides, etc. and artificial food additives, drugs, sugar, Coca-Cola, and other environmental toxins. These poisons/toxins suffocate your cells; eliminating them allows your cells to start living again. There are various detox methods that help your body purge out the poisons: A gastrointestinal cleanse is foremost important to improve regularity and your gut health. A liver cleanse and nutritional support is necessary to help the liver filter the blood more effectively. Beetroot juice is one of the most effective foods for this purpose. Heavy metal poisoning is difficult to detoxify unless you know what foods help... A juice cleanse helps to detoxify the system, especially apple juice, followed by eating apples after the juice fast OR juice and drink water for 14–28 days. Detoxification is a very wide topic and with every individual, BASED ON THEIR TOXICITY LEVELS, healing times will vary. To help the effectiveness of any detoxification, drink one litre of water for every 22 kilos of body weight, daily.

Eat More Organic, Fresh, Raw Fruits & Vegetables:

It is a known fact that eating more fresh, raw fruits and vegetables is an essential part of a healthy lifestyle. Fruits and vegetables provide your body with all of the nutrients your body needs, without any side effect except higher energy and health: phytonutrients, antioxidants, enzymes, vitamins, minerals, flavonoids, amino acids, fibre and anti-inflammatory properties.

Fast foods are void of these nutrients on their own but require them for digestion, thus causing nutrient deficiencies that contribute to deterioration of health. If you haven't been eating many fruits and vegetables, you will have a lot to catch up on. Drinking freshly extracted juices will help speed up your healing. The key is to eat/drink them raw and all organic (without pesticides, and other pharma chemicals). Green juices contain high levels of chlorophyll, which is powerful for healing the gut and detoxifying the body of heavy metals. Start drinking green juices in small amounts, gradually building up to two or three glasses per day. Moringa tea and green matcha tea are very rich in chlorophyll and anti-cancer properties.

Avoid Excess Iron:

The main cause of Parkinson's Disease is heavy metal toxicity in the blood. Heavy metal poisoning also causes low blood pressure, which results in dizziness and fainting.

With initial diagnosis, most PD sufferers may be prescribed iron supplements and over an extended amount of time may find that their brain health will further deteriorate. This is especially so in male PD sufferers who have no way of losing blood, unlike women who have their monthly menstruation. Do you see the vicious cycle here? Excess iron resulting from iron supplements causes iron overload (a condition aka hemochromatosis) that contributes to oxidation of the blood and the brain cells.

Eat Fermented Foods for Probiotics:

Our lack of gut health or any digestive disorders usually starts from having a severely imbalanced gut flora and an overload of fauna. Many people underestimate the importance of gut health and often disregard the care of a healthy gut by eating foods that undermine gut health. Fermented foods are some of the best foods for replenishing your gut with beneficial bacteria to strengthen gut health and the immune system. Some of the fermented foods you could add to your diet include kefir, organic yogurt, kombucha, sauerkraut, kimchi, tofu, and tempeh (fermented soy). Replenishing your gut flora with beneficial bacteria will enable your body to break down environmental toxins and detoxify heavy metals more efficiently.

Eat Good Mood Foods:

Since Parkinson's and other neuro-degenerative diseases are about the inability of the brain to produce dopamine, it makes sense to help the body by eating foods that help with dopamine production. Eat nuts and seeds—they all have a healthy content of Omega 3s, 6s, and 9s. Omega 3 contains two essential fatty acids that are crucial to brain health: DHA and EPA. Half of your brain is made up of DHA fat, which wards off brain inflammation, promotes neuron growth and protects the function of neurotransmitters. Never have fish oil! You'll be surprised to know that free-range organic eggs are one of the healthiest foods to help boost brain power. Coconut oil has been proven to help reverse Alzheimer's, it can do the same for Parkinson's. Foods that are high in antioxidants help to neutralize free radicals that attack the brain. All berries are very healthy and filled with antioxidants: Goji berries, Wild blueberries, Dark chocolate, Pecans, Artichoke, Elderberries, Kidney beans, Cranberries, Blackberries, and Cilantro. Include foods that are high in anti-inflammatory properties, which not only help reduce inflammation in the body but also in the brain. All Berries, Broccoli, Avocado, all Peppers, Mushrooms, Grapes, Turmeric, Extra Virgin Olive oil, Dark Chocolate, Tomatoes, and Cherries.

Lifestyle:

Walking, swimming, dancing and laughing, listening to music you loved while in your teenage years and 20s and singing the words verbatim can activate memory function.

Goddess Warrior

To you, Goddess Warrior, I whisper the song of sweet surrender
Stop holding ... stop fighting ... be soft ... be still...

Goddess of the Sacred Temple who knows hatred not
for you have dared to face the devil within and slay the demons lurking
beneath the shadow of the mind...
Delving into the deepest depths of the Dark Night of the Soul and
begging to be torn apart, until tears of terror burned the cheeks of the
forlorn child within, like acid on a silken gown, leaving her exhausted ...
breathless ... silent...

To you, Goddess Warrior, I whisper the song of sweet surrender
Stop holding ... stop fighting ... be soft ... be still...

Spirit Warrior, why is it that you fight the light and suppress your truth?
There is no greater love than self-love, no acceptance more precious
than that of thy own.
Look into the sacred waters within and you will find mirrored there,
perfection, and beauty in its fullest, most magnificent expression...

Sovereign Being of Love and Light
Accept the glory bestowed upon you as you journeyed through the
tunnel of life
from the womb of flesh, to be cocooned by the warm embrace of your
beloved Mother Earth.
Be free now of the chains that suppress your soul and hold you prisoner
to your human form.
Allow now for that smouldering ember to burn brightly and rage wildly
with passion and desire for life.
For like a bird with clipped wings she longs to fly, to soar like an eagle
on the ever-changing winds of life, and rule like a Queen over her inner
kingdom...

To you, Goddess Warrior, I whisper the song of sweet surrender
Stop holding ... stop fighting ... be soft ... be still...

For only then will you know truth and disregard without haste all forms of
self-judgement, criticism and the unworthiness that torments your soul.
Only then will you claim your divinity and allow the light of truth to
illuminate the world both inside and out, in an offering of unconditional
love, peace and freedom.
Only then will you know the eternal existence of life and hear the whisper
of Spirit on every breath of air, every crashing ocean wave and every ray
of sunshine that penetrates your skin and permeates your soul.
Only then will you embrace eyes that truly see and ears that hear the
sound of your own true sacredness.

To you, Goddess warrior, I whisper the song of sweet surrender.
Stop holding ... stop fighting ... be soft ... be still...

Lynnie Nichols

Is Your Physical Body Meant to be Your Spaceship?

Can we learn how to travel through time and space...body intact and remember it? There are records of the past, from nearly every culture, that say yes! It's been said many times over, for thousands of years, that 'if your dream is big enough the facts don't count!'

The observational studies of the 'electrum' goes back to the earliest dynasties of Egypt and even the Inca, Mayan, Anasazi and the Orient. The studies of the 'atomos' (atoms) took place at high levels of understanding in the Greco-Roman Classical period of Rome 600 B.C. and earlier. Pythagorus and other vegetarian scholars of innate, inherent genius and self-taught by the way, all embraced the philosophy that, 'the only evil is violence against innocence', and that 'pleasure is the highest good.' They all agreed on the Principle of Light as the only real law that permeates the entire cosmos. In other words, 'that all events on this earth and in the entire cosmos occur and are ultimately based upon the motions and interactions of 'atoms' moving in empty space'. All matter is 99.99% empty space. Your cells, all 10,000 trillion of them that make up your 'physical body' is 99.99% empty space. Light, visible or not, fills all of space and is what matter is made of. When 'Light' condenses into 'gasses' it can then condense into 'liquids' such as water, which can then condense into 'solids.' All solids are mostly space that is filled with Light. Light appears and forms into patterns, so do gases, liquids, and solids. These patterns are referred to as 'geometric forms.' There are lines, spirals, circles, ellipses, triangles, rectangles, polygons and more. The study of comparisons in natures geometric patterns of the 13 Solar planets, the 13 Archimedean polygons, the 13 Astrological personality types, the 13 Men and 13 women of Christian beginnings (Jesus and the 12=13 and each of their wives or girlfriends), which was the extended polyamorous groupings of 13 couples (called the MazzaRoth or MazzaLoth in Hebrew), meaning 'Family of Light' shining as bright as the stars/sun, creating an environment for celestial pursuit of cosmic genius and the Light of understanding existence and it's possibilities. There are 8 more comparisons but the point is, it led ancient thinkers to the place of realizing that patterns could be named and numbered. Two of the patterns they observed and saw in nature, was in everything. They named these two patterns and called them, 'transcendental numbers.' Transcendental meant, 'to go above and beyond ordinary experience', that in order to comprehend possible realities that do not yet exist in one's life, you use the principles of thought and imagination, intuition, reflection, pondering, and recording dreams in order to interpret them into useable ideas. Hence, Da Vinci and helicopters, airplanes and parachutes etc. centuries before they existed materially on this earth.

Are Transcendental Numbers the Forgotten Key to Time and Space Travel Experiences? They are observable as nature's most used Principles of Light that form creative cosmological designs in energetic frequency's and solid material forms and were expressed by polymaths of the ancient world as PHi: 1:1.6 & Pi: 3.14. Ancient scholars taught that 'they are the keys' to unlocking and discovering regeneration, healing, physical immortality (over coming death & return) and transmuting the atoms, molecules and cells into a 'retrofit of one's body/temple/sacred abode into the 'spaceship of life' and an infinite ever expanding intelligence', a living hydrogen and solar fuelled vehicle that can travel at supra-luminal speeds to other worlds, solar systems and galaxies in order to meet other Children of Light, 'Godlings' as it were, that have already achieved this level of existence and performance and live forever in what was called 'celestial bliss', where they are planning, organizing and building new galaxies, solar systems and worlds to infinitely perpetuate the 'evolution' of intelligence from subatomic particle, to molecular, to cellular, then into and through all material life forms and all the while keeping nuclear records (dna) at the atomic level of the neter, or individual (not dividable) not lost, so that upon each return and new 'life form' of one's individual experience, any amount of Light or intelligence obtained in the previous life would re-rise with you as an advantage in that new life experience, so that we could build a more complex 'house-body' to live in. What if some on the earth today are ready for this 'elevated' step into cosmological fulfillment into a body for space/time travel? Anciently, in Latin, Light was called the Magus. Those who studied Light (everything is made of Light) were called, The Magi. Then as they acted upon Principles of Light they were filled with spectrums or oscillating frequencies of Light and spirits (air/gases/to breathe) that gave them greater Creata Magus or Creative Light, today called 'intelligence'. They called Creative Light, or the 'powers of imagi-nation', MAGIC. Even Albert

Einstein declared that 'imagination is more important than knowledge.' He went on to say that, 'imagination is everything.' The Ancients wrote that by embracing behaviours that attract the highest celestial frequency's, it gave them cognitive functional capacities that allowed them to 'see' into and even 'hear' other people of the same harmonic on other worlds.

What the early Alchemists had learned from records left behind from the City of Enoch (records show that it didn't sink in the ocean, but rather, that it lifted off the earth and flew into space) was that oxygen means 'acid maker'. Oxygen lets us live, but eventually rusts us out as we return the body to the earth. Nitrogen means 'spark maker'. Hydrogen means 'water maker'. Three levels of Light intensity were observed. They called them; Telestial, Terrestrial and Celestial levels of Light that could be understood, embraced, acted upon and absorbed. They referred to these three levels of Light brightness or intensity as, the Sun, Moon and Stars. One could go from oxygen breather to hydrogen breather and in this, red blood cells which carry oxygen were no longer needed, so the red blood cells came out of the body as sacral fluids, were activated and lifted up the spinal column into the 'heavens' or upper rooms of the temple/queendom/kingdom, today called the cranial cavity, that houses the brain. When Celestial behaviours that attract that frequency of light where embraced and performed, one moved into the path of turning the 'Lead of Death' into the 'Gold of Immortal Condition' as the atoms, molecules and cells reconstructed their orbital spins to supra-luminal (faster than light) speeds.

Let's look at the possibility of physical immortality through the idea of quantum physics, the level at which matter becomes energy. In 'Ageless Body, Timeless Mind', Deepak Chopra describes this level; 'your body appears to be composed of solid matter that can be broken down into molecules and atoms, but quantum physics tells us that every atom is more than 99.9999% empty space, and the sub-atomic particles moving at lightning speed through this space are actually bundles of vibrating energy.' 'These vibrations aren't random and meaningless however, they carry information- the essential stuff of the cosmos, including your body is non-stuff, but it isn't ordinary non-stuff, it's thinking non-stuff, or intelligent energy.' So, the body has moved from a solid object to a fluid river of energy. With this understanding, ancient philosophers taught we are similar to a flow of potter's clay, to be moulded at will by the potter, which is your mental, emotional, physical and social selves, and your trust in the process of life self (anciently called the Moneta self). And remember, the energy is intelligent! Is this intelligence what some call your spiritual self, waiting to be moulded by your mental, emotional, and physical selves, or perhaps wishing to be allowed to be manifest into material reality without obstruction? Deepak Chopra tells us 'India, China, Japan and to a lesser extent, the Christian West, have given birth to sages who realized their essential nature as a flow of intelligence.' 'By preserving that flow and nurturing it year after year, they overcame entropy from a deeper level of nature.

LET'S CUT TO THE CHASE: There are collections in different cultures that recorded the process of going from death to a state of immortality. They mention plants that are thousands of years old and how amaranth seeds and other special flowers, leaves, roots, needles, saps and essential oils of these plants, when offered to a body that is prepared by fasting on water for a specific number of days, based upon the individual themselves, would generate the re-growth of what today we call the telomeres. They would begin to use more hydrogen when breathing which meant the 'red blood' was no longer needed, so it surfaces to the pores of the skin and drops off as the hydronium fluids of the brain are condensed with celestial spectrums of light. An immortal condition is achieved in a 3-day (72 hour) DNA driven and activated process. They believed that this is part of one's heritage as an entity of the Cosmic Community.

Cowboy Don

NATURE'S DOCTRINE OF SIGNATURES

Here's a few of nature's signatures; Brain... walnut, Eye... carrot, Ear... prune, mushroom, Pineal... pine nut, Pituitary... pea, macadamia, Lungs... potato, Bronchial Tubes... broccoli, Heart... tomato, red capsicum, Bones... celery, rhubarb, Stomach... ginger, Liver... lemon, Pancreas... sweet potato , Intestines... long green beans, Kidneys... kidney beans, Ovaries... olives, Testicles... figs, Womb... avocado, Cells... onion, Blood Cells... red and green grapes

The CIRCULATORY SYSTEM

Consists of... heart, veins and arteries.

Chakra- Third Eye (indigo) / **Endocrine Gland and Function** ... The pituitary gland is situated at the base of the skull and is often called the 'master gland'; it secretes a thyroid-stimulating hormone (THS), follicle-stimulating hormone (FSH) and adrenocorticotropic hormone (ACTH) into the blood in order to control the activity of many other endocrine glands such as the thyroid, ovaries, adrenal, etc. It releases hormones that control blood pressure and is itself controlled by hormones produced by a part of the brain called the hypothalamus, which links the nervous and endocrine systems. The circulatory system transports endocrine information around the body.

Holds Emotional Molecules of... love, pleasure, graciousness, sadness, rejection and loneliness.

Foods That Support This System Are... apples, capsicum, beetroot, cherries, grapefruit, grapes, kale, mango, strawberry, tomato, watercress, spinach.

Support the Emotional/Physical Healing of This System with... INDIGO/BLUE and ORANGE foods.

Blue wholefoods support this system for longevity and promote feelings of fulfilment.

Orange wholefoods help with the release of blood disorders in this system whilst assisting the body to release emotions of loneliness and grief/broken heart.

Stare at the green heart for no less than one minute; then look at the white heart and see what colour you project into that heart.

You should project the colour **RED**

***NUGGET... *Did you know that these words are all connected, based on the Wisdom of the Ancients? EAR, HEAR, HEART, EARTH AND TEAR...*

When we listen to our Heart and Hear feelings of love, joy, excitement, truth and more, it heals the body's systems.

Rain was called 'Mother Earth's Tears of Joy' (T-EARS).

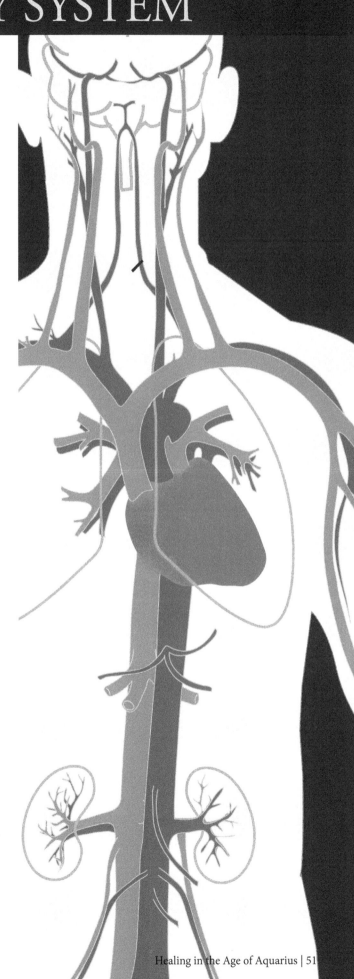

HEART

BODY *FOODS THAT HEAL*	MIND *POSSIBLE EMOTIONAL CAUSE*	SPIRIT *IMBALANCED CHAKRA*
SIGNATURE FOODS... tomato, red capsicum and for the heartbeat- beetroot, strawberries	Are you holding on to painful emotions from the past? Are you sacraficing love and joy for material status or wealth?	Third Eye Chakra- **colour indigo** / Heart Chakra- colour Emerald Green

***NUGGET... *Both capsicum and tomato are red and have four chambers just like the heart. Be sure to eat the seeds and pulp of the capsicum as this is a type of pectin that is very beneficial to the heart. Red capsicum targets the strengthening of the heart whilst green capsicum targets the removal of waste.*

CIRCULATORY SYSTEM
SPICY MANGO CAPSICUM CUPS

Ingredients: 2 red capsicums- halved, 2 tomatos diced, ½ red onion- diced finely, 1 mango- diced, 1 chilli- diced finely, 2 tablespoons fresh lime juice, ⅛ cup watercress, ¼ cup coriander, baby spinach leaves

Method: Cut capsicums into halves, scooping out the insides. Dice the pith of inner capsicums then add to diced tomato and mango. Dice the onion and chilli finely and add to salsa mix. Add the watercress and coriander. Mix the ingredients well before spooning into the capsicum halves. Serve on a bed of baby spinach leaves

ARTERIES

BODY	MIND	SPIRIT
FOODS THAT HEAL	*POSSIBLE EMOTIONAL CAUSE*	*IMBALANCED CHAKRA*
---	---	---
SIGNATURE FOODS... red-veined leaves such as beetroot and chard, cabbage	Are you feeling bored, negative, lacking in joy?	Third Eye Chakra- **colour indigo**

***NUGGET... *Eat three ruby-red grapefruit daily for arterial cleansing.*

CIRCULATORY SYSTEM
BEETROOT SALAD

Ingredients: Red-veined chard and/or beetroot leaves shredded finely, 1 large beetroot with skin scrubbed clean or peeled, ½ large red capsicum diced, ½ punnet cherry tomatoes left whole or halved, watercress to taste, 1 cup slithered almonds toasted on a dry oven tray

ROAST CAPSICUM DRESSING; 1 red capsicum, halved and seeded, ½ cup organic olive oil, ¼ teaspoon sea salt

Method: Cut the beetroot into small cubes and bake in the oven with coconut oil until soft, or slice into matchsticks with mandolin for raw version. Lightly toast the slithered almonds on an oven tray or in a dry pan. Place the red-veined leaves, capsicum and tomatoes in a salad bowl. Toss the warm toasted almonds through the salad. Drizzle with the roast capsicum dressing and serve immediately

Roast Capsicum Dressing; roast the capsicum halves in the oven until soft. Peel the skins off and let the capsicum cool. Place in a blender with olive oil and salt. Blend on high until it becomes a smooth dressing consistency

*For a non-vegan version, add some crumbled organic goat's feta

BODY	MIND	SPIRIT
FOODS THAT HEAL	*POSSIBLE EMOTIONAL CAUSE*	*IMBALANCED CHAKRA*
---	---	---
SIGNATURE FOODS... chives, white-veined leaves such as spinach, kale, cabbage and turnip greens, radichio	Are you stopping the flow of love and joy? Are you holding feelings of guilt, fear or rejection?	Third Eye Chakra- **colour indigo**

CIRCULATORY SYSTEM
CHILLI KALE SALAD WITH TAHINI DRESSING

Ingredients: 3 large kale leaves shredded finely, 2 beetroot leaves shredded finely, ¼ red cabbage shredded finely, 1 red onion diced or sliced finely, 1 red chilli diced finely, 1 red capsicum with pith diced, ½ raw beetroot peeled and cut into matchsticks, 1 container cherry tomatoes halved or 2 diced tomato, watercress to taste, Himalayan salt.

(This recipe specifically uses wholefoods that support the circulatory system. Feel free to add whatever else you desire such as carrot, cucumber, mushrooms, parsley, mint etc.)

TAHINI DRESSING; **(see recipe under Dressings in back of book)**

Method: Toss all salad ingredients together in a bowl. Just before serving, dress with tahini dressing and a sprinkle of Himalayan or sea salt

BLOOD

BODY	MIND	SPIRIT
FOODS THAT HEAL	*POSSIBLE EMOTIONAL CAUSE*	*IMBALANCED CHAKRA*
---	---	---
SIGNATURE FOODS... red and green grapes, beets, berries, black eyed peas, navy beans, cherries, grapefruit. Coconut water, coconut milk/cream are all beneficial blood builders	Are you feeling defeated and unloved? Are you blocking the flow of joy in your life by holding on to unresolved emotional issues?	Third Eye Chakra- **colour indigo**

NOTE... *Allspice is a blood purifier.*

NUGGET... *Drinking coconut water will restore the blood count. In World War II, coconut water was actually transfused into the body instead of blood.*

CIRCULATORY SYSTEM
BLOODY GOOD JUICE ☺

Ingredients: ½ litre coconut water, 1 large beet, 1 cup mixed berries, 1 cup of red and green grapes, tiny pinch of allspice

Method: Juice the beet, berries and grapes then add to the coconut water and allspice. Drink immediately.

DIS-EASES/DISORDERS OF
The CIRCULATORY SYSTEM

ANAEMIA

***WHAT IS IT?...** **Anaemia** is a condition in which there are less red blood cells than normal, or there is a deficiency of haemoglobin (an iron-containing compound) in each blood cell. Red blood cells carry oxygen around the body so the result of anaemia is a person looking very pale or feeling constant tiredness. Less common symptoms include heart palpitations, headaches, and ringing in the ears.

***BODY – EPICURE*
- Get off all medication and supplements- herbs in the form of powders or teas are okay. You may have 72 hours of feeling toxicities leave the bloodstream.
- **Fastest...** Water fast for 7–10 days **OR...**
- 21–28 days on dark leafy green juices and smoothies.
- Eat three or four stalks of celery each day and drink celery juice.
- Have plenty of nature-made salt (Ra 24ct Gold See Salt is especially healing).
- Eat tubers such as potato, carrots, rutebaga and all other foods that grow under the ground.
- Eat a variety of fruit, vegetables, nuts and seeds, especially red heart foods such as beetroot, red capsicum, tomato, red grapes, red apples, red capsicum, cherries, red grapefruit and strawberries.
- Drink one glass of water every hour on the hour for 10 hours of each day, for 30 days or drink one litre of water per 22 kilos of bodyweight each day.
- Walk for 30–45 minutes every day.
- Develop the darkest suntan you can by covering your body in Divine Body Butter or coconut oil and then exposing at least 70% of your body to the sun for one hour every day (30 mins each side).
- **ESSENTIAL OIL...** lemon, orange, ginger, grapefruit.
- (Divine and Ra 24ct gold salt available in the USA **www.thedontolman.com/store** and Australia **www.lynnienichols.com/shop**)

BODY *FOODS THAT HEAL THE CNS*	MIND *POSSIBLE EMOTIONAL CAUSE*	SPIRIT *IMBALANCED CHAKRA*
---	---	---
SIGNATURE FOODS... apples, capsicum, beetroot, cherries, grapefruit, grapes, kale, mango, strawberry, tomato, watercress, spinach	• Are you feeling stressed, overwhelmed by worries and fear? • Are you feeling like life is a struggle, there's no joy or fun? • Are you lacking in self-love?	Third Eye Chakra- **colour Indigo**

***NUGGET...** *Celery and salt target the bones and the red blood cells.*

CIRCULATORY SYSTEM
IRON BOOSTER JUICE

Ingredients: 3–4 red apples, ½ cup baby spinach leaves, 1 large kale leaf, 2 large stalks celery, 1 small beetroot, 2 large beetroot leaves

Method: Juice all ingredients together and drink immediately

ARRHYTHMIAS

***WHAT IS IT?...** **Arrhythmias** are irregular or abnormal heartbeats, tachycardia meaning the heart beat is too fast and bradycardia the heart beat is too slow. Arrhythmias are caused when the electrical signals that coordinate the heartbeats are not working correctly.

***BODY – EPICURE*

- Get off all medication and supplements- herbs in the form of powders or teas are okay. You may have 72 hours of feeling toxicities leave the bloodstream.
- **Fastest...** Water fast for 7–10 days **OR...**
- 10–14 day cabala juice fast to balance the gasses and correct arrythmias.
- Eat two or three ruby-red grapefruit every day, including the pith of one of the grapefruit as well as lots of tomatoes, red capsicum and vitamin E foods such as almonds, legumes, sunflower seeds, safflower and wheatgerm oil, hazelnuts, peanuts, Brazil nuts, olives in salt brine, spinach, papaya, mustard greens, Swiss chard, blueberries, organic corn, pinenuts, avocados, turnip greens, and apricots.

- Drink one glass of water every hour on the hour for 10 hours of each day, for 30 days or drink one litre of water per 22 kilos of bodyweight each day.
- Have plenty of nature made salt (Ra 24ct Gold See Salt is especially healing).
- Develop the darkest suntan you can by covering your body in Divine Body Butter or coconut oil and then exposing at least 70% of your body to the sun for one hour every day (30 mins each side).
- **ESSENTIAL OIL...** helichrysum, rose.
- (Divine and Ra 24ct gold salt available in the USA **www. thedontolman.com/store** and Australia **www. lynnienichols.com/shop**)

BODY	MIND	SPIRIT
FOODS THAT HEAL	*POSSIBLE EMOTIONAL CAUSE*	*IMBALANCED CHAKRA*
---	---	---
SIGNATURE FOODS... apples, capsicum, beetroot, cherries, grapefruit, grapes, kale, mango, strawberry, tomato, watercress, spinach	• Are you feeling insecure, unloved or lacking in self-love? • Are you putting work and money before love and joy? • Are you feeling uninspired, bored, not listening to your heart's desires? • Are you feeling broken-hearted or afraid of having your heart broken?	Third Eye Chakra- **colour Indigo** / Heart Chakra- colour Emerald Green

***NOTE...** High iron can create imbalance in gasses. Foods with high calcium content such as organic yoghurt, cheeses, milk, broccoli and green leafy foods balance high iron levels.*

***NUGGET...** Bend over and exaggerate a cough for one minute and then drink one litre of water—this resets the gases.*

CIRCULATORY SYSTEM
HEART BALANCING SALAD

Ingredients: 1 cup of green or brown lentils, ⅛ cup sunflower seeds, ½ cup Kalamata olives in salt brine, 1 cup each of torn mustard greens and Swiss chard, ½ cup blueberries, 1 cob of organic corn, 1/8 cup pinenuts, 1 whole large avocado, ⅛ cup each of slithered almonds and peanuts

DRESSING; ½ cup wheatgerm oil, pinch of Himalayan salt, 1 heaped teaspoon honey and ½ cup lemon juice

Method: Place the torn mustard greens and Swiss chard in a salad bowl. Add the cooked cold lentils, sunflower seeds, Kalamata olives deseeded, blueberries, raw corn cut off the cob and chunky diced avocado. Lightly toast the slithered almonds and peanuts in a dry pan then add to the salad. Mix all dressing ingredients together in a jar then pour over the salad. (serves 2)

AORTIC ANEURYSM

***WHAT IS IT?...* **Aortic aneurysm** is where pressure within a weakened section of the aorta, the body's largest artery that carries oxygen-rich blood from the heart to the rest of the body, causes the artery to bulge or balloon, creating what's known as an aneurysm.

***BODY – EPICURE*

- Get off all medication and supplements- herbs in the form of powders or teas are okay. You may have 72 hours of feeling toxicities leave the bloodstream.
- **Fastest...** Water fast for 7–10 days **OR...**
- 21–28-day cabala juice fast, with added celery, whilst snacking on grapefruit.
- Eat two or three ruby-red grapefruit every day, including the pith of one of the grapefruit, as well as one pomegranate and three or four sticks of celery for 30–90 days.
- Drink one glass of water every hour on the hour for 10 hours of each day, for 30 days or drink one litre of water per 22 kilos of bodyweight each day.
- Drink celery juice and have plenty of nature-made salt (Ra 24ct Gold See Salt is especially healing).
- Salt Covenant- have two teaspoons of sea salt in one litre of water first thing in the morning before you eat—the salinity of this is like the blood and will get rid of intestinal pressures/blockages that lead to high blood pressure. It will dilate the blood vessels.
- Have cold showers/swim in cold water and put ice on the chest.
- Apply cypress oil to the heart, temples and bottoms of feet to increase circulation and strengthen vascular walls. Massage helichrysum oil into the area.
- Develop the darkest suntan you can by covering your body in Divine Body Butter or coconut oil and then exposing at least 70% of your body to the sun for one hour every day (30 mins each side).
- **ESSENTIAL OIL...** cypress, helichrysum, frankincense, rosemary, basil.
- (Divine and Ra 24ct gold salt available in the USA **www.thedontolman.com/store** and Australia **www.lynnienichols.com/shop**)

BODY	MIND	SPIRIT
FOODS THAT HEAL	**POSSIBLE EMOTIONAL CAUSE**	**IMBALANCED CHAKRA**
---	---	---
SIGNATURE FOODS... apples, capsicum, beetroot, cherries, grapefruit, grapes, kale, mango, strawberry, tomato, watercress, spinach	• Are you refusing to face long-held emotional problems? • Are you putting others' desires before yours/neglecting your own joy?	Heart Chakra- colour Emerald Green and Third Eye Chakra- **colour Indigo**

CIRCULATORY SYSTEM
CELERY AND POMEGRANATE SALAD with HONEY DRESSING

Ingredients: 3–4 sticks celery, 1 pomegranate, 1 red grapefruit, 1 tbs honey, ½ cup olive oil, Himalayan salt

DRESSING; ½ cup olive oil, 1tbs honey, pinch of salt

Method: Finely slice the celery, dice the grapefruit, and remove the pulp from a pomegranate. Combine in a bowl. Mix dressing ingredients together and drizzle over the salad. (serves 1)

ARTERIOSCLEROSIS/HIGH CHOLESTEROL

***WHAT IS IT?... **Arteriosclerosis** is a disease in which plaque builds up inside of the blood vessels that carry oxygen-rich blood away from the heart, called arteries. This plaque creates a thickening, narrowing and hardening of the artery walls. Cholesterol is a type of fat (lipid) that your body makes and needs; however, bad cholesterol comes from the foods you eat and too much of this is the cause of arteriosclerosis/high cholesterol.

***BODY – EPICURE

- Get off all medication and supplements- herbs in the form of powders or teas are okay. You may have 72 hours of feeling toxicities leave the bloodstream.
- **Fastest...** Water fast for 7–10 days **OR...**
- 21–28-day cabala juice fast, with added celery, whilst snacking on grapefruit.
- Eat two or three ruby-red grapefruit every day for 90 days, and be sure to eat the pith of one of the grapefruit.
- Drink one glass of water every hour on the hour for 10 hours of each day, for 30 days or drink one litre of water per 22 kilos of bodyweight.
- Drink celery juice and have plenty of nature made salt (Ra 24ct Gold See Salt is especially healing).
- Drink tea made from the lemongrass leaf. Mix 1-2 drops lemongrass oil with a carrier oil and ingest daily. Studies have shown lemongrass oil to contain terpenoid compounds that decrease cholesterol levels.
- Have a lot of fruit in the diet including nuts and seeds.
- Salt Covenant- have two teaspoons of sea salt in one litre of water first thing in the morning before you eat—the salinity of this is like the blood and will get rid of intestinal pressures/blockages that lead to high blood pressure. It will dilate the blood vessels.
- Walk for at least 45mins every day.
- Sungazing morning and evenings in 13-second intervals; look at the sun until it reaches a 10-degree arc, or a clenched fist sitting on horizon as sun comes up, stop at top of fist. At night, start gazing as sun hits top of fist until it's gone.
- Develop the darkest suntan you can by covering your body in Divine Body Butter or coconut oil and then exposing at least 70% of your body to the sun for one hour every day (30 mins each side).
- Do a colon cleanse to remove toxicity and plaque from the body.
- **ESSENTIAL OIL...** lemongrass, rosemary, lavender, myrrh, clove, oregano.
- (Divine and Ra 24ct gold salt available in the USA **www.thedontolman.com/store** and Australia **www.lynnienichols.com/shop**)

BODY *FOODS THAT HEAL*	MIND *POSSIBLE EMOTIONAL CAUSE*	SPIRIT *IMBALANCED CHAKRA*
---	---	---
SIGNATURE FOODS... apples, capsicum, beetroot, cherries, grapefruit, grapes, kale, mango, strawberry, tomato, watercress, spinach	• Are you feeling possessive yet wanting more? • Are you constantly criticising yourself for not being perfect? • Are you being cold-hearted and narrow-minded, judgemental of others? • Are you blocking yourself from feeling joy?	Third Eye Chakra- **colour Indigo**

***NOTE... *90–95% of the time, high cholesterol is not real.*

***NUGGET... *The acid in grapefruit thins the blood quicker than any drug and will turn clogged fat into soluble form and remove it from the body. Red grapefruit targets the circulatory system heart/blood, whilst yellow grapefruit targets the spleen, thymus and liver.*

CIRCULATORY SYSTEM
MANGO, STRAWBERRY AND GRAPEFRUIT SMOOTHIE BOWL

Ingredients: Flesh of 2 large sweet mango, 1 tub of strawberries, 1 small red grapefruit peeled and deseeded, 2 large banana, shredded coconut

Method: Put a little of the mango, banana and strawberries aside for garnishing. Place remaining ingredients in a blender on high speed, until thick and creamy. Pour into a shallow bowl and garnish with diced mango, banana, slices of strawberry and toasted coconut

BROKEN CAPILLARIES

***WHAT IS IT?...* **Broken capillaries** are tiny spider veins beneath the skin's surface that occur when blood capillaries dilate.

***BODY – EPICURE*

- **Fastest...** Water fast for 7–10 days **OR...**
- Cabala juice fast 14–28 days.
- Cypress oil massaged into the heart, temples and bottoms of feet increases circulation and strengthens capillary walls. Rosemary and basil oil also assist blood circulation.
- Apply Divine body butter and then go in the sun for 30–

45 mins for seven days. Eat one or two cucumbers every day during this.

- **ESSENTIAL OIL...** lemon, cypress, rosemary, basil.
- (Divine, Congest Ease, essential oil of lemon, Himalayan rock salt, Ra 24ct See Salt, available in the USA **www.thedontolman.com/store** and Australia **www.lynnienichols.com/shop**)

BODY	MIND	SPIRIT
FOODS THAT HEAL	*POSSIBLE EMOTIONAL CAUSE*	*IMBALANCED CHAKRA*
---	---	---
SIGNATURE FOODS... apples, capsicum, beetroot, cherries, grapefruit, grapes, kale, mango, strawberry, tomato, watercress, spinach	• Are you seeing the small details rather than big picture?	Third Eye Chakra- **colour Indigo**

CIRCULATORY SYSTEM
REFRESHING CUCUMBER FACE MASK

Ingredients: 2 large cucumbers with skin, juice of 1 lemon

Method: Mash cucumber with a fork... leave skin on if possible for maximum benefit, then smother all over the face and neck. Leave for 30 mins then rinse off and apply lemon juice to the skin. Do this every day for 7–28 days until the capillary infusion has gone away.

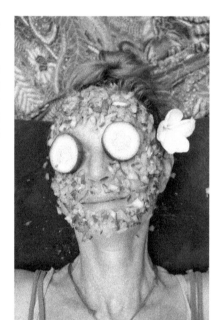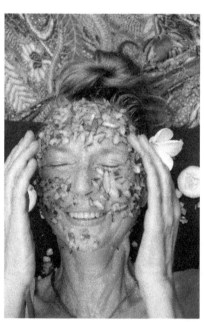

hehe, not the most glamorous look... but oh, so worth it 😊

DEEP VEIN THROMBOSIS (DVT)

***WHAT IS IT?...** **Deep vein thrombosis** is a blood clot in a vein lying deep below the skin, most often the thigh or lower leg. These blood clots are caused by the blood thickening and clumping together and are often a result of long periods of immobility during long-distance travel.

***BODY – EPICURE**

- Get off all medication and supplements- herbs in the form of powders or teas are okay. You may have 72 hours of feeling toxicities leave the bloodstream.
- **Fastest...** Water fast for 7–10 days **OR...**
- 21–28 day cabala juice fast.
- Go vegan or vegetarian.
- Eat one or two ruby red grapefruit three times per week, be sure to eat the pith of one of the grapefruit.
- Eat blood thinning foods such as kiwi fruit and green leafy vegetables and other high vitamin E foods such as papaya, chard, kale, broccoli, spinach, wholegrains, sunflower seeds, coconut and coconut milk/water, oils such as sunflower and wheatgerm oils.
- Have ginger to eat or as a tea, three or four times daily. Also, eat ginger, tumeric, chillies, avocado and cherries can help to prevent and clear bloodclots, as well as curry powder, cinnamon, oregano and thyme.
- Have ½ teaspoon of cayenne pepper in fresh green juice daily.
- Have one tablespoon of turmeric powder in warm water with unfiltered raw organic honey daily.
- Drink one glass of water every hour on the hour for 10 hours of each day, for 30 days or drink one litre of water per 22 kilos of bodyweight.
- Have lots of nature made salt (Ra 24ct Gold See Salt is especially healing).
- Have fruit smoothies with added sunflower or wheatgerm oil.
- Helichrysum oil massaged directly into the area is said to break down coagulated blood. Cypress oil massaged into the heart, temples and bottoms of feet increases circulation and strengthens vascular walls. Rosemary and basil oil also assist blood circulation.
- Salt Covenant- have two teaspoons of sea salt in one litre of water first thing in the morning before you eat—the salinity of this is like the blood and will get rid of intestinal pressures/blockages. It will dilate the blood vessels.
- Elevate the limb above the heart and lay there for 20–30 mins per day.
- Walk 45–60 minutes daily.
- Use compression stocking or wraps.
- Sungazing morning and evenings in 13-second intervals; look at the sun until it reaches a 10-degree arc, or a clenched fist sitting on horizon as sun comes up, stop at top of fist. At night, start gazing as sun hits top of fist until it's gone.
- Develop the darkest suntan you can by covering your body in Divine Body Butter or coconut oil and then exposing at least 70% of your body to the sun for one hour every day (30 mins each side).
- Do a colon cleanse to remove toxicity from the body.
- **ESSENTIAL OIL...** helichrysum, rosemary, basil.
- (Divine and Ra 24ct gold salt available in the USA **www.thedontolman.com/store** and Australia **www.lynnienichols.com/shop**)

BODY _FOODS THAT HEAL_	MIND _POSSIBLE EMOTIONAL CAUSE_	SPIRIT _IMBALANCED CHAKRA_
---	---	---
SIGNATURE FOODS... apples, capsicum, beetroot, cherries, grapefruit, grapes, kale, mango, strawberry, tomato, watercress, spinach	• Are you blocking the joy in life? • Is fear stopping your joy/success?	Third Eye Chakra- colour Indigo / Root Chakra- colour Red

***NUGGET...** Apple seeds contain plant synthesised arsenic which is blood thinning and harmless to man. Along with apple seeds, wheatgrass, apricot kernels and all other seeds except for citrus, are great sources of B17, known by many as Nature's Chemo!*

CIRCULATORY SYSTEM
GREEN BLOOD-THINNING SMOOTHIE

Ingredients: 2 kiwi fruit peeled, 1 large red apple with seeds and peel, 1 kale leaf, ½ cup baby spinach leaves, little bit ginger, ¼ cup sunflower oil, 1 large banana, ½-1 cup water, pinch of cinnamon

Method: Blend all ingredients, except cinnamon, together on high speed until thick and creamy. Garnish with a sprinkle of cinnamon. (serves 1)

ECLAMPSIA/PRE-ECLAMPSIA/GESTATIONAL HYPERTENSION

***WHAT IS IT?...** **Eclampsia** is a rare, serious condition causing convulsions and even coma during pregnancy, posing a threat to both mother and baby. Preeclampsia, formerly called toxaemia, is characterised by protein in the urine and high blood pressure after the 20th week of pregnancy and most often is a precursor to eclampsia.

***BODY – EPICURE*

- Get off all medication and supplements- herbs in the form of powders or teas are okay. You may have 72 hours of feeling toxicities leave the bloodstream.
- **Fastest...** Water fast for 7–10 days **OR...**
- 21–28 day cabala juice fast.
- Eat two or three ruby red grapefruit per day to drop blood pressure—be sure to eat the pith of one of the grapefruit.
- Eat a good, healthy plant-based diet with eggs and good organic dairy.
- Drink celery juice and have plenty of nature made salt (Ra 24ct Gold See Salt is especially healing).
- Drink one glass of water every hour on the hour for 10 hours of each day, for 30 days or drink one litre of water per 22 kilos of bodyweight.
- Salt Covenant- have two teaspoons of sea salt in one litre of water first thing in the morning before you eat—the salinity of this is like the blood and will get rid of intestinal pressures/blockages. It will dilate the blood vessels.
- Sungazing morning and evenings in 13-second intervals; look at the sun until it reaches a 10-degree arc, or a clenched fist sitting on horizon as sun comes up, stop at top of fist. At night, start gazing as sun hits top of fist until it's gone.
- Develop the darkest suntan you can by covering your body in Divine Body Butter or coconut oil and then exposing at least 70% of your body to the sun for one hour every day (30 mins each side).
- **ESSENTIAL OIL...** ylang ylang, eucalyptus, lavender, clover, clary sage, lemon.
- (Divine and Ra 24ct gold salt available in the USA **www.thedontolman.com/store** and Australia **www. lynnienichols.com/shop**)

BODY	MIND	SPIRIT
FOODS THAT HEAL	*POSSIBLE EMOTIONAL CAUSE*	*IMBALANCED CHAKRA*
---	---	---
SIGNATURE FOODS... apples, capsicum, beetroot, cherries, grapefruit, grapes, kale, mango, strawberry, tomato, watercress, spinach	• Are you letting your emotions rule you? • Are you too focused on what others are doing rather than minding your own business? • Is someone making your 'blood boil'? • Is pressure from a situation causing you to block your own feelings?	Third Eye Chakra- **colour Indigo**

***NOTE...** *Elevated blood pressure is a natural part of the childbirth process... The body has to elevate the blood pressure to prepare for delivery!*

***NUGGET...** *AVOID ECLAMPSIA/PRE-ECLAMPSIA by walking for 45 minutes every day until the birth—especially the first eight months, eating a good, healthy plant-based diet with eggs and good organic dairy, drinking one litre of water per 22 kilos of bodyweight each day, getting fresh electrified air.*

CIRCULATORY SYSTEM
SCRAMBLED EGGS

Ingredients: ¼ cup organic cow's milk, ½ cup grated organic animal rennet-free cheese, 3 organic eggs, 1 clove garlic, ½ onion, ½ tsp Himalayan salt, 2 cups baby spinach leaves. Coconut oil for cooking

Method: Place the eggs in a bowl and whisk until fluffy, add the grated cheese, milk, salt, garlic, onion and shredded spinach. Heat a little coconut oil in a frypan then add the egg mixture. Cook on medium heat, stirring occasionally until the eggs are light and fluffy. (serves 1)

ENDOCARDITIS (IE)

***WHAT IS IT?...** **Endocarditis,** also called infectious endocarditis (IE) or bacterial endocarditis (BE), is where the heart valve, inner membrane, or a blood vessel of the heart is infected by bacteria entering the bloodstream. Although endocarditis is not common, people who have pre-existing heart disease are at increased risk of developing this.

***BODY – EPICURE**

- Get off all medication and supplements- herbs in the form of powders or teas are okay. You may have 72 hours of feeling toxicities leave the bloodstream.
- **Fastest...** Water fast for 7–10 days **OR...**
- 21–28 day cabala juice fast whilst eating two or three grapefruit each morning. If you can't fast, combine this with snacking on cherries, strawberries, mango, tomatoes, capsicum and all of the other heart foods.
- Eat and juice a locally grown, fresh, raw organic vegan diet for highest nutritional force, making sure that every day you eat raw wholefoods that support the circulatory system.
- Drink one glass of water every hour on the hour for 10 hours of each day, for 30 days or drink one litre of water per 22 kilos of bodyweight.
- Have lots of nature-made salt (Ra 24ct Gold See Salt is especially healing).
- Walk for 10–20 minutes each day.
- Salt Covenant- have two teaspoons of sea salt in one litre of water first thing in the morning before you eat—the salinity of this is like the blood and will get rid of intestinal pressures/blockages. It will dilate the blood vessels.
- Use oils with antibacterial properties.
- Sungazing morning and evenings in 13-second intervals; look at the sun until it reaches a 10-degree arc, or a clenched fist sitting on horizon as sun comes up, stop at top of fist. At night, start gazing as sun hits top of fist until it's gone.
- Develop the darkest suntan you can by covering your body in Divine Body Butter or coconut oil and then exposing at least 70% of your body to the sun for one hour every day (30 mins each side).
- **ESSENTIAL OIL...** peppermint, lavender, lemon, lemongrass, eucalyptus.
- (Divine and Ra 24ct gold salt available in the USA **www.thedontolman.com/store** and Australia **www.lynnienichols.com/shop**)

BODY	MIND	SPIRIT
FOODS THAT HEAL	*POSSIBLE EMOTIONAL CAUSE*	*IMBALANCED CHAKRA*
---	---	---
SIGNATURE FOODS... apples, capsicum, beetroot, cherries, grapefruit, grapes, kale, mango, strawberry, tomato, watercress, spinach	• Is it time to love and put yourself first for a change? • Are you favouring money and position over joy and love? • Do you have the belief 'life wasn't meant to be easy'?	Third Eye Chakra- **colour Indigo** / Heart Chakra- colour Emerald Green

---

***NOTE... *May take 90 days to heal.*

CIRCULATORY SYSTEM
STRAWBERRY and WATERCRESS SALAD

Ingredients: 1 punnet of strawberries washed and halved lengthways, 1 cup of fresh watercress, 2 cups of baby spinach leaves

Method: Place all ingredients together in a salad bowl. Add lemon dressing (see recipe under Dressings in back of book). Add feta cheese for a non-vegan option. (serves 1)

HAEMOPHILIA

***WHAT IS IT?...** **Haemophilia** is a condition where the blood does not clot normally, resulting in an extended length of bleeding and/or a greater blood loss than normal, even from minor injuries. Typically, this condition is caused by a lack of coagulation factor.

***BODY – EPICURE*

- Get off all medication and supplements- herbs in the form of powders or teas are okay. You may have 72 hours of feeling toxicities leave the bloodstream.
- **Fastest...** Water fast for 7–10 days **OR...**
- 21–28-day cabala juice fast whilst eating two or three grapefruit each morning. If you can't fast, combine this with snacking on cherries, strawberries, mango, tomatoes, capsicum and all of the other heart foods.
- Drink coconut water/milk to restore the blood count. Can also drink one litre of grape juice with two egg yolks blended together—this acts like a transfusion.
- Eat free-range organic omelettes, buckwheat, fresh ginger, organic apricots- fresh and dried, lots of onions and garlic- raw and/or cooked.
- Eat a variety of fermented foods such as organic yoghurts, kefirs, aged cheeses, olives in brine, sauerkraut, etc.
- Drink and eat a lot of citrus.
- Drink one glass of water every hour on the hour for 10 hours of each day, for 30 days or drink one litre of water per 22 kilos of bodyweight.
- Have lots of nature made salt (Ra 24ct Gold See Salt is especially healing).
- Have a daily bath with one or two cups of sea salt and bicarb each morning.
- Use oils with coagulant properties.
- Sungazing morning and evenings in 13-second intervals; look at the sun until it reaches a 10-degree arc, or a clenched fist sitting on horizon as sun comes up, stop at top of fist. At night, start gazing as sun hits top of fist until it's gone.
- Develop the darkest suntan you can by covering your body in Divine Body Butter or coconut oil and then exposing at least 70% of your body to the sun for one hour every day (30 mins each side).
- **ESSENTIAL OIL...** helichrysum, myrrh and geranium.
- (Divine and Ra 24ct gold salt available in the USA **www.thedontolman.com/store** and Australia **www.lynnienichols.com/shop**)

BODY *FOODS THAT HEAL*	MIND *POSSIBLE EMOTIONAL CAUSE*	SPIRIT *IMBALANCED CHAKRA*
---	---	---
SIGNATURE FOODS... apples, capsicum, beetroot, cherries, grapefruit, grapes, kale, mango, strawberry, tomato, watercress, spinach	- Are you lacking in self-love? - Are you holding unforgiveness toward yourself?	Third Eye Chakra- **colour Indigo**

***NUGGET... *Onions represent the different-sized cells in the body and target all 10,000 trillion cells.*

CIRCULATORY SYSTEM
NATURE'S BLOOD MAKER

Ingredients: 1 litre of grape juice, 2 egg yolks

Method: Place both ingredients together in a blender and mix well, drink immediately

HEART DISEASE/CARDIOVASCULAR DISEASE

***WHAT IS IT?...** **Heart disease/Cardiovascular disease** is the umbrella term referring to conditions that involve blocked or narrowed blood vessels leading to chest pain (angina) or, more severely, a heart attack or stroke. Conditions affecting the heart's muscle, valves or rhythm also come under the umbrella term of heart disease.

***BODY – EPICURE*

- Get off all medication and supplements- herbs in the form of powders or teas are okay. You may have 72 hours of feeling toxicities leave the bloodstream.
- Fastest... Water fast for 7–10 days OR...
- 21–28-day cabala juice fast whilst eating two or three grapefruit each morning. If you can't fast, combine this with snacking on cherries, strawberries, mango, tomatoes, capsicum and all of the other heart foods.
- Eat and juice a locally grown, fresh, raw organic vegan diet for highest nutritional force, making sure that every day you eat raw wholefoods that support the circulatory system.
- Drink water, lemon juice and cayenne pepper combined for circulation.
- Drink one glass of water every hour on the hour for 10 hours of each day, for 30 days or drink one litre of water per 22 kilos of bodyweight.
- Have lots of nature made salt (Ra 24ct Gold See Salt is especially healing).
- Walk for 10–45 minutes each day.

- Salt Covenant- have two teaspoons of sea salt in one litre of water first thing in the morning before you eat—the salinity of this is like the blood and will get rid of intestinal pressures/blockages. It will dialate the blood vessels.
- Sungazing morning and evenings in 13-second intervals; look at the sun until it reaches a 10-degree arc, or a clenched fist sitting on horizon as sun comes up, stop at top of fist. At night, start gazing as sun hits top of fist until it's gone.
- Develop the darkest suntan you can by covering your body in Divine Body Butter or coconut oil and then exposing at least 70% of your body to the sun for one hour every day (30 mins each side).
- This is a 90-day healing protocol.
- **ESSENTIAL OIL...** basil, ginger, cinnamon bark, helichrysum, clary sage, cypress, eucalyptus.
- (Divine and Ra 24ct gold salt available in the USA **www.thedontolman.com/store** and Australia **www. lynnienichols.com/shop**)

BODY FOODS THAT HEAL	MIND POSSIBLE EMOTIONAL CAUSE	SPIRIT IMBALANCED CHAKRA
---	---	---
SIGNATURE FOODS... apples, capsicum, beetroot, cherries, grapefruit, grapes, kale, mango, strawberry, tomato, watercress, spinach	• Are you holding on to painful experiences/situations from the past? • Have you become hard-hearted? • Where's the joy and love? Is your Inner Child longing to laugh, have fun and be loved by you?	Third Eye Chakra- **colour Indigo** / Heart Chakra- colour Emerald Green

***NOTE...** *Heart Disease is the world's leading cause of death and disability. An Australian dies every 10 minutes as a result of heart disease.*

CIRCULATORY SYSTEM
BLOOD-CIRCULATOR JUICE

Ingredients: 1 litre pure water, 3 lemons juiced, cayenne pepper

Method: Use a commercial juicer to juice lemons with skin on. Mix ingredients together and drink throughout the day to improve blood circulation

HEART ATTACK/CARDIAC ARREST

***WHAT IS IT?...** **Heart attack** happens when there is a sudden complete blockage of an artery or can be the result of arrhythmias, where the heart beat becomes rapid (tachycardia), or chaotic (ventricular fibrillation), or extremely slow (bradycardia).

Cardiac arrest is the sudden loss of heart function. Death can occur within minutes of symptoms appearing, especially where a person is suffering from heart disease.

***BODY – EPICURE*

- Get off all medication and supplements- herbs in the form of powders or teas are okay. You may have 72 hours of feeling toxicities leave the bloodstream.
- Fastest... Water fast for 7–10 days OR...
- 21–28-day cabala juice fast whilst eating two or three grapefruit each morning. If you can't fast, combine this with snacking on cherries, strawberries, mango, tomatoes, capsicum and all of the other heart foods.
- Eat and juice a locally grown, fresh, raw organic vegan diet for highest nutritional force, making sure that every day you eat raw wholefoods that support the circulatory system.
- Eat raspberry flavoured Pulse, this targets the heart and blood.
- Drink water, lemon juice and cayenne pepper combined for circulation.
- Drink one glass of water every hour on the hour for 10 hours of each day, for 30 days or drink one litre of water per 22 kilos of bodyweight.
- Have lots of nature made salt (Ra 24ct Gold See Salt is especially healing).
- Walk for 10–45 minutes each day.
- Salt Covenant- have two teaspoons of sea salt in one litre of water first thing in the morning before you eat—the salinity of this is like the blood and will get rid of intestinal pressures/blockages. It will dialate the blood vessels.
- Sungazing morning and evenings in 13-second intervals; look at the sun until it reaches a 10-degree arc, or a clenched fist sitting on horizon as sun comes up, stop at top of fist. At night, start gazing as sun hits top of fist until it's gone.
- Develop the darkest suntan you can by covering your body in Divine Body Butter or coconut oil and then exposing at least 70% of your body to the sun for one hour every day (30 mins each side).
- **ESSENTIAL OIL...** helichrysum, basil, clary sage, cypress, eucalyptus.
- (Pulse, Divine and Ra 24ct gold salt available in the USA **www.thedontolman.com/store** and Australia **www.lynnienichols.com/shop**)

BODY *FOODS THAT HEAL*	MIND *POSSIBLE EMOTIONAL CAUSE*	SPIRIT *IMBALANCED CHAKRA*
---	---	---
SIGNATURE FOODS... apples, capsicum, beetroot, cherries, grapefruit, grapes, kale, mango, strawberry, tomato, watercress, spinach	• Are you preferencing money and status over joy and love? • Are you feeling unworthy of love and joy, not good enough? • Are you living and doing for others and making yourself less important? • Are you blocking feelings of and joy flowing into your life?	Third Eye Chakra- **colour Indigo** / Heart Chakra- colour Emerald Green

***NOTE...** *Prevent a heart attack by eating three red grapefruit every day.*

***NUGGET...** *To stop a heart attack, when you feel the pain, bend over and exaggerate a cough until the pain stops, then drink one litre of water. If it happens at night, sit up and bend over, close your mouth tight and force the air out between the lips—this creates a balancing of gasses almost immediately.*

CIRCULATORY SYSTEM
RASBERRY PULSE

Ingredients: Nuts, seeds, fruit including rasberry

Method: Raspberry Pulse and Mango Pulse are healing heart foods, made to phi ratio and available in the USA **www.thedontolman.com/store** and Australia **www.lynnienichols.com/shop**)

HEART FAILURE

***WHAT IS IT?...** **Heart Failure** is a severe condition in which the heart muscle is either unable to fill with enough blood or unable to pump enough blood to meet the body's need for fresh blood and oxygenation.

***BODY – EPICURE**

- Get off all medication and supplements- herbs in the form of powders or teas are okay. You may have 72 hours of feeling toxicities leave the bloodstream.
- **Fastest...** Water fast for 7–10 days **OR...**
- 21–28-day cabala juice fast whilst eating two or three grapefruit each morning. If you can't fast, combine this with snacking on cherries, strawberries, mango, tomatoes, capsicum and all of the other heart foods.
- Eat and juice a locally grown, fresh, raw organic vegan diet for highest nutritional force, making sure that every day you eat raw wholefoods that support the circulatory system.
- Eat raspberry flavoured Pulse, this targets the heart and blood.
- Drink water, lemon juice and cayenne pepper combined for circulation.
- Drink one glass of water every hour on the hour for 10 hours of each day, for 30 days or drink one litre of water per 22 kilos of bodyweight.
- Have lots of nature made salt (Ra 24ct Gold See Salt is especially healing).
- Walk for 10–45 minutes each day.
- Salt Covenant- have two teaspoons of sea salt in one litre of water first thing in the morning before you eat—the salinity of this is like the blood and will get rid of intestinal pressures/blockages. It will dilate the blood vessels.
- Sungazing morning and evenings in 13-second intervals; look at the sun until it reaches a 10-degree arc, or a clenched fist sitting on horizon as sun comes up, stop at top of fist. At night, start gazing as sun hits top of fist until it's gone.
- Develop the darkest suntan you can by covering your body in Divine Body Butter or coconut oil and then exposing at least 70% of your body to the sun for one hour every day (30 mins each side).
- **ESSENTIAL OIL...** helichrysum, basil, clary sage, cypress, eucalyptus.
- (Pulse, Divine and Ra 24ct gold salt available in the USA **www.thedontolman.com/store** and Australia **www.lynnienichols.com/shop**)

BODY *FOODS THAT HEAL*	MIND *POSSIBLE EMOTIONAL CAUSE*	SPIRIT *IMBALANCED CHAKRA*
---	---	---
SIGNATURE FOODS... apples, capsicum, beetroot, cherries, grapefruit, grapes, kale, mango, strawberry, tomato, watercress, spinach	• Have you stopped the flow of love and joy? • Are you feeling unworthy of love, joy and forgiveness/not good enough? • Do you believe you are unlovable?	Third Eye Chakra- **colour Indigo** / Heart Chakra- colour Emerald Green

CIRCULATORY SYSTEM
HEART-STARTER CRUMBLE

Ingredients: 4 large grated red apples including skin and seeds, 1 cup grapes cut into halves, 1 large mango diced, 1 punnet of strawberries cut in halves, 1 cup shaved coconut.

CRUMBLE TOPPING: 1 cup LSA (linseed, soy, almond meal), ½ cup coconut oil, 2 tbsp honey, 1 tsp cinnamon, 1 cup shredded toasted coconut, ½ cup salted toasted cashews chopped, ½ cup salted pistachios chopped.

Method: Toss all ingredients together in a bowl to make a fruit salad. Place half of the mixture into each bowl and top with a generous handful of crumble topping. Garnish with a sprig of mint.

Crumble Topping; Place all ingredients together in a bowl. Use your hands to mix and rub the ingredients until it becomes the desired crumble texture. Add more coconut oil if needed. (serves 2)

HEMACHROMATOSIS

***WHAT IS IT?...* **Hemachromatosis** is a condition where there is an overload of iron in the body, which can lead to liver damage and diabetes mellitus. Iron is a part of haemoglobin, a very important molecule in the blood that carries oxygen from the lungs to the body tissues; however, too much iron can cause hemachromatosis.

***BODY – EPICURE*

- Get off all medication and supplements- herbs in the form of powders or teas are okay. You may have 72 hours of feeling toxicities leave the bloodstream.
- Fastest... Water fast for 7–10 days OR...
- 21-day cabala juice fast.
- Eat all different colour cabbage and sauerkraut every day.
- Eat high-calcium foods such as organic yoghurt, cheese and milk as well as broccoli and green leafy vegetables.
- Drink one glass of water every hour on the hour for 10 hours of each day, for 30 days or drink one litre of water per 22 kilos of bodyweight.
- Suck on Himalayan rock salt, have the size of the last segment of your little finger each day.
- Sungazing morning and evenings in 13-second intervals; look at the sun until it reaches a 10-degree arc, or a clenched fist sitting on horizon as sun comes up, stop at top of fist. At night, start gazing as sun hits top of fist until it's gone.
- Develop the darkest suntan you can by covering your body in Divine Body Butter or coconut oil and then exposing at least 70% of your body to the sun for one hour every day (30 mins each side).
- **ESSENTIAL OIL...** oregano oil.
- (Divine and Ra 24ct gold salt available in the USA **www.thedontolman.com/store** and Australia **www. lynnienichols.com/shop**)

BODY *FOODS THAT HEAL*	MIND *POSSIBLE EMOTIONAL CAUSE*	SPIRIT *IMBALANCED CHAKRA*
---	---	---
SIGNATURE FOODS... apples, capsicum, beetroot, cherries, grapefruit, grapes, kale, mango, strawberry, tomato, watercress, spinach	• Are you lacking in joy and self-love?	Third Eye Chakra- **colour Indigo**

***NOTE...** Foods with high calcium content such as organic yoghurt, cheeses, milk, broccoli and green leafy foods balance high iron levels.*

***NUGGET...** Cabbage – all colours including sauerkraut – is nature's chelator to remove over-stored iron in the blood and body.*

CIRCULATORY SYSTEM
RAW GADO GADO

Ingredients: ¼ red cabbage, ¼ green cabbage, 1 med carrot, ½ bunch spinach, 1 large kale leaf, 1 small red capsicum, 1 tsp ginger, ½ tsp turmeric, chilli and sea salt to taste

SESAME PEANUT DRESSING; ½ cup organic peanut butter, ¾ cup olive oil, pinch sea salt, ¼ cup sesame oil

Method: Finely shred the red and green cabbage, spinach, kale and red capsicum. Mix well. Dice the ginger, turmeric and chilli and add to the mix with a couple of pinches of salt. Mix dressing ingredients together in a jar. Pile the salad into serving bowls and top with a generous amount of dressing. (serves 2)

HIGH BLOOD PRESSURE/HYPERTENSION

***WHAT IS IT?...* **High blood pressure/Hypertension** is when the pressure in the arteries over a long period of time as the heart beats is 140 systolic or higher, or 90 diastolic or higher. Normal blood pressure is 120/80. The top number of 120, called systolic, is the pressure in the arteries when the heart beats and the bottom number of 80, called diastolic, is the pressure when the heart rests between beats. High blood pressure can lead to a heart attack or stroke and may also affect the kidneys.

***BODY – EPICURE*

- Get off all medication and supplements- herbs in the form of powders or teas are okay. You may have 72 hours of feeling toxicities leave the bloodstream.
- **Fastest...** Water fast for 7–10 days **OR...**
- 21–28-day cabala juice fast, with added celery, whilst snacking on grapefruit.
- Eat two or three ruby-red grapefruit every day and be sure to eat the pith of one of the grapefruit.
- Drink one glass of water every hour on the hour for 10 hours of each day, for 30 days or drink one litre of water per 22 kilos of bodyweight.
- Drink celery juice and have plenty of nature made salt (Ra 24ct Gold See Salt is especially healing).
- Have a lot of fruit in the diet.
- Walk for 10–45 minutes each day.
- Salt Covenant- have two teaspoons of sea salt in one litre of water first thing in the morning before you eat—the salinity of this is like the blood and will get rid of intestinal pressures/blockages that lead to high blood pressure. It will dilate the blood vessels.
- Sungazing morning and evenings in 13-second intervals; look at the sun until it reaches a 10-degree arc, or a clenched fist sitting on horizon as sun comes up, stop at top of fist. At night, start gazing as sun hits top of fist until it's gone.
- Develop the darkest suntan you can by covering your body in Divine Body Butter or coconut oil and then exposing at least 70% of your body to the sun for one hour every day (30 mins each side).
- Do a colon cleanse to remove toxicity from the body.
- **ESSENTIAL OIL...** lavender, ylang ylang, marjoram, neroli, bergamot, cedarwood.
- (Divine and Ra 24ct gold salt available in the USA **www.thedontolman.com/store** and Australia **www. lynnienichols.com/shop**)

BODY *FOODS THAT HEAL*	MIND *POSSIBLE EMOTIONAL CAUSE*	SPIRIT *IMBALANCED CHAKRA*
---	---	---
SIGNATURE FOODS... apples, capsicum, beetroot, cherries, grapefruit, grapes, kale, mango, strawberry, tomato, watercress, spinach	• Are you holding on to feelings of hate, resentment and/or revenge? • Are you feeling pressured, overwhelmed by demands?	Third Eye Chakra- **colour Indigo**

CIRCULATORY SYSTEM
GRAPEFRUIT, CELERY & APPLE JUICE

Ingredients: 1 ruby-red grapefruit with pith, 2 stalks of celery, 1 large red apple, 1 large green apple

Method: Juice all ingredients and drink immediately

LONG QT SYNDROME (LQTS)

***WHAT IS IT?...** **Long QT** is a disorder of the electrical activity of the heart, which can cause sudden dangerous heart rhythms called arrhythmias. Arrhythmias affect the way your heart circulates blood and oxygenates the body.

***BODY – EPICURE*

- Get off all medication and supplements- herbs in the form of powders or teas are okay. You may have 72 hours of feeling toxicities leave the bloodstream.
- Fastest... Water fast for 7–10 days OR...
- 10–14-day cabala juice and green juice fast to balance the gasses and correct arrythmias.
- Eat two or three ruby-red grapefruit every day, including the pith of one of the grapefruit, as well as lots of tomatoes and red capsicum.
- Eat vitamin E foods such as almonds, legumes, sunflower seeds, safflower and wheatgerm oil, hazelnuts, peanuts, Brazil nuts, olives in salt brine, spinach, papaya, mustard greens, Swiss chard, blueberries, organic corn, pinenuts, avocados, turnip greens, and apricots.
- Drink one glass of water every hour on the hour for 10 hours of each day, for 30 days or drink one litre of water per 22 kilos of bodyweight each day.
- Have plenty of nature made salt (Ra 24ct Gold See Salt is especially healing).
- Develop the darkest suntan you can by covering your body in Divine Body Butter or coconut oil and then exposing at least 70% of your body to the sun for one hour every day (30 mins each side).
- **ESSENTIAL OIL...** bergamot, cedarwood, lavender, ylang ylang, marjoram, neroli.
- (Divine and Ra 24ct gold salt available in the USA **www.thedontolman.com/store** and Australia **www. lynnienichols.com/shop**)

BODY *FOODS THAT HEAL*	MIND *POSSIBLE EMOTIONAL CAUSE*	SPIRIT *IMBALANCED CHAKRA*
---	---	---
SIGNATURE FOODS... apples, capsicum, beetroot, cherries, grapefruit, grapes, kale, mango, strawberry, tomato, watercress, spinach	• Are you feeling insecure, unloved or are you lacking self-love? • Are you putting work and money before love and joy? • Are you feeling uninspired, bored, not listening to your heart's desires? • Are you feeling broken hearted or afraid of having your heart broken?	Third Eye Chakra- **colour Indigo** / Heart Chakra- colour Emerald Green

CIRCULATORY SYSTEM
VITAMIN E SMOOTHIE

Ingredients: ¼ cup almonds, ¼ cup sunflower seeds, ½ cup papaya, ½ cup Swiss chard, ½ cup spinach, ½ cup dried apricots, ¼ cup wheatgerm oil, 1 cup coconut milk/cream

Method: Place all ingredients together in a blender on high and mix until smooth and creamy—add extra coconut milk, if necessary, to create the desired consistency, (serves 1)

METABOLIC SYNDROME

WHAT IS IT?... **Metabolic syndrome** is a group of physiological and biochemical abnormalities that often occur together and are associated with the development of type 2 diabetes, cardiovascular disease and stroke. Components of metabolic syndrome include high blood pressure, obesity, high blood triglycerides, insulin resistance and low levels of HDL cholesterol.

BODY – EPICURE

- **Fastest...** Water fast for 7–10 days **OR...**
- 21–28-day cabala juice fast, with added celery, whilst snacking on grapefruit.
- Eat two or three ruby-red grapefruit every day and be sure to eat the pith of one of the grapefruit.
- Drink one glass of water every hour on the hour for 10 hours of each day, for 30 days or drink one litre of water per 22 kilos of bodyweight.
- Drink celery juice and have plenty of nature made salt (Ra 24ct Gold See Salt is especially healing).
- Eat orange sweet potato and have a lot of fruit in the diet.
- Walk for 10–45 minutes each day.
- Salt Covenant- have two teaspoons of sea salt in one litre of water first thing in the morning before you eat—the salinity of this is like the blood and will get rid of intestinal pressures/blockages that lead to high blood pressure. It will dilate the blood vessels.
- Sungazing morning and evenings in 13-second intervals; look at the sun until it reaches a 10-degree arc, or a clenched fist sitting on horizon as sun comes up, stop at top of fist. At night, start gazing as sun hits top of fist until it's gone.
- Develop the darkest suntan you can by covering your body in Divine Body Butter or coconut oil and then exposing at least 70% of your body to the sun for one hour every day (30 mins each side).
- Do a colon cleanse to remove toxicity from the body.
- **ESSENTIAL OIL...** cinnamon, lemongrass, lavender, ylang ylang, marjoram, neroli.
- (Divine and Ra 24ct gold salt available in the USA **www.thedontolman.com/store** and Australia **www.lynnienichols.com/shop**)

BODY *FOODS THAT HEAL*	MIND *POSSIBLE EMOTIONAL CAUSE*	SPIRIT *IMBALANCED CHAKRA*
---	---	---
SIGNATURE FOODS... apples, capsicum, beetroot, cherries, grapefruit, grapes, kale, mango, strawberry, tomato, watercress, spinach	• Are you feeling dislike, hatred or rejection toward yourself? • Are you feeling miserable/fearful and blocking the flow of love and joy?	Third Eye Chakra- **colour Indigo** / Heart Chakra- colour Emerald Green

CIRCULATORY SYSTEM
SWEET POTATO PIZZA

Ingredients: 2 large orange sweet potato, ½ cup Kalamata olives, 4 large tomatoes, 2 large red capsicum, 1 tbsp dried oregano, 1 large red onion, 2 large cloves garlic, 1 cup organic cheese, coconut oil

Method: Cut the sweet potato into long, thin slices and bake in a moderate oven with coconut oil until golden. Place in a casserole dish as the pizza base. Roast the capsicum until the skin goes black, remove the skins and then dice. Dice the tomato and onion; finely dice the garlic and slice the olives. Mix all of the diced ingredients together, add a tbsp oregano and a pinch or two of salt then spread over the sweet potato. Top with grated, organic, non-animal-rennet cheese and place in the oven until the sweet potato is hot and cheese is melted. An option is to use a fry pan instead of casserole dish. (Vegan option- once pizza is hot, drizzle with cashew mayonnaise- (see recipe under Dressings in back of book)

Serves 2

MYELOMA/MULTIPLE MYELOMA

***WHAT IS IT?...* **Myeloma** is a cancer of the plasma cells in the bone marrow.

***BODY – EPICURE*

- **Fastest...** Water fast for 7–10 days **OR...**
- Do the five-week 35% food-grade hydrogen peroxide protocol combined with a cabala juice/coconut water fast for 14–28 days. Snack on fresh coconut.
- For seven days drink one litre of red grape juice or orange juice blended with two raw egg yolks to support the capacity of the bloodstream.
- Drink coconut water/milk to restore the blood count.
- Eat a variety of fermented foods such as organic yoghurts, kefirs, aged cheeses, olives in brine, sauerkraut, etc. as well as fresh coconut and boiled eggs.
- Eat one medium-sized potato every day, the starch cleanses the lymphatic stream.
- Eat lots of onions and garlic, raw and cooked.
- Eat lots of fruit, especially red and white grapes for the blood cells.
- Drink one glass of water every hour on the hour for 10 hours of each day, for 30 days or drink one litre of water per 22 kilos of bodyweight.
- Have lots of nature-made salt (Ra 24ct Gold See Salt is especially healing).
- Have a daily bath with one or two cups of sea salt and bicarb each morning.
- Oxygenate the blood by walking for 45 mins to 1 hr every day.
- Sungazing morning and evenings in 13-second intervals; look at the sun until it reaches a 10-degree arc, or a clenched fist sitting on horizon as sun comes up, stop at top of fist. At night, start gazing as sun hits top of fist until it's gone.
- Develop the darkest suntan you can by covering your body in Divine Body Butter or coconut oil and then exposing at least 70% of your body to the sun for one hour every day (30 mins each side).
- Drink one cup of lemon juice every day, can mix with pure water.
- Do a colon cleanse to remove toxicity from the body.
- **ESSENTIAL OIL...** lemon, lavender, rosemary, eucalyptus, camomile, ylang ylang, jasmin.
- (Divine and Ra 24ct gold salt available in the USA **www.thedontolman.com/store** and Australia **www.lynnienichols.com/shop**)

BODY *FOODS THAT HEAL*	MIND *POSSIBLE EMOTIONAL CAUSE*	SPIRIT *IMBALANCED CHAKRA*
---	---	---
SIGNATURE FOODS... apples, capsicum, beetroot, cherries, grapefruit, grapes, kale, mango, strawberry, tomato, watercress, spinach	- Are you judging life and making it good or bad rather than just accepting? - Have you lost all joy and gratitide for life?	Third Eye Chakra- **colour Indigo** / Root Chakra- **colour Red**

CIRCULATORY SYSTEM
CREAMY EGG & POTATO SALAD

Ingredients: 1 small red onion, 2 cloves of garlic, 2 eggs, 3 large potatoes, ½ cup parsley, 1 tsp sea salt, cashew mayonnaise (see recipe under Dressings in back of book)

Method: Dice the potato into cubes and steam until just soft; put aside to cool. Boil eggs for 5 minutes until hard inside then peel, mash and add to the steamed potato. Finely dice and add the parsley, red onion and garlic. Season with salt. Add a generous amount of cashew mayonnaise and serve, (serves 4)

MYELODYSPLASTIC SYNDROME (MDS)

***WHAT IS IT?...** **Myelodysplastic syndrome** is a group of disorders that affect the normal blood cell production in bone marrow, producing abnormal immature blood cells that fail to mature properly. MDS is also known as 'bone marrow failure disorder.'

***BODY – EPICURE*

- **Fastest...** Water fast for 7–10 days **OR...**
- 21–28-day cabala juice fast.
- Drink coconut water/milk to restore the blood count. Can also drink one litre of grape juice with two egg yolks blended together—this acts like a transfusion.
- Drink one cup of lemon juice every day, can mix with pure water.
- Eat a variety of fermented foods such as organic yoghurts, kefirs, aged cheeses including blue cheese, olives in brine, sauerkraut, etc. as well as lots of onions and garlic, raw and cooked.
- Eat one medium-sized potato every day, the starch cleanses the lymphatic stream.
- Eat lots of fruit.
- Oxygenate the blood by walking for 45 mins to 1 hr every day.
- Drink one glass of water every hour on the hour for 10 hours of each day, for 30 days or drink one litre of water per 22 kilos of bodyweight.
- Have lots of nature-made salt (Ra 24ct Gold See Salt is especially healing).
- Have a daily bath with one or two cups of sea salt and bicarb each morning.
- Sungazing morning and evenings in 13-second intervals; look at the sun until it reaches a 10-degree arc, or a clenched fist sitting on horizon as sun comes up, stop at top of fist. At night, start gazing as sun hits top of fist until it's gone.
- Develop the darkest suntan you can by covering your body in Divine Body Butter or coconut oil and then exposing at least 70% of your body to the sun for one hour every day (30 mins each side).
- **ESSENTIAL OIL...** lemon, myrrh.
- (Divine and Ra 24ct gold salt available in the USA **www.thedontolman.com/store** and Australia **www.lynnienichols.com/shop**)

BODY *FOODS THAT HEAL*	MIND *POSSIBLE EMOTIONAL CAUSE*	SPIRIT *IMBALANCED CHAKRA*
---	---	---
SIGNATURE FOODS... apples, capsicum, beetroot, cherries, grapefruit, grapes, kale, mango, strawberry, tomato, watercress, spinach	• Are you feeling defeated? Have you given up? • Are you lacking love, laughter and joy in your life?	Third Eye Chakra- colour Indigo / Root Chakra- colour Red

CIRCULATORY SYSTEM
STUFFED POTATOES WITH FERMENT

Ingredients: ½ cup sliced Kalamata olives in brine, 4 large organic potatoes with skins, 1 large clove garlic diced, 1 small red onion diced, sea salt, pepper, ½ cup parsley, 1 cup sauerkraut or fermented veg. Vegan option; ½ cup cashew mayonnaise **(see recipe under Dressings in back of book)**, non-vegan option; ¼-½ cup blue cheese.

Method: Scrub the skins of the potatoes, prick with a fork and place in the oven on high temperature until the skins go crunchy and the insides are soft. Set aside to cool slightly, then cut in half width-wise. Gently scoop out the filling with a teaspoon and place in a mixing bowl with the sliced olives, onions, parsley, (blue cheese or cashew mayo) and garlic. Mix well and season with salt and pepper. Spoon the mixture back into the potato skins and place in the oven again to heat before serving. Garnish with a spoon of fermented veggies and a dollop of natural yoghurt or cashew mayonnaise. (serves 4)

VON WILLEBRAND'S DISEASE (VWD)

***WHAT IS IT?...** **Von Willebrand's disease** is a disorder caused by defective or missing clotting protein called von Willebrand factor, thus affecting the ability of the blood to clot efficiently.

***BODY – EPICURE*

- Get off all medication and supplements- herbs in the form of powders or teas are okay. You may have 72 hours of feeling toxicities leave the bloodstream.
- **Fastest...** Water fast for 7–10 days **OR...**
- 21–28-day cabala juice fast.
- Drink coconut water/milk to restore the blood count. Can also drink one litre of grape juice with two egg yolks blended together—this acts like a transfusion.
- Eat free range organic omelettes, buckwheat, fresh ginger, organic apricots- fresh an dried, lots of onions and garlic raw and/or cooked.
- Eat a variety of fermented foods such as organic yoghurts, kefirs, aged cheeses, olives in brine, sauerkraut, etc.
- Drink and eat a lot of citrus.
- Drink one glass of water every hour on the hour for 10 hours of each day, for 30 days or drink one litre of water per 22 kilos of bodyweight.
- Have lots of nature-made salt (Ra 24ct Gold See Salt is especially healing).
- Have a daily bath with one or two cups of sea salt and bicarb each morning. Add oils with coagulant properties
- Sungazing morning and evenings in 13-second intervals; look at the sun until it reaches a 10-degree arc, or a clenched fist sitting on horizon as sun comes up, stop at top of fist. At night, start gazing as sun hits top of fist until it's gone.
- Develop the darkest suntan you can by covering your body in Divine Body Butter or coconut oil and then exposing at least 70% of your body to the sun for one hour every day (30 mins each side).
- **ESSENTIAL OIL...** helichrysum, myrrh and geranium.
- (Divine and Ra 24ct gold salt available in the USA **www.thedontolman.com/store** and Australia **www.lynnienichols.com/shop**)

BODY	MIND	SPIRIT
FOODS THAT HEAL	*POSSIBLE EMOTIONAL CAUSE*	*IMBALANCED CHAKRA*
---	---	---
SIGNATURE FOODS... apples, capsicum, beetroot, cherries, grapefruit, grapes, kale, mango, strawberry, tomato, watercress, spinach	• Are you lacking self-love? • Are you unable to forgive yourself?	Third Eye Chakra- **colour Indigo**

CIRCULATORY SYSTEM
SAVOURY BUCKWHEAT PANCAKE

Ingredients: 2 cups buckwheat flour, 2 eggs, 2 cups coconut milk, pinch of sea salt, coconut oil for cooking, 1 cup grated organic non-animal rennett cheese, 1 red onion, 4 cloves garlic, 1 cup sliced Kalamata olives in brine, 2 cups mushroom, 1 tsp ginger, 4 tomatoes, 2 red capsicum, sauerkraut or fermented veggies, 1 cup parsley.

Method: Dice capsicum, onion, garlic, ginger, tomato, mushroom and place in a mixing bowl with sliced olives. For non-vegan option grate organic animal-rennet-free cheese and place in a separate bowl. In a mixing bowl, place the buckwheat flour and salt. Create a well in the middle of the mix, add the eggs and then gradually pour in the coconut milk, mixing well between additions. Continue until the mix becomes a smooth, medium consistency—not too runny, not too thick.

Heat some coconut oil in a frypan. Once hot, add a soup ladle of the buckwheat mix. Cook on gentle heat until it begins to bubble and become golden; then turn over and cook the other side. Lay the hot pancake on a serving plate and cover half with the filling ingredients. Top with grated cheese if non-vegan. Fold the other side of the pancake over the filling. Garnish with a sprinkle of chopped parsley and a spoonful of fermented veggies. (serves 4)

Cowboy 'Nuggets' of Wisdom

ALKALINE DIET… The body is an alchemist! When you eat acidic wholefoods, the body naturally creates alkaline and vice versa. Fruit nuts and seeds, especially lemon, cause the body to create alkaline. This is nature's way of maintaining a healthy, balanced pH level in the body. Bacteria such as pylori bacteria actually create and thrive in an alkaline environment. Acid kills bacteria! Beware of alkaline diets suggesting you cut out all of these powerful, healing, healthy acidic foods for an extended period of time. Also beware of the hype around alkaline water as the hydroxides in alkaline water neutralise stomach acid!

BONE BROTH… Bone broth from any animal has the highest concentration of mercury, even more so than seafood, which also has high levels due to big businesses dumping toxic waste in the ocean.

DAIRY… Raw good un-homogenised dairy does not create mucous in the body. It is healthy and healing. Raw organic milk can heal autism and remove mercury from the brain… pasteurised dairy has been irradiated!

FRUIT SUGAR… There are only two types of sugars … fast and slow. Fast sugars are toxic—their tiny molecular structure allows them to cross the blood-brain barrier so fast that it sends the brain into chaos and confusion. The pancreas then produces insulin to make the person tired and cause them to lie down as the brain thinks it's a dangerous situation. It tells the body to lay down layers of fat myelin sheath to protect the body. Fast sugars are all refined sugars—they cause diabetes. Slow sugars are healthy and healing. Our ancestors knew these were the most sacred foods to the body temple. They are large molecular sugars that cross the blood-brain barrier so slowly that the brain and body are energised. The pancreas produces glucagon and turns it into adrenalin. Human energy comes from this. Fruit is the most healing of all foods!

GOOD AND BAD FAT… Any and all organic virgin cold pressed nut, seed or veggie oils are wonderful for internal and external use. Olive oil is amazing for the skin. Some oils become rancid, causing free radicals when they are heated, so only cook with oils that can be heated without the molecular structure changing, such as coconut oil. Fish oil is extremely high in mercury and therefore not recommended. Good fats are needed for the myelin sheath around the nerves/cells as well as to stabilize blood sugar levels and balance emotions and hormones. A high, good-fat diet helps to stop inflammation. Healthy fats include avocado, butter, dairy and cheeses from ethical grass-fed animals, nuts, coconut oil, chia, flax and more.

HEALING CRISIS… When healing the body of disease naturally, there is a three-part remission as the body heals deeper and deeper. Once you begin the natural healing journey, it is very common that a disease will go away, only to return again several months later and then repeat this again a third time, after which the disease will be gone completely. This is very normal and healing… Sometimes things have to get worse before they get better!

HEAVY METALS/VACCINATIONS… Many heavy metals are stored in the base of the brain. The pectin in apples is the best wholefood to cross the blood-brain barrier and remove the toxicity. The white pith of capsicums is also a great source of pectin. Eat strawberries and omegas such as nuts, seeds and avocados. Protocol for removing heavy metals… Eat two apples per day along with any/all omegas. Eat one cup of natural yoghurt and kefirs for 14 days, along with white organic cheese from goats or cows without animal rennet/gelatin. Take bentonite clay internally. Get plenty of sunshine and lemon for the liver. After medical procedures and vaccinations… Eat three or four apples every day and do a 10-day water fast. Eat garlic and eggs for their sulphur (msm), eat zinc foods, turmeric to reduce inflammation, vitamin C and D to activate the immune system.

PALEO DIET… When you go back into the geologic ages and archaeology, the paleo period is an age they registered that started 2.6 million years ago and ended in 8000 BC, over 10,000 years ago. No records have ever been found dating back that far; in fact, there are no records dating back more than 5–7000 years. The oldest records ever found came out of Egypt, and it is documented in the ancient 'Archaen collections' that all Egyptians were total vegetarians. Every human fossil ever found on the earth has been studied using all of the different technologies ... electrochemically, microscopically, etc. They've studied the teeth and nothing has ever been found other than plant-based residues—no animal residues or DNA on the teeth of these fossils whatsoever!

PARASITES...
Animals that eat animals are the highest source of parasites, and some of these parasites are known to target the heart and the brain! Tests have shown that there is a parasite that lives in pigs that will survive even if the pork has been burnt to charcoal. Parasites that live in animals cannot live in plants.

PROBIOTICS...
95% of the time, bought probiotics are cultured from human faeces, 100% of the time when it is in capsule form. Another drawback of bought capsule probiotics is the limited number of strains contained. Normally these range from one to 18 strains, where the body needs/has several thousands. Good probiotics are natural ferments such as natural yoghurts and kefirs, cheese without animal rennet, especially blue cheese, ferments such as sauerkraut, fermented veggies, kim-chi, olives in brine, etc. Prebiotics are fibres from raw fruit and vegetables that feed the flora already existing in the body. Powerful 'prebiotics' that feed all strains are oat bran, B vitamins, apple, seaweed and rice bran.

RADIATION AND THE COLOUR YELLOW...
Uncle Richard Tolman and Albert Einstein were best friends. Richard was a professor of physics at California's Technical Institute, which is now called Cal Tech. They discovered, by an unusual accident that occurred in Marysville Nuclear Energy Lab in Tennessee, that the colour yellow changes the energy frequency of radioactive materials in such a way that it blocks and changes the damaging wave into a safe energy pattern. They knew they had to protect themselves and other lab members from radiation of the uranium in testing for nuclear fission and splitting of the atoms. They had created a 10-foot-thick (over three metres) lead wall and tested it and it didn't block anything, radiation came through the Geiger counters and radiation-detecting equipment. From out of nowhere a young worker walked past a pile of uranium and the detectors showed no radiation reading. Everyone thought there was an electric energy shutoff, so they shut everything down and restarted the system, but it was obvious that nothing had shut off. They couldn't figure it out. Finally, Richard Tolman asked to bring the young guy in to see if he was carrying anything that may have caused this. The young man had nothing. Albert asked him to go and walk past the uranium again, and once again all readings stopped. They asked to borrow his yellow shirt and did testing. What they discovered was that the yellow stopped it—they couldn't measure the radiation at all, it had changed in its oscillating energy fields. Later, Einstein warned that this knowledge of the colour yellow would be taken from the masses. When bomb shelters were being built underground in case of nuclear war, they were painted bright yellow inside. Bomb shelter symbols were and still are a mix of yellow and black triangles. To this day, every time there is a nuclear power plant meltdown, clean-up personnel wear bright yellow boots, pants, shirts, jackets and helmets. Richard and Albert said, 'The ability to measure the change in frequency to a safe one is so complex we cannot measure it. It may be so complex that even future technologies won't be able to do it!' And even if it is figured out, they warned, 'Beware, the powers that be may not allow it to be known. So please use the colour yellow for all EMF presentations to the public for safety purposes.'

It is interesting that even yellow lemons have anions not cations like all other fruits and veggies. I know from experience working with laboratories in the neurosciences that colours do have an impact on the brain cells and the neurochemistry of the brain and its cognitive functions, even our emotions! Yellow is the colour of Happiness, Joy, and Protection from harmful EMF waves. Be safe from radiation—embrace happiness and joy; get into the light of the yellow sun.

SO, WHERE DO YOU GET YOUR PROTEIN?...
This is one of the most common questions asked of any vegetarian or vegan. Did you know that every plant in nature has all 2000 proteins in varying amounts? The strongest, most muscular animals on the face of the earth are vegans ... cows, gorillas and elephants. And yes, cows do have a different digestive system than human Beings; however, the gorilla has

exactly the same physiology as a human and all they eat is berries and leaves! Meat is a secondary protein, the animal it comes from eats plants or other animals that ate plants. Nut milks are an excellent source of protein—soak one-part nuts and then add to four parts water in a blender and then squeeze out the milk through a nut bag. Coconut yoghurts are full of amino acids to build muscle. Nuts, seeds, fruits, vegies and greens are all excellent sources of primary proteins and brilliant for vegan bodybuilders!

WHEAT…

For ever and a day, humans have eaten wheat, so why all of a sudden is everybody gluten intolerant? The fact is the reactions people are experiencing are caused by products such as melamine (ground up asbestos) that grains are being soaked in, along with other toxic products used to prepare the silos in order to store the grains for extended periods of time, five to 15 years in many cases. Eat organic wheat or a grain that's stored for a maximum of one to two years. Grains are healthy and healing.

WORTH YOUR SALT?…

Salt, water and sunshine mixed, is the very basis of all life and even health of a given life. The earth is 70% water, so are our bodies. 90% of the Earth's water is salt water. 90 % of our bodies water is salt water. When sunlight shines on salt water, it ionizes into calcium. That's why the ocean is filled with calcium, as it settles on the ocean floor. Coral calcium exists because of this. All sea shells and crustacean's shells are made of calcium. The overload of calcium ionizes into magnesium, then iron, then all of the known nutritional and non-nutritional minerals. Your body does the same thing when you eat salt, drink water and get into the sunlight. Most people are mal-illuminated. Good salt such as sea and rock salt, water and sunshine are the keys to health, especially heart health. 27% of the body's salt is in the bones. Osteoporosis results when the body needs more salt and takes it from the bones. Bones are 22% water. Is it not obvious what happens to the bones when we're deficient in salt or water or both?

Here's some truths about salt: SALT is most effective in stabilizing irregular heartbeats, and contrary to the misconception that it causes high blood pressure, is actually essential for the regulation of blood pressure in conjunction with water. Naturally the proportions are critical. SALT is vital to the extraction of excess acidity from the cells in the body, particularly the brain cells. SALT is vital for balancing the sugar levels in the blood; a needed element in diabetics. SALT is vital for the generation of hydroelectric energy in cells in the body. It is used for local power generation at the sites of energy need by the cells. SALT is vital for absorption of food particles through the intestinal tract. SALT is vital for the clearance of mucus plugs and sticky phlegm from the lungs, particularly in asthma and cystic fibrosis. SALT is vital for clearing up catarrh and congestion of the sinuses. SALT is a strong naturel histamine neutralizer. SALT is essential for the prevention of muscle cramps. SALT is vital to prevent excess saliva production to the point that it flows out of the mouth during sleep. Needing to constantly mop up excess saliva indicates salt shortage. SALT is absolutely vital to making the structure of bones firm. Osteoporosis, in a major way, is a result of salt and water shortage in the body. SALT is vital for sleep regulation. It is a nature hypnotic. SALT is a vitally needed element in the treatment of diabetics. SALT on the tongue will stop persistent dry coughs. SALT is vital for the prevention of gout and gouty arthritis. SALT is vital for maintaining sexuality and libido. SALT is vital for preventing varicose veins and spider veins on the legs and thighs. SALT is vital to the communication and information processing nerve cells the entire time the brain cells work, from conception to death. SALT is vital for reducing a double chin. When the body is short of salt, it really means the body is short of water. The salivary glands sense the salt shortage and are obliged to produce more saliva to lubricate the act of chewing and swallowing and also, to supply the stomach with water it needs for breaking down foods. Circulation to the salivary glands increases and the blood vessels become 'leaky' in order to supply the glands with water to manufacture saliva. The 'leakiness' spills beyond the area of the glands themselves, causing the creased bulk under the skin of the chin, the cheeks and into the neck. SEA SALT contains about 80 mineral elements that the body needs. Some of these elements are needed in trace amounts. Unrefined sea salt is a better choice of salt than other types of slat on the market. Ordinary table salt from supermarkets has been stripped of its companion elements and contains additive elements such as aluminium silicate to keep it powdery and porous. Aluminium is a very toxic element in our nervous system and is implicated as one of the primary causes of Alzheimer's disease.

Toxic Relationships & Healing Through Forgiveness

I sometimes have a giggle to myself when I hear people stating proudly how long they have been married, especially when I know damn well that those people have hardly spoken a civil word to each other for goodness knows how long, let alone a loving one! The sad part of this, though, is that it really is not a laughing matter, in fact, quite the opposite. The root cause of so much disease these days is toxic relationships. I see this all of the time, and have even had women tell me they know the cause of their cancer is the fact that they have been miserable in their marriage for the last 20 years! I've also had women tell me that they would rather die than have to face the consequences of making changes.

Unfortunately, past programming based on religious beliefs and fear is what holds people in these unhealthy situations, to their detriment. The suppression of fear, anger, resentment, guilt, hatred, sadness, grief etc. fester away and, over time, manifest into physical pain or disease in some form. Toxic relationships cause severe stress to the body, and stress in any form will play havoc on the body's organs. Often when a person is relieved of stress, miraculous healings take place. Have you ever heard of people diagnosed with cancer and given a prognosis of just months to live who quit their jobs, sell everything up and head off on a holiday to enjoy the rest of the time they have on Earth, only to discover that the cancer goes away and they live on happily and healthily for many more years? Or a situation where a person is ill with a serious disease and after leaving their relationship, the illness goes away completely and they regain their health?

FORGIVENESS is the key to miraculous healing! When we release the burden of emotional toxicity from the body, cellular changes and healing begins to take place immediately. I've been absolutely blown away by the miraculous healings that have taken place in as little as days, hours and in one case, instantly. I've seen clients that have undergone every scan under the sun, to no avail, every medical treatment, also to no avail, and yet, after just one or two journey emotional healing sessions, they've experienced true healing and transformation. I've witnessed people in intense physical pain become pain-free within hours, people who have had very limited movement of body-parts regain full range of movement less than 24 hours later. I've seen clients who have tried many different types of medicine to absolutely no avail, and yet, when they access the degenerative cellular memories and the powerful emotions attached to them and find full forgiveness with the past, they achieve the results they have been searching for.

 I once heard it explained like this... "If you pull the main root of a tree, the entire tree collapses." Similarly, if you access the core degenerative cellular memory and emotions attached to that and find full forgiveness and closure, the whole physical issue can drop away in the time it takes for each cell of that organ/body part to be regenerated without the old cellular memory. On the other hand, if we are not completely open to seeing and feeling what's beneath the surface, it is likely that we will access one of the smaller roots and therefore the tree/dis-ease will get a bit wobbly but continue to survive.

Skeptical by nature, if I hadn't witnessed these, so called, miracles with my own two eyes, I probably would not believe it. Seeing this first hand has given me 100% faith in the human body/mind/spirit's ability to heal from almost anything, unless, of course, spiritually it is our time to leave this physical plane, returning to that from which we came. Our past is only scary when we keep it suppressed. It's like a shadow in the dark, petrifying until we turn on the light and see it for what it really is. We must have the courage to face our past in order to heal and make the necessary changes to regain loving, healthy relationships, or, where this is impossible, leave the situation entirely.

You are not here to struggle and suffer through life...you are here to thrive, to love and be loved

Lynnie xx

The RESPIRATORY SYSTEM

Consists of... throat, trachea, tongue, hypothalamus, diaphragm, bronchi and lungs.

Chakra- Throat (sky blue) /Endocrine Gland and Function... The thyroid gland is located in the front of the neck and regulates the body's metabolism by secreting the thyroid hormone. The four parathyroid glands secrete the parathyroid hormone; they are located behind the thyroid and have absolute control over calcium levels in the body.

Holds Emotional Molecules of trauma, shock, terror, compulsiveness, acceptance, relief, tolerance and cooperativeness.

Foods That Support the Physical Healing of This System Are... apples, artichoke, broccoli, caraway seeds, raw honey, onions, peppermint, potatoes, radish, rosemary, turmeric, yams, and carrots.

Support the Emotional/Physical Healing of This System with... ORANGE and BLUE foods.

Blue wholefoods are calming for this system and support life force and feelings of family.

Orange wholefoods help with the release of 'fight or flight' emotions as well as trapped, traumatic experiences and overwhelm.

***NUGGET... Did you know that the starch in potatoes targets the lungs by acting as tiny sponges that absorb and remove heavy metals?

LUNGS AND BRONCHI

BODY *FOODS THAT HEAL* ---	MIND *POSSIBLE EMOTIONAL CAUSE* ---	SPIRIT *IMBALANCED CHAKRA* ---
SIGNATURE FOODS... potato, yam, radish, broccoli, collard and mustard greens.	Are you holding feelings of grief, depression, anguish or sadness? Are you feeling unworthy or not good enough?	Throat Chakra- colour Sky Blue / Heart Chakra- colour Green

***NUGGET... *To target **Aspergillus Lung Fungus**; Garlic... a natural antifungal, antimicrobial and blood cleanser. Garlic was a health tonic used in the ancient Greek and Chinese times. Goldenseal Root... an effective antifungal and antiviral when consumed orally. Olive Oil and Olive Leaf Extract... contain chemical oleuropein, a strong antifungal which disrupts the reproductive cycle of Aspergillus species and stops their proliferation and spread. Coconut oil and cut onions can also help clear lung infections.*

THE RESPIRATORY SYSTEM
STUFFED HORSERADISH AND ROSEMARY POTATOES WITH CARAWAY SAUCE

Ingredients: 4 large organic potatoes with skins scrubbed (I love the Dutch Cream variety), 1cm horseradish peeled and diced finely, 2–3 teaspoons of fresh rosemary diced finely

CARAWAY SAUCE; 3 artichoke hearts (I use ones already prepared and stored in oil), ¼ cup soaked cashews, 2 tsp caraway seeds, ½ cup water (add more if needed to get ideal sauce consistency), sea salt to taste

CIDER BROCCOLI; 1 head of broccoli including stem, ⅛ cup organic olive oil, ⅛ cup apple cider vinegar

Method: Bake the potatoes whole in a 200 degree oven until outsides are hard and crunchy and insides are soft. Allow to cool slightly then cut the potatoes in half and, using a teaspoon, scoop the soft insides into a mixing bowl. Set skins aside for refilling later. Mash or process the potato to a smooth consistency before adding the finely diced horseradish and rosemary to the mix. Spoon the potato mixture back into the skins and place in the oven to warm before serving.

Caraway Sauce; place the caraway seeds, cashews, artichoke and water in a blender on high speed until smooth and creamy.

Broccoli; pulse in a blender until it becomes rice like. Combine the olive oil and apple cider vinegar together and drizzle over the salad.

Place the cider broccoli onto a serving platter as the base, add the heated potatoes, top with caraway sauce and serve.

MOUTH

BODY	MIND	SPIRIT
FOODS THAT HEAL	*POSSIBLE EMOTIONAL CAUSE*	*IMBALANCED CHAKRA*
---	---	---
HEALING FOOD... suck on rock salt	Are you closed-minded with strong opinions?	Throat Chakra- colour Sky Blue

THE RESPIRATORY SYSTEM
SATE' POTATO BALLS

Ingredients: 6 large organic potatoes steamed and mashed, 5 large curly kale leaves shredded finely, 2 cloves garlic diced finely, 1 teaspoon nature made salt, ¼ cup nutritional yeast, extra sea salt and pepper for seasoning

SATE' PEANUT SAUCE; 1 onion diced, 1 clove garlic crushed or diced finely, 2 tablespoons coconut oil, ¼ cup crunchy peanut butter, ½ cup water, 1 ½ teaspoons curry powder, 1 teaspoon sea salt

Method: In a large mixing bowl combine the mashed or processed potato with the shredded kale, diced garlic, nutritional yeast and sea salt, mix well—I love to get my hands into it! At this point taste the mixture and, if need be, add more salt and some pepper to taste. Make this mixture into fist-sized balls

Sate' Peanut Sauce; combine onion, garlic and oil in a pan, cook on high for 2 minutes. Stir in the peanut butter, water, curry and salt and continue to stir on low heat until heated through.

Place the heated potato balls onto a serving platter. Drizzle with peanut sauce and serve

THROAT

BODY *FOODS THAT HEAL*	MIND *POSSIBLE EMOTIONAL CAUSE*	SPIRIT *IMBALANCED CHAKRA*
---	---	---
HEALING FOOD – suck on rock salt and honey	Are you swallowing emotions of fear, anger or sadness? Are you afraid to speak your truth or holding in angry words?	Throat Chakra- colour Sky Blue

THE RESPIRATORY SYSTEM
CRISPY POTATO WITH STUFFED BAKED ONIONS

Ingredients: Large brown or red onions with skins left on, 1 cup water, 8 medium potatoes, ½ cup coconut oil, ½ teaspoon sea salt. 1 teaspoon cumin, 1 large stick of fresh rosemary diced finely.

TABBOULEH; Large bunch of parsley, 1 clove garlic diced finely, ½ red capsicum diced finely, 1/8 cup cooked quinoa.

Method: Remove the tops of the onions. Place these, along with the whole onions, in a casserole dish. Pour 1 cup of water into the base of the dish. Combine the cumin, salt and coconut oil and drizzle this into the onions, cover with a lid and pop in the oven for 1 hour. When cooked, scoop out the soft insides of the onions making sure to leave a few layers around the shell so that the onion stays intact. Stuff the onion centres with tabbouleh mix.

Tabbouleh; finely dice the parsley, garlic and capsicum, add to quinoa.

Potatoes; combine coconut oil and finely diced rosemary together in a bowl. Make slices in the potatoes from one side to another approximately ½ cm from each other, being sure not to cut all the way through so that the potatoes stay intact. (It helps to place a wooden spoon or chopstick on the cutting board so you can only cut so far). Open the potato slices and brush the rosemary oil through thoroughly. Drizzle the remainder over the top then place the potatoes in a moderate oven until crispy.

DIS-EASES/DISORDERS OF
The RESPIRATORY SYSTEM

ADENOIDITIS

***WHAT IS IT?...** **Adenoiditis** is an inflammation of the adenoids, usually caused by infection. The adenoids are lymphatic tissue found in the throat and along with the tonsils are our first line of defence against viruses and bacteria.

***BODY – EPICURE*
- Get off all supplements and medication immediately.
- **Fastest...** Water fast for 7–10 days **OR...**
- Cabala juice fast 14–28 days.
- Eat and juice a locally grown, fresh, raw organic vegetarian diet for highest nutritional force and gentle detox.
- Get plenty of salt in the diet and suck on Himalayan rock salt daily—the size of the end section of your little finger.
- Use a nettie pot and a mix of water/tea tree oil to cleanse the nasal passage—this can also be done with Breathe Eze.
- Take one teaspoon of turmeric powder with warm milk, this can be nutmilk, every morning and night.
- Garlic—inhibits growth of pollups. Take one teaspoon of garlic chopped up small, twice per day.
- Teatree oil—place two drops of teatree oil on your finger and suck up into each nostril and into the throat then swallow.
- Eat two or three oranges every day and one cup of fresh picked dandelion greens—this will shrink and clear up pollups.
- Sungazing morning and evenings in 13-second intervals; look at the sun until it reaches a 10-degree arc, or a clenched fist sitting on horizon as sun comes up, stop at top of fist. At night, start gazing as sun hits top of fist until it's gone.
- **ESSENTIAL OIL...** teatree oil.
- (Breathe Ez, essential oil of tea tree and peppermint, Himalayan rock salt, Ra 24ct See Salt available at in the USA **www.thedontolman.com/store** and Australia **www.lynnienichols.com/shop**)

BODY FOODS THAT HEAL	MIND POSSIBLE EMOTIONAL CAUSE	SPIRIT IMBALANCED CHAKRA
---	---	---
SIGNATURE FOODS... apples, artichoke, broccoli, caraway seeds, raw honey, onions, peppermint, potatoes, radish, rosemary, turmeric, yams, carrots	• Are you feeling unloved, left out, unwelcome? • Are you constantly dealing with family arguments?	Throat Chakra- colour Sky Blue

***NOTE...** *Pollups are simply clogged/dried up mucosal linings.*

RESPIRATORY SYSTEM
ORANGE AND DANDELION SALAD

Ingredients: 3 oranges, 1 cup of fresh dandelion greens

DRESSING; 1 cup fresh squeezed orange juice, 1 tbsp caraway seeds, 1 tbsp raw honey, 1 cup cold pressed virgin olive oil, ½ tsp sea salt

Method: Peel and dice the oranges into 2 cm cubes and mix in a bowl with the dandelion greens. Mix all dressing ingredients together in a jar and let sit for half hr. Drizzle over salad to serve (serves 1)

ASBESTOSIS

***WHAT IS IT?...** **Asbestosis** is a lung fibrosis disease resulting from the inhalation of asbestos particles, which causes excess connective tissue in the lungs. Symptoms include respiratory problems such as coughing, wheezing, etc.

***BODY – EPICURE*

- Get off all medication and supplements- herbs in the form of powders or teas are okay.
- **Fastest...** Water fast for 7–10 days **OR...**
- Cabala juice fast 14–28 days.
- Suck on Himalayan rock salt daily, the size of the end section of your little finger.
- Drink one litre of water per 22 kilos of bodyweight every single day.
- Slice raw red-skinned potato sliced into 1 cm-thick cookies, squeeze fresh lemon juice over the potato and top with good nature-made salt—eat one good-sized potato every day for six months.
- Eat one or two cups of white or red radishes every day as well as lots of onion and garlic.
- Put two or three drops of peppermint oil in a bowl of hot water then drape a towel over your head and breathe the steam in and out through the mouth for three to five minutes, two or three times per day.
- Add ½ cup bicarb and ¼ tsp peppermint oil and some sea salt to a hot bath and soak in this daily.
- Walking daily for 30 mins each day—place two drops of peppermint oil in your hands and, whilst walking, cup your hands over your nose and breathe the peppermint in; once lungs are full, blow out through the mouth.
- Develop the darkest suntan you can by covering your body in Divine Body Butter or coconut oil and then exposing at least 70% of your body to the sun for one hour every day (30 mins each side).
- **ESSENTIAL OIL...** peppermint, rosemary, myrrh, frankincense, eucalyptus, oregano, geranium, thyme.
- (Divine, Breathe Ez, essential oil of peppermint, Himalayan rock salt, Ra 24ct See Salt available in the USA **www.thedontolman.com/store** and Australia **www.lynnienichols.com/shop**)

BODY *FOODS THAT HEAL*	MIND *POSSIBLE EMOTIONAL CAUSE*	SPIRIT *IMBALANCED CHAKRA*
---	---	---
SIGNATURE FOODS... apples, artichoke, broccoli, caraway seeds, raw honey, onions, peppermint, potatoes, radish, rosemary, turmeric, yams, carrots	• Are you feeling suppressed, sad, yearning for something else? • Are you finding it difficult to stand up for yourself? • Are you lacking in self-love?	Throat Chakra- colour Sky Blue / Heart Chakra- colour Emerald Green

***NUGGET... *Potato particles are not used by the body for nutrients, they go to the lymphatic system and act like sponges inside the bloodstream, clearing toxicities and heavy metals from the body.*

RESPIRATORY SYSTEM
RAW RED-SKINNED POTATO COOKIES

Ingredients: 1 medium to large red skin potato, Don's Ra 24ct See Salt, lemon juice

Method: Cut the potato into 1 cm-thick rounds, drizzle lemon juice over the top and sprinkle with salt. Eat one potato per day. (serves 1)

ASTHMA

***WHAT IS IT?...** **Asthma** is a respiratory condition affecting the bronchi of the lungs. Symptoms include wheezing, coughing, chest tightness and breathing difficulties.

***BODY – EPICURE*

- Get off all medication immediately—no asthma sprays
- **Fastest...** Water fast for 7–10 days **OR...**
- Cabala juice fast 14–28 days.
- Put two or three drops of peppermint oil in a bowl of hot water then drape a towel over your head and breathe the steam in and out through the mouth for three to five minutes, two or three times per day.
- Add ½ cup bicarb and ¼ tsp peppermint oil and some sea salt to a hot bath and soak in this daily.
- Suck on Himalayan rock salt daily, the size of the end section of your little finger.
- Drink one litre of water per 22 kilos of bodyweight every single day.
- Slice raw red-skinned potato into 1 cm-thick cookies, squeeze fresh lemon juice over the potato and top with good nature-made salt.
- Eat one or two cups of white or red radishes every day as well as lots of onion and garlic, raw and cooked.
- Use Congest Ease on throat, chest and feet.
- Walking daily for 30 mins each day—place 2 drops of peppermint oil in your hands and, whilst walking, cup your hands over your nose and breathe the peppermint in; once lungs are full, blow out through the mouth.
- Develop the darkest suntan you can by covering your body in Divine Body Butter or coconut oil and then exposing at least 70% of your body to the sun for one hour every day (30 mins each side).
- No airconditioning, sleep with the windows open; electrify the air with fans and windows.
- **ESSENTIAL OIL...** peppermint, rosemary, myrrh, frankincense, eucalyptus, oregano, geranium, thyme.
- (Divine, Congest Ease, essential oil of peppermint, Himalayan rock salt, Ra 24ct See Salt available in the USA **www.thedontolman.com/store** and Australia **www.lynnienichols.com/shop**)

BODY *FOODS THAT HEAL*	MIND *POSSIBLE EMOTIONAL CAUSE*	SPIRIT *IMBALANCED CHAKRA*
---	---	---
SIGNATURE FOODS... apples, artichoke, broccoli, caraway seeds, raw honey, onions, peppermint, potatoes, radish, rosemary, turmeric, yams, carrots	• Are you feeling smothered, unable to breahe for yourself? • Are you unable to love and accept yourself? • Are you doing what others want instead of what you desire?	Throat Chakra- colour Sky Blue / Heart Chakra- colour Emerald Green

***NOTE...** One particular ventolin spray/puffer quadrupled the death rate in New Zealand in just one year—it was banned.*

***TESTIMONIAL...** When my son was young, he suffered with asthma. Not knowing any better at the time, we seeked medical advice and were given ventolin inhalers, which he carried around with him and puffed on each time he began to wheeze. That was until I discovered WATER was the healer! From then on, each time he showed asthmatic signs, I'd make him stop what he was doing and drink a few glasses of pure water and guess what... His asthma miraculously disppeared along with the ventolin inhalers! Lynnie*

RESPIRATORY SYSTEM
ROSEMARY ROSTI

Ingredients: 3 large red-skinned potatoes, 1 red onion, 3 cloves garlic, Himalayan salt, 1 tbsp fresh or dried rosemary, 1 egg, coconut oil

Method: Grate the potatoes with a coarse grater and squeeze out the excess juice. Put the dry grated potato into a bowl with diced onion, finely diced garlic, Himalayan salt, pepper, and rosemary. Add an egg and mix well. Heat some coconut oil in a frypan and place large spoonsful of the mixture into the pan and fry. When golden brown, turn over and cook the other side. (Use as an alternative to bread for breakfast with smashed avo or eggs)

BRONCHITIS

***WHAT IS IT?...** **Bronchitis** is a swelling or inflammation of the mucous membrane in the air passages between the lungs and the nose called the bronchial tubes.

***BODY – EPICURE*

- Get off all medication immediately—NO asthma sprays.
- **Fastest...** Water fast for 7–10 days **OR...**
- Cabala juice fast 14–28 days.
- Suck on Himalayan rock salt daily, the size of the end segment of your little finger.
- Drink one litre of water per 22 kilos of bodyweight every single day.
- Slice raw red-skinned potato sliced into 1 cm-thick cookies, squeeze fresh lemon juice over the potato and top with good nature-made salt.
- Eat one or two cups of white or red radishes every day as well as lots of onion and garlic, raw and cooked.
- Drink three or four cups of hot water with the juice of a lemon and 1 teaspoon of raw honey.
- Put two or three drops of peppermint oil in a bowl of hot water then drape a towel over your head and breathe the steam in and out through the mouth for three to five minutes, two or three times per day.
- Add ½ cup bicarb and ¼ tsp peppermint oil and some sea salt to a hot bath and soak in this daily.

- Walking daily for 30 mins each day—place two drops of peppermint oil in your hands and, whilst walking, cup your hands over your nose and breathe the peppermint in; once lungs are full, blow out through the mouth.
- Develop the darkest suntan you can by covering your body in Divine Body Butter or coconut oil and then exposing at least 70% of your body to the sun for one hour every day (30 mins each side).
- No airconditioning, sleep with fans on and/or windows open to electrify the air.
- Put Congest Ease on the chest, back and feet once or twice per day.
- Sniff Breathe Eze up the nose, also spray in the mouth and swallow.
- **ESSENTIAL OIL...** peppermint, rosemary, frankincense, eucalyptus, oregano, geranium, thyme.
- (Divine, Congest Ease, Breathe Ez, essential oil of peppermint, Himalayan rock salt, Ra 24ct See Salt available in the USA **www.thedontolman.com/store** and Australia **www.lynnienichols.com/shop**)

BODY	MIND	SPIRIT
FOODS THAT HEAL	*POSSIBLE EMOTIONAL CAUSE*	*IMBALANCED CHAKRA*
---	---	---
SIGNATURE FOODS... apples, artichoke, broccoli, caraway seeds, raw honey, onions, peppermint, potatoes, radish, rosemary, turmeric, yams, carrots	• Are you feeling fearful, like things are out of your control? • Are you in an angry, argumentative environment?	Throat Chakra- colour Sky Blue / Heart Chakra- colour Emerald Green

***NUGGET...** *Apple seeds contain plant synthesised arsenic which is blood thinning and harmless to man. Along with apple seeds, wheatgrass, apricot kernels and all other seeds except for citrus, are great sources of B17, known by many as Nature's Chemo!*

RESPIRATORY SYSTEM
CREAMY BROCCOLI BOWL

Ingredients: 1 large head of broccoli, 3 brown onions, 4 cloves garlic, 1 sliced red radish, 2 tbsp coconut oil for frying, nature-made salt and pepper

CURRY SAUCE; 1 cup cashews, 2 tsp curry powder, 1 clove garlic, ½ cup water, ⅛ cup nutritional yeast, dash of apple cider vinegar, 1 tsp sea salt

Method: Dice the brown onions and garlic and fry in a pan. Steam the broccoli for two or three minutes only, so that it softens but is still predominately raw. Place the broccoli, onion and garlic together in a serving bowl. Add the sliced radish and a good dose of curry sauce and mix well. Season with salt and pepper if desired. Serve immediately whilst broccoli is still hot

Curry Sauce; Soak the raw cashews for half hour in water, strain and place in a blender with the water, ACV, salt, curry powder and garlic. Blend on high speed for a few minutes until very smooth and creamy. (serves 2)

CHRONIC OBSTRUCTIVE PULMONARY DISEASE (COPD)

***WHAT IS IT?...** **Chronic obstructive pulmonary disease** is an umbrella term used to describe a group of lung diseases such as chronic asthma, emphysema, chronic bronchitis, that prevent a person's ability to breathe properly.

***BODY – EPICURE*

- Get off all medication immediately. NO asthma sprays!
- **Fastest...** Water fast for 7–10 days **OR...**
- Cabala juice fast 14–28 days.
- Suck on Himalayan rock salt daily, the size of the end segment of your little finger.
- Do the water protocol—one glass of water every hour on the hour, or drink one litre of water per 22 kilos of bodyweight every single day.
- Slice raw red-skinned potato sliced into 1 cm-thick cookies, squeeze fresh lemon juice over the potato and top with good nature made salt. Eat one good-sized potato every day.
- Eat one or two cups of white or red radishes every day as well as lots of onion and garlic, raw and cooked.
- Eat three grapefruit every morning, scrape the white pulp from the inside of one of the fruit and eat for 21 days to six weeks.
- Put two or three drops of peppermint oil in a bowl of hot water then drape a towel over your head and breathe the steam in and out through the mouth for three to five minutes, two or three times per day.
- Add ½ cup bicarb and ¼ tsp peppermint oil and some sea salt to a hot bath and soak in this daily.
- Drink three or four cups of hot water with the juice of a lemon and 1 teaspoon of raw honey.
- Walking daily for 30 mins each day—place two drops of peppermint oil in your hands and, whilst walking, cup your hands over your nose and breathe the peppermint in; once lungs are full, blow out through the mouth.
- Develop the darkest suntan you can by covering your body in Divine Body Butter or coconut oil and then exposing at least 70% of your body to the sun for one hour every day (30 mins each side).
- No airconditioning, sleep with fans on and/or windows open to electrify the air.
- Put Congest Ease on the chest, back and feet once or twice per day.
- Sniff Breathe Eze up the nose, also spray in the mouth and swallow.
- **ESSENTIAL OIL...** peppermint, rosemary, myrrh, frankincense, eucalyptus, oregano, geranium, thyme.
- (Divine, Congest Ease, Breathe Ez, essential oil of peppermint, Himalayan rock salt, Ra 24ct See Salt, available in the USA **www.thedontolman.com/store** and Australia **www.lynnienichols.com/shop**)

BODY FOODS THAT HEAL	MIND POSSIBLE EMOTIONAL CAUSE	SPIRIT IMBALANCED CHAKRA
---	---	---
SIGNATURE FOODS... apples, artichoke, broccoli, caraway seeds, raw honey, onions, peppermint, potatoes, radish, rosemary, turmeric, yams, carrots	• Are you feeling fearful, like things are out of your control? • Are you in an angry, argumentative environment?	Throat Chakra- colour Sky Blue / Heart Chakra- colour Emerald Green

***NOTE...** *The pectin in grapefruit will target the clearing of the arteries, heart and bloodstream.*

RESPIRATORY SYSTEM
CREAMY LUNG-CLEARING GARLIC POTATOES

Ingredients: 6 large red-skinned potatoes, 1 large red onion, 6 large red radishes, parsley to garnish, salt and pepper. Rosemary Oil; ½ cup olive oil, 1 tbsp fresh finely chopped rosemary

GARLIC SAUCE; 2 cups cashews, ¼ cup nutritional yeast, 4 cloves garlic, 1½ cups water, splash of apple cider vinegar, 1 tsp sea salt.

Method: Wash and cut the potatoes into thin slices. Steam until just soft, then place into a serving dish with the finely sliced radish and diced onion. Gently mix the garlic sauce through. Add extra salt and pepper if desired. Garnish with a drizzle of rosemary oil and parsley.

Garlic Sauce: Soak the cashews for 1 hour then place in a blender on high speed with all other ingredients until smooth, thick and creamy. (serves 4)

CYSTIC FIBROSIS (CF)

WHAT IS IT?... **Cystic fibrosis** is a condition that predominately affects the lungs, blocking the bronchi with the production of thick, sticky mucus, causing constant lung infections and resulting in difficulty breathing. CF can also affect/damage the pancreatic ducts and intestines.

BODY – EPICURE

- Get off all medication immediately. NO asthma sprays!
- Fastest... Water fast for 7–10 days OR...
- Cabala juice fast 14–28 days.
- Suck on Himalayan rock salt daily, the size of the end segment of your little finger.
- Do the water protocol—one glass of water every hour on the hour, or drink one litre of water per 22 kilos of bodyweight every single day.
- Slice raw red-skinned potato into 1 cm-thick cookies, squeeze fresh lemon juice over the potato and top with good nature-made salt. Eat one good-sized potato every day.
- Eat one or two cups of white or red radishes every day as well as lots of onion and garlic, raw and cooked.
- Eat three grapefruit every morning, scrape the white pulp from the inside of one of the fruit and eat for 21 days to six weeks.
- Put two or three drops of peppermint oil in a bowl of hot water then drape a towel over your head and breathe the steam in and out through the mouth for three to five minutes, two or three times per day.
- Add ½ cup bicarb and ¼ tsp peppermint oil and some sea salt to a hot bath and soak in this daily.
- Drink three or four cups of hot water with the juice of a lemon and 1 teaspoon of raw honey.
- Walking daily for 30 mins each day—place two drops of peppermint oil in your hands and, whilst walking, cup your hands over your nose and breathe the peppermint in; once lungs are full, blow out through the mouth.
- Develop the darkest suntan you can by covering your body in Divine Body Butter or coconut oil and then exposing at least 70% of your body to the sun for one hour every day (30 mins each side).
- No airconditioning, sleep with fans on and/or windows open to electrify the air.
- Put Congest Ease on the chest, back and feet once or twice per day.
- Sniff Breathe Eze up the nose, also spray in the mouth and swallow.
- **ESSENTIAL OIL...** peppermint, lavender, helichrysum, camomile, clary sage, lemongrass.
- (Divine, Congest Ease, Breathe Ez, essential oil of peppermint, Himalayan rock salt, Ra 24ct See Salt, available in the USA **www.thedontolman.com/store** and Australia **www.lynnienichols.com/shop**)

BODY *FOODS THAT HEAL*	MIND *POSSIBLE EMOTIONAL CAUSE*	SPIRIT *IMBALANCED CHAKRA*
---	---	---
SIGNATURE FOODS... apples, artichoke, broccoli, caraway seeds, raw honey, onions, peppermint, potatoes, radish, rosemary, turmeric, yams, carrots	• Are you feeling sorry for yourself, stuck in the 'poor me, it's not fair' victim mentality? • Are you feeling that life's too hard and nothing works for you? • Are you nursing old hurts?	Throat Chakra- colour Sky Blue / Heart Chakra- colour Emerald Green

RESPIRATORY SYSTEM
HORSERADISH AND POTATO CAKES

Ingredients: 6 large red-skinned potatoes, 2 eggs, 1 tbsp sea salt, rosemary, 4 cloves of garlic, 2 brown onions, ½ tsp horseradish, ½ cup coconut oil

Method: Grate the potatoes and squeeze out the extra juice. Peel and finely dice the garlic, horseradish and onions, add this to the potato. Add the eggs, rosemary and salt.

Heat some coconut oil in a pan and fry spoonsful of the potato mix until golden brown on both sides. (serves 4)

EMPHYSEMA

***WHAT IS IT?...** **Emphysema** is progressive lung disease characterised by increasing breathlessness.

***BODY – EPICURE*

- Get off all medication immediately—absolutely NO asthma sprays.
- **Fastest...** Fastest... Water fast for 7–10 days **OR...**
- Cabala juice fast 14–28 days.
- Suck on Himalayan rock salt daily, the size of the end segment of your little finger.
- Do the water protocol—one glass of water every hour on the hour, or drink one litre of water per 22 kilos of bodyweight every single day.
- Slice raw red-skinned potato sliced into 1 cm-thick cookies, squeeze fresh lemon juice over the potato and top with good nature-made salt. Eat one good-sized potato every day.
- Eat one or two cups of white or red radishes every day as well as lots of onion and garlic, raw and cooked.
- Drink three or four cups of hot water with the juice of a lemon and 1 teaspoon of raw honey.
- Put two or three drops of peppermint oil in a bowl of hot water then drape a towel over your head and breathe the steam in and out through the mouth for three to five minutes, two or three times per day.
- Add ½ cup bicarb and ¼ tsp peppermint oil and some sea salt to a hot bath and soak in this daily.
- Walking daily for 30 mins each day—place two drops of peppermint oil in your hands and, whilst walking, cup your hands over your nose and breathe the peppermint in; once lungs are full, blow out through the mouth.
- Develop the darkest suntan you can by covering your body in Divine Body Butter or coconut oil and then exposing at least 70% of your body to the sun for one hour every day (30 mins each side).
- No airconditioning, sleep with fans on and/or windows open to electrify the air.
- Put Congest Ease on the chest, back and feet once or twice per day.
- Sniff Breathe Eze up the nose, also spray in the mouth and swallow.
- If you can't quit smoking, at least switch to pure tobacco.
- **ESSENTIAL OIL...** peppermint, rosemary, frankincense, helichrysum, eucalyptus, oregano, geranium, thyme.
- (Divine, Congest Ease, Breathe Ez, essential oil of peppermint, Himalayan rock salt, Ra 24ct See Salt, available in the USA **www.thedontolman.com/store** and Australia **www.lynnienichols.com/shop**)

BODY *FOODS THAT HEAL*	MIND *POSSIBLE EMOTIONAL CAUSE*	SPIRIT *IMBALANCED CHAKRA*
---	---	---
SIGNATURE FOODS... apples, artichoke, broccoli, caraway seeds, raw honey, onions, peppermint, potatoes, radish, rosemary, turmeric, yams, carrots	• Are you afraid of life? • Are you feeling suppressed, unable to be your authentic self?	Throat Chakra- colour Sky Blue / Heart Chakra- colour Emerald Green

RESPIRATORY SYSTEM
TUMERIC LUNG JUICE

Ingredients: 4 apples, 1 cm tumeric, 2 large carrots, 1 tbsp honey

Method: Juice the apple, tumeric and corrots. Add the honey and serve

INFLUENZA / COLD / FEVER

***WHAT IS IT?...** **Influenza, commonly known as 'the flu',** is a contagious viral infection of the respiratory system affecting the throat, nose, bronchial tubes and the lungs. Symptoms include fever, coughing, runny nose, sore throat and aching.

***BODY – EPICURE*

- Get off all medication and supplements- herbs in the form of powders or teas are okay, but no pills or capsules! No neurophin or panadol as this ruins the digestive system function.
- **Fastest...** Water fast for 7–10 days **OR...**
- Cabala juice fast 14–28 days.
- Eat and juice a locally grown, fresh, raw organic vegan diet for highest nutritional force, for 28 days.
- Eat and drink lots of citrus... If it's a breastfed baby that has the fever/influenza the mother should eat and drink the citrus.
- FEVER... Do an enema... If it's a child/baby that has the high temperature, use a rubber syringe bulb and warm water with 1 tsp sea salt; oil the tip of the syringe with a good organic oil and insert into baby's anus, give the enema. Typically, the fever is gone within 1hr, if it comes back, do it again. (Enema douche travel kits available from **www.lynnienichols.com/shop**)
- Cut an onion in half and breathe the fumes into the nose, mouth and lungs. It can help to place cut onions around the bedroom in order to absorb.
- Cook a variety of legumes and beans in a crockpot with lots of onion – red, brown and white and lots of garlic. Eat 1 bowl of this per day. If kids don't like this, make it into a soup.
- Eat one or two cups of white or red radishes every day as well as lots of onion and garlic.
- Drink warm lemonade using lemon and honey.
- Eat raw red-skinned potato—cut slices the thickness of your little finger, sprinkle with good nature-made salt and drizzle lemon juice over. Eat one medium or large potato every day.
- Suck on rock salt every day, the size of the end segment of your little finger.
- Drink one litre per 22 kilos bodyweight of pure water every day.
- Put two or three drops of peppermint oil in a bowl of hot water then drape a towel over your head and breathe the steam in and out through the mouth for three to five minutes, two or three times per day
- Walking daily for 30 mins each day—place 2 drops of peppermint oil in your hands and, whilst walking, cup your hands over your nose and breathe the peppermint in, once lungs are full, blow out through the mouth.
- Add ½ cup bicarb and ¼ tsp peppermint oil and some sea salt to a hot bath and soak in this daily.
- Develop the darkest suntan you can by covering your body in Divine Body Butter or coconut oil and then exposing at least 70% of your body to the sun for one hour every day (30 mins each side).
- No airconditioning, sleep with fans on and/or windows open to electrify the air.
- Put Congest Ease on the chest, back and feet once or twice per day.
- Sniff Breathe Eze up the nose, also spray in the mouth and swallow.
- **ESSENTIAL OIL...** peppermint, eucalyptus, thyme, lavender, tea tree.
- (Divine, Congest Ease, essential oil of peppermint and eucalyptus, Himalayan rock salt, Ra 24ct See Salt available in the USA **www.thedontolman.com/store** and Australia **www.lynnienichols.com/shop**)

BODY *FOODS THAT HEAL*	MIND *POSSIBLE EMOTIONAL CAUSE*	SPIRIT *IMBALANCED CHAKRA*
---	---	---
SIGNATURE FOODS... apples, artichoke, broccoli, caraway seeds, raw honey, onions, peppermint, potatoes, radish, rosemary, turmeric, yams, carrots	• INFLUENZA... Are you only seeing the negatives? • Are you living in fear, afraid to consider anything outside of your own beliefs? • COLDS... Are you feeling mentally overwhelmed from constant, confusing mind chatter? • Are you manifesting a belief that it is normal to get sick each year? • FEVER... Are you burning up with bitterness/anger?	Throat Chakra- colour Sky Blue / Heart Chakra- colour Emerald Green

***NOTE...** Fever is the body heating you up to burn out bacterial overwhelm.

***NUGGET...** People often get the flu in the colder seasons when meat intake is kicked up and also around Christmas/holiday season when meat and sweets are eaten together. When you eat sweets withy meat, there's a fermentation process that takes place so fast that it results in the body needing to cleanse via vomiting, fever and the runs. Flu is natural and healthy, it's your body's way of healing and ridding toxicity; it is trying to throw out an offence taken in by you!

COMMON COLD (see influenza)

***WHAT IS IT?...* **A cold** is a condition of the upper respiratory system (nose and throat) caused by a virus. Symptoms include runny nose, sneezing, coughing, headaches and fever.

MIND *POSSIBLE EMOTIONAL CAUSE*	SPIRIT *IMBALANCED CHAKRA*
---	---
• Are you feeling overwhelmed mentally from constant mind chatter that's causing confusion? • Are you manifesting your belief in getting sick each year?	Throat Chakra- colour Sky Blue / Heart Chakra- colour Emerald Green

RESPIRATORY SYSTEM
POTATO AND BROCCOLI with HORSERADISH CREAM

Ingredients: 1 medium head of broccoli, 4 large potatoes, 1 tsp sea salt, 2 cloves garlic, 1-2 tsp fresh lemon thyme

HORSERADISH CREAM; 1 tsp finely diced horseradish, 1 cup cashews, ¾ cup water, ⅛ cup nutritional yeast, 2 tbsp lemon juice, 1 tbsp raw honey, ½ tsp sea salt

Method: Scrub the potatoes, cut into 2–3 cm cubes and steam until just soft. Place in a salad bowl and allow to cool. Grate or process the broccoli into rice size, finely dice the garlic and add both to the cooled potato. Add thyme.

Horseradish Cream; Soak the cashews in water for 1 hour. Strain and place in a blender with all other ingredients until smooth and creamy. Taste and season with more salt if desired. Mix this through the potato salad and serve. (serves 4)

LARYNGITIS

WHAT IS IT?... **Laryngitis** is caused by an infection or overuse of the larynx (voice box), which creates a swelling of the larynx at the back of the throat. Symptoms include loss of voice, sore throat and hoarseness.

BODY – EPICURE

- Get off all medication and supplements- herbs in the form of powders or teas are okay, but no pills or capsules!
- **Fastest...** Water fast for 7–10 days **OR...**
- Cabala juice fast 14–28 days.
- Suck on rock salt every day, the size of the end segment of your little finger.
- Eat one heaped teaspoon of organic raw honey, insalivate before swallowing.
- Make a warm drink of honey, lemon and apple cider vinegar and drink throughout the day.
- Sniff Breathe Eze up the nose, also spray in the mouth and swallow. Put two or three drops of peppermint oil in a bowl of hot water then drape a towel over your head and breathe the steam in and out through the mouth for three to five minutes, two or three times per day.
- Drink one litre per 22 kilos bodyweight of pure water every day.
- Develop the darkest suntan you can by covering your body in Divine Body Butter or coconut oil and then exposing at least 70% of your body to the sun for one hour every day (30 mins each side).
- No airconditioning, sleep with fans on and/or windows open to electrify the air.
- Put Congest Ease on the chest, back and feet once or twice per day.
- **ESSENTIAL OIL...** peppermint, ginger, eucalyptus, lemon, thyme, orange.
- (Divine, Congest Ease, Breathe-Ez, essential oil of peppermint, Himalayan rock salt, Ra 24ct See Salt, 35% food-grade hydrogen peroxide available in the USA **www.thedontolman.com/store** and Australia **www.lynnienichols.com/shop**)

BODY *FOODS THAT HEAL*	MIND *POSSIBLE EMOTIONAL CAUSE*	SPIRIT *IMBALANCED CHAKRA*
---	---	---
SIGNATURE FOODS... apples, artichoke, broccoli, caraway seeds, raw honey, onions, peppermint, potatoes, radish, rosemary, turmeric, yams, carrots	• Are you fearful of speaking up for yourself? • Are you feeling so angry that you can't speak? • Are you resenting authority?	Throat Chakra- colour Sky Blue

RESPIRATORY SYSTEM
WARM LEMONADE

Ingredients: 1 tbsp honey, 2 lemons, 1 tbsp apple cider vinegar, 1 cup hot water

Method: Juice the lemons with a commercial juicer in order to get healing benefits from the skin. Pour into hot water, add ACV and honey.

LUNG CANCER

***WHAT IS IT?... **Lung cancer** is a growth of abnormal cells that begins in one or both lungs and rapidly divides to form malignant tumours.

***BODY – EPICURE

- Get off all medication and supplements- herbs in the form of powders or teas are okay, but no pills or capsules!
- **Fastest...** Water fast for 7–10 days **OR...**
- Cabala juice fast 14–28 days.
- Do the five-week 35% food-grade hydrogen peroxide protocol combined with a cabala juice fast for 14–28 days ... if needed, can have raw vegan food also.
- Eat and juice a locally grown, fresh, raw organic vegan diet for highest nutritional force, concentrating on eating and juicing fresh, locally grown organic broccoli, carrots, kale, spinach, potatoes, yams and large leaves with white veins.
- Eat one or two cups of white or red radishes every day as well as lots of onion and garlic.
- Eat raw red-skinned potato—cut slices the thickness of your little finger, sprinkle with good nature-made salt and drizzle lemon juice over. Eat one medium or large potato every day.
- Put two or three drops of peppermint oil in a bowl of hot water then drape a towel over your head and breathe the steam in and out through the mouth for three to five minutes, two or three times per day.
- Add ½ cup bicarb and ¼ tsp peppermint oil and some sea salt to a hot bath and soak in this daily.
- Walking daily for 30 mins each day—place 2 drops of peppermint oil in your hands and, whilst walking, cup your hands over your nose and breathe the peppermint in; once lungs are full, blow out through the mouth.
- Suck on rock salt every day, the size of the end segment of your little finger.
- Drink one litre per 22 kilos bodyweight of pure water every day.
- Have daily a berry, asparaus smoothie, consisting of two cups berries and 12 stalks of asparagus (can add a banana to sweeten) plus water to desired consistency. Drink within 45 minutes of making it. Can eat the foods instead if preferred.
- Develop the darkest suntan you can by covering your body in Divine Body Butter or coconut oil and then exposing at least 70% of your body to the sun for one hour every day (30 mins each side).
- No airconditioning, sleep with fans on and/or windows open to electrify the air.
- Put Congest Ease on the chest, back and feet once or twice per day.
- **ESSENTIAL OIL...** peppermint, frankincense, vetiver, lavender, thyme, oregano, myrrh, cannabis.
- (Divine, Congest Ease, essential oil of peppermint, Himalayan rock salt, Ra 24ct See Salt, 35% food-grade hydrogen peroxide available in the USA **www.thedontolman.com/store** and Australia **www.lynnienichols.com/shop**)

BODY	MIND	SPIRIT
FOODS THAT HEAL	**POSSIBLE EMOTIONAL CAUSE**	**IMBALANCED CHAKRA**
---	---	---
SIGNATURE FOODS... apples, artichoke, broccoli, caraway seeds, raw honey, onions, peppermint, potatoes, radish, rosemary, turmeric, yams, carrots	• Are you holding on to deep-seated grief or sadness? • Are you harbouring a broken heart and unforgiveness?	Throat Chakra- colour Sky Blue / Heart Chakra- colour Emerald Green

BROCCOLI WITH CARAMELISED ONION ON GARLIC YAM

Ingredients: 6 medium yam, 1 medium head of broccoli, 2 large brown onions, 4 large cloves garlic, 1 tsp sea salt, pepper, 2 cups of shredded spinach, 3 tbsp honey, ¼ – ½ cup coconut oil, 2 tbsp extra coconut oil.

Method: Boil the yams until soft and then peel and cut into thin slices. Place in a frying pan with the coconut oil, spinach, salt and pepper. Heat until the yam is hot and spinach is wilted.

Broccoli; Chop into small 1 cm pieces then place into a bowl of boiling hot water for 2 minutes; strain and set aside. In a frypan, heat coconut oil and fry the brown onions and garlic until golden. Add the honey and continue to fry on low heat until the onion caramelises. Add the broccoli and stir-fry for 2 minutes. Arrange the hot yam mix on a serving plate. Top this with the broccoli/onion mix and serve while hot. (serves 2)

MESOTHELIOMA

***WHAT IS IT?...** **Mesothelioma** *is rare form of cancer that primarily develops in the lining of the lungs (pleural mesothelioma) or can also develop in the abdomen (peritoneal mesothelioma). It is associated with asbestos exposure and affects the mesothelial cells that cover most internal organs.*

***BODY – EPICURE*

- Get off all medication and supplements- herbs in the form of powders or teas are okay, but no pills or capsules!
- **Fastest...** Water fast for 7–10 days **OR...**
- Cabala juice fast 14–28 days.
- Suck on Himalayan rock salt daily, the size of the end segment of your little finger.
- Do the water protocol—one glass of water every hour on the hour, or drink one litre of water per 22 kilos of bodyweight every single day.
- Eat raw red-skinned potato sliced into 1 cm-thick cookies; squeeze fresh lemon juice over the potato and top with good nature-made salt. Eat one good-sized potato every day for six months to clear asbestos.
- Eat one or two cups of white or red radishes every day as well as lots of onion and garlic, raw and cooked.
- Eat a high vitamin E diet—wholegrains, sunflower seeds, olive oil, safflower and sunflower oil, corn, avocado, garlic, and broccoli.
- Drink three or four cups of hot water with the juice of a lemon and 1 teaspoon of raw honey.
- Walking daily for 30 mins each day—place two drops of peppermint oil in your hands and, whilst walking, cup your hands over your nose and breathe the peppermint in; once lungs are full, blow out through the mouth.
- Peppermint Oil- Put two or three drops of peppermint oil in a bowl of hot water then drape a towel over your head and breathe the steam in and out through the mouth for three to five minutes, two or three times per day. Put a little peppermint oil on your lip, rub on the back of neck, chest and bottom of feet first thing in the morning.
- Add ½ cup bicarb and ¼ tsp peppermint oil and some sea salt to a hot bath and soak in this daily.
- Develop the darkest suntan you can by covering your body in Divine Body Butter or coconut oil and then exposing at least 70% of your body to the sun for one hour every day (30 mins each side).
- No airconditioning, sleep with fans on and/or windows open to electrify the air.
- Put Congest Ease on the chest, back and feet once or twice per day.
- Sniff Breathe Eze up the nose, also spray in the mouth and swallow.
- **ESSENTIAL OIL...** peppermint, frankincense, vetiver, lavender, thyme, myrrh, cannabis.
- (Divine, Breathe Ez, Congest Ease, essential oil of peppermint, Himalayan rock salt, Ra 24ct See Salt, available in the USA **www.thedontolman.com/store** and Australia **www.lynnienichols.com/shop**)

BODY	MIND	SPIRIT
FOODS THAT HEAL	*POSSIBLE EMOTIONAL CAUSE*	*IMBALANCED CHAKRA*
---	---	---
SIGNATURE FOODS... apples, artichoke, broccoli, caraway seeds, raw honey, onions, peppermint, potatoes, radish, rosemary, turmeric, yams, carrots	• Are you feeling depressed, not good enough, not worthy of life? • Are you holding on to grief and sadness? • Are you allowing yourself to be controlled by others because you feel unworthy, not good enough?	Throat Chakra- colour Sky Blue / Heart Chakra- colour Emerald Green

RESPIRATORY SYSTEM
TAMARI RICE CAKE WITH GUACAMOLE

Ingredients: Rice: 2 cups brown rice, ½ cup sunflower seeds, 2 cobs organic corn, 2 cloves of garlic, 2 large onions, ¼ cup tamari sauce, himalayan salt, pepper

GUACAMOLE; see recipe in back of book

Method: Boil the rice until soft, use just enough water so that the rice becomes a little gluggy. Fry the brown onion and garlic in a little coconut oil, add to the rice along with the crunchy fresh corn cut from the cobs, sunflower seeds and tamari, season with Himalayan salt and pepper. Make a rice cake by pressing a large spoonful of mix together on a serving plate. Top with guacamole and garnish with coriander. (serves 4)

MOUTH ULCERS/CANKER SORES

***WHAT IS IT?... **Mouth ulcers** are lesions on the mucous membrane of the mouth or tongue thought to be bought on by stress and/or anxiety, by accidentally biting the area of the mouth, or if there's not enough salt in the diet acids can overwhelm the mucosal lining of the mouth, resulting in ulceration.

***BODY – EPICURE

- Get off all medication immediately.
- **Fastest...** Water fast for 7–10 days **OR...**
- Cabala juice fast 14–28 days.
- Drink one cup of freshly juiced lemon juice each day, with peels on if using a juice extractor.
- Make sure you have enough nature-made salt in your diet.
- Suck on sea rock salt daily, the size of the end segment of your little finger, then swish with lemon juice and swallow.
- Do salt water mouth rinsing and then rub organic raw honey onto the sores.
- Use one tbsp of good oil such as coconut oil or organic virgin olive oil and swish in the mouth for one minute until it foams up; then spit out and rinse with bicarbonate of soda (not baking soda).
- Apply tea tree oil directly onto the ulcer using a cotton bud.
- Eat ferments such as organic kefirs and yoghurts, sauerkraut, kombucha, olives in salt brine, tempeh, organic blue cheese without animal rennet etc. and snack on soy beans, bananas, nuts and seeds.
- Do the water protocol—one glass of water every hour on the hour, or drink one litre of water per 22 kilos of bodyweight every single day.
- Develop the darkest suntan you can by covering your body in Divine Body Butter or coconut oil and then exposing at least 70% of your body to the sun for one hour every day (30 mins each side).
- **ESSENTIAL OIL...** tea tree.
- (Divine, Ra 24ct See Salt, Himalayan rock salt available in the USA **www.thedontolman.com/store** and Australia **www.lynnienichols.com/shop**)

BODY *FOODS THAT HEAL*	MIND *POSSIBLE EMOTIONAL CAUSE*	SPIRIT *IMBALANCED CHAKRA*
---	---	---
SIGNATURE FOODS... apples, artichoke, broccoli, caraway seeds, raw honey, onions, peppermint, potatoes, radish, rosemary, turmeric, yams, carrots	• Are you being closed-minded and opinionated? • Are you unable to consider new ideas and situations?	Throat Chakra- colour Sky Blue

RESPIRATORY SYSTEM
SALTED CARAWAY POTATO WEDGES

Ingredients: 4 large potatoes scrubbed and cut into wedges, ½ cup coconut oil, 1 tbsp caraway seeds, sea salt

Method: Cut the potatoes into wedges. Toss in a mix of coconut oil and caraway seeds. Place on a baking tray and cook until golden brown both sides. Sprinkle with a good dose of sal. (serves 2)

MYCOPLASMA

***WHAT IS IT?...* **Mycoplasma pneumonia** is a respiratory infection that is contagious; however, most people with this infection do not develop pneumonia.

***BODY – EPICURE*

- Get off all medication immediately—absolutely no asthma sprays.
- **Fastest...** Water fast for 7–10 days **OR...**
- Cabala juice fast 14–28 days.
- Drink one cup of freshly juiced lemon juice each day, with peels on if using a juice extractor.
- Suck on rock salt daily, the size of the end segment of your little finger.
- Eat ferments such as organic kefirs and yoghurts, sauerkraut, kombucha, olives in salt brine, tempeh, organic blue cheese without animal rennet etc. and snack on soy beans, bananas, nuts and seeds.
- Do the water protocol—one glass of water every hour on the hour, or drink one litre of water per 22 kilos of bodyweight every single day.
- Drink three or four cups of hot water with the juice of a lemon and one teaspoon of raw honey.
- Cinnamon Oil—rub between your hands until warm and then rub all over the hands and up to the shoulders two or three times per day in order to assist the lymphatic stream.
- Develop the darkest suntan you can by covering your body in Divine Body Butter or coconut oil and then exposing at least 70% of your body to the sun for one hour every day (30 mins each side).
- Put Congest Ease on the chest, back and feet once or twice per day.
- Sniff Breathe Eze up the nose, also spray in the mouth and swallow.
- **ESSENTIAL OIL...** cinnamon, eucalyptus, bergamot, peppermint, tea tree.
- (Divine, Breathe Eze and Congest Ease available in the USA **www.thedontolman.com/store** and Australia **www.lynnienichols.com/shop**)

BODY *FOODS THAT HEAL*	MIND *POSSIBLE EMOTIONAL CAUSE*	SPIRIT *IMBALANCED CHAKRA*
---	---	---
SIGNATURE FOODS... apples, artichoke, broccoli, caraway seeds, raw honey, onions, peppermint, potatoes, radish, rosemary, turmeric, yams, carrots	• Are you feeling attacked? • Are you feeling irritated, angry, bitter?	Throat Chakra- colour Sky Blue / Heart Chakra- colour Emerald Green

RESPIRATORY SYSTEM
FERMENTED VEGGIES

Ingredients: ¼ large red cabbage, 1½ large green cabbage, 3 tbsp ginger, 3 tbsp turmeric, 3 small beetroot, 3 large carrots, 2 ½ tbsp sea salt, 1-2 tbs raw honey

OPTIONAL; parsley, coriander, lemon thyme, chilli, onion

Method: Finely shred the cabbage, finely dice the ginger and turmeric, and slice the beetroot and carrots into fine matchsticks with a mandolin. Place all ingredients together in a mixing bowl with sea salt. Massage with your hands until the bowl is full of juice. Place in jars, pressing down firmly after each spoonful is added to remove excess air. Make sure the vegetables are covered with juice and if not, you can add a little water. Place some folded cabbage leaf on top to keep the ingredients submerged. Secure the lid tightly and leave on a bench, out of the sun, for six days until the vegetables have fermented. Check each day to ensure the ingredients are under the liquid. Once ready, place into smaller jars and store in the fridge

Enjoy fermented veggies before every meal for good gut flora.

OBSTRUCTIVE SLEEP APNEA

***WHAT IS IT?...** **Obstructive sleep apnea** is where the muscles of the throat intermittently relax and obstruct the airways, causing breathing to stop and start.

***BODY – EPICURE**

- Get off all supplements and medication immediately.
- **Fastest...** Water fast for seven days **OR...**
- Cabala juice fast 14–28 days followed by a colon cleanse to remove toxicity/plaque.
- Eat a vegetarian diet.
- Get plenty of salt in the diet—suck on good nature-made rock salt.
- Have your evening meal at least two hours before bed and drink a mug of warm raw, organic cow's milk or a warm nut milk mixed with raw organic honey just before bed.
- Eat dark organic chocolate or drink one or two unfiltered organic wheat beers an hour or so before bed.
- Walking daily, morning and night if possible, for 30–45 minutes.
- Mix 1 tsp of lavender oil with a cup of water and spray on the pillow and bed, can also massage some of this on temples and the back of the neck just before bed.
- Sungazing morning and evenings in 13-second intervals; look at the sun until it reaches a 10-degree arc, or a clenched fist sitting on horizon as sun comes up, stop at top of fist. At night, start gazing as sun hits top of fist until it's gone.
- Take up meditation and practice this just before you go to bed.
- **ESSENTIAL OIL...** lavender, geranium, marjoram, valerian, chamomile.
- (Divine, essential oil of lavender, Ra 24ct See Salt, Himalayan rock salt, colon cleanses available in the USA **www.thedontolman.com/store** and Australia **www. lynnienichols.com/shop**)

BODY *FOODS THAT HEAL*	MIND *POSSIBLE EMOTIONAL CAUSE*	SPIRIT *IMBALANCED CHAKRA*
---	---	---
SIGNATURE FOODS... apples, artichoke, broccoli, caraway seeds, raw honey, onions, peppermint, potatoes, radish, rosemary, turmeric, yams, carrots	• Are you not wanting to face your feelings and what your heart truly desires? • Are you feeling extreme pressure and not wanting to face life? • Are you holding on to supressed anger, unforgiveness over past experiences?	Throat Chakra- colour Sky Blue

***NUGGET... *Our ancestors understood that when you have lemon combined with fermented drinks in the form of organic wine and unfiltered organic beer, socially with friends, it creates electrical energy amongst all gathered and is one of the greatest sacraments to the 'living temple'.*

RESPIRATORY SYSTEM
WARM CHAI LATE

Ingredients: ½ cup organic coconut milk, ½ cup cashew milk, 1-2 tsp honey, ½ tsp cardomon, ½ tsp cinnamon, ¼ tsp nutmeg

Method: Place all ingredients in a saucepan and slowly bring to the boil. Turn off before it reaches boiling point

Cashew Milk; Place 1 cup cashews and 1 litre of water in a blender and mix on high speed until a smooth liquid. Pour into a nut-milk bag and squeeze the milk into a bowl

PNEUMONIA

WHAT IS IT?... **Pneumonia** is infection/inflammation in the alveoli (air sacs) in one or both lungs, which fill with fluid and make it extremely hard to breathe. Pneumonia is most commonly caused by a virus, bacteria or fungi.

BODY – EPICURE

- Get off all medication immediately.
- **Fastest...** Water fast for seven days **OR...**
- Cabala juice fast 14–28 days
- Eat raw red-skinned potato sliced into 1 cm-thick cookies; squeeze fresh lemon juice over the potato and top with good nature-made salt.
- Eat one or two red grapefruit per day—be sure to scrape out and eat the white part of the fruit.
- Eat one or two cups of white or red radishes every day as well as lots of onion and garlic, raw and cooked.
- Suck on Himalayan rock salt daily, the size of the end segment of your little finger.
- Do the water protocol—one glass of water every hour on the hour, or drink one litre of water per 22 kilos of bodyweight every single day.
- Eat carrots, broccoli, kale, spinach, pumpkin, tomatoes, turnips, sweet potatoes, red potatoes, squash.
- Eat a high vitamin E diet—wholegrains, sunflower seeds, olive oil, safflower and sunflower oil, corn, avocado, garlic, and broccoli.
- Drink three or four cups of hot water with the juice of a lemon and 1 teaspoon of raw honey.
- Peppermint Oil- put two or three drops of peppermint oil in a bowl of hot water then drape a towel over your head and breathe the steam in and out through the mouth for three to five minutes, two or three times per day. Put a little peppermint oil on your lip, rub on the back of neck, chest and bottom of feet first thing in the morning.
- Add ½ cup bicarb and ¼ tsp peppermint oil and some sea salt to a hot bath and soak in this daily.
- Walking daily for 30 mins each day—place two drops of peppermint oil in your hands and, whilst walking, cup your hands over your nose and breathe the peppermint in; once lungs are full, blow out through the mouth.
- Develop the darkest suntan you can by covering your body in Divine Body Butter or coconut oil and then exposing at least 70% of your body to the sun for one hour every day (30 mins each side).
- No airconditioning, sleep with fans on and/or windows open to electrify the air.
- Put Congest Ease on the chest, back and feet once or twice per day.
- Sniff Breathe Eze up the nose, also spray in the mouth and swallow.
- **ESSENTIAL OIL...** peppermint, rosemary, frankincense, oregano, eucalyptus, geranium.
- (Divine, essential oil of peppermint, Ra 24ct See Salt, Himalayan rock salt, Breathe Eze, Congest Ease available in the USA **www.thedontolman.com/store** and Australia **www.lynnienichols.com/shop**)

BODY *FOODS THAT HEAL*	MIND *POSSIBLE EMOTIONAL CAUSE*	SPIRIT *IMBALANCED CHAKRA*
---	---	---
SIGNATURE FOODS... apples, artichoke, broccoli, caraway seeds, raw honey, onions, peppermint, potatoes, radish, rosemary, turmeric, yams, carrots	• Are you holding emotional hurts from the past? • Are you feeling controlled?	Throat Chakra- colour Sky Blue / Heart Chakra- colour Emerald Green

RESPIRATORY SYSTEM
LUNG-LOVER STEW

Ingredients: 2 large carrots, ¼ pumpkin, 1 turnip, 2 large sweet potatoes, 2 large red potatoes, 2 large yam, 4 squash, 2 organic corn cobs, 1 medium head broccoli, 3 large kale leaves, 3 large spinach leaves, ½ kilo tomatoes, 6 large cloves garlic, 2 large red onions, 1 tsp rosemary, 1 tsp fresh tumeric, 1 tbsp sea salt, 3 tbsp coconut oil

Method: Peel, or if organic scrub the skins of the vegetables—chop into chunky pieces. Peel the onion, garlic and turmeric and dice. Cut the squash into quarters, cut the corn from the cobs, chop the broccoli into bite-sized pieces and finely shred the spinach and kale

Fry the onion and garlic in coconut oil for 2 minutes, add the rosemary and turmeric and fry for a further minute. Add the root vegetables, salt and a little water and continue to stir-fry for five minutes. Add the remaining water and bring to the boil. Once boiling, turn down and continue to simmer until the vegetables are soft but not mushy. Add the broccoli, kale, spinach, tomatoes and corn and continue to simmer for 5 minutes. Taste and add extra rosemary or salt if needed. Season with pepper and serve. (serves 2)

PULMINARY EMBOLISM

***WHAT IS IT?...** **Pulminary Embolism** is the sudden blockage of a major artery in the lung caused by a blood clot. Large clots can stop the blood flow to the lung resulting in death; however, most clots are smaller and may damage the lung due to restricted blood flow but are not fatal.

***BODY – EPICURE*

- Get off all medication immediately.
- **Fastest...** Water fast for seven days **OR...**
- Cabala juice fast 14–28 days
- Eat raw red-skinned potato sliced into 1 cm-thick cookies; squeeze fresh lemon juice over the potato and top with good nature-made salt
- Eat one or two red grapefruit per day—be sure to scrape out and eat the white part of the fruit.
- Eat one or two cups of white or red radishes every day as well as lots of onion and garlic, raw and cooked.
- Suck on rock salt daily, the size of the end segment of your little finger.
- Do the water protocol—one glass of water every hour on the hour, or drink one litre of water per 22 kilos of bodyweight every single day.
- Eat carrots, broccoli, kale, spinach, pumpkin, tomatoes, turnips, sweet potatoes, red potatoes, squash.
- Eat a high vitamin E diet—wholegrains, sunflower seeds, olive oil, safflower and sunflower oil, corn, avocado, garlic, and broccoli.
- Drink three or four cups of hot water with the juice of a lemon and one teaspoon of raw honey.
- Peppermint Oil- put two or three drops of peppermint oil in a bowl of hot water then drape a towel over your head and breathe the steam in and out through the mouth for three to five minutes, two or three times per day. Put a little peppermint oil on your lip, rub on the back of neck, chest and bottom of feet first thing in the morning.
- Add ½ cup bicarb and ¼ tsp peppermint oil and some sea salt to a hot bath and soak in this daily.
- Walking daily for 30 mins each day—place two drops of peppermint oil in your hands and, whilst walking, cup your hands over your nose and breathe the peppermint in; once lungs are full, blow out through the mouth.
- Develop the darkest suntan you can by covering your body in Divine Body Butter or coconut oil and then exposing at least 70% of your body to the sun for one hour every day (30 mins each side).
- No airconditioning, sleep with fans on and/or windows open to electrify the air.
- Put Congest Ease on the chest, back and feet once or twice per day.
- Sniff Breathe Eze up the nose, also spray in the mouth and swallow.
- **ESSENTIAL OIL...** peppermint, helichrysum.
- (Divine, essential oil of peppermint, Ra 24ct See Salt, Himalayan rock salt, Breathe Eze, Congest Ease available in the USA **www.thedontolman.com/store** and Australia **www.lynnienichols.com/shop**)

BODY	MIND	SPIRIT
FOODS THAT HEAL	*POSSIBLE EMOTIONAL CAUSE*	*IMBALANCED CHAKRA*
---	---	---
SIGNATURE FOODS... apples, artichoke, broccoli, caraway seeds, raw honey, onions, peppermint, potatoes, radish, rosemary, turmeric, yams, carrots	• Are you feeling depressed and fearful? • Are you supressing yourself due to feeling unworthy?	Throat Chakra- colour Sky Blue / Heart Chakra- colour Emerald Green

***NOTE...** *Vitamin E has protector and inhibitor fats... Garlic and avocado are extremely powerful for thinning the blood.*

***NUGGET...** *All tree nuts and even peanuts have a blood-thinning agent.*

RESPIRATORY SYSTEM
TUBER STACK WITH ROSEMARY OIL

Ingredients: 2 large carrots, ½ pumpkin, 1 turnip, 2 large sweet potatoes, 2 large red potatoes, 3 brown onions, 5 large cloves garlic, 1 tsp cumin, 3 tbsp honey, 2 tbsp fresh diced rosemary, 1 cup cold pressed virgin olive oil, 1 avocado

Method: Peel the garlic and brown onions and chop the onions into quarters. Cut the skin from the pumpkin and scrub the skins of all other vegetables (peel if not organic). Chop the vegetables into small pieces and place in a bowl with the chopped onion, full garlic cloves, coconut oil and a good dose of sea salt. Toss until coated well with coconut oil... add extra oil if necessary. Place on a baking tray in a moderate oven until soft and golden brown

Make the Stack; mash the pumpkin and cumin together with a fork and place a spoonful on each plate as the base of your stack. Place a large serving spoon of the baked veggies on top of the pumpkin. Add a generous drizzle of rosemary oil and garnish with a couple of thick slices of avocado. (serves 4)

SINUSITIS

WHAT IS IT?... **Sinusitis** is where the sinuses become inflamed and swollen, which causes blockage and mucus buildup, normally due to infection; however, sometimes the cause can be nasal polyps

BODY – EPICURE

- Get off all medication immediately.
- Every morning, one of the first things to do is to put a thumb or finger on one nostril and blow out the other—this clears any mucous and stops blocking of the sinus. Do this out in the open air or in a steamy shower.
- Spray salt water (10/13 drops eucalyptus, peppermint, two or three tbsp salt and one litre water) and spray up the nose and blow out.
- Suck on rock salt daily, the size of the end segment of your little finger.
- Heat pan of water until steamy, put towel over your head and breathe in steam through the nose and out through the mouth... Can add two or three drops eucalyptus, peppermint or teatree oil.
- Use Breathe Eze—hold head back when spraying this so it gets up into the sinus; swallow the Breathe Eze that runs down into the throat.
- Use Congest Ease on throat, chest and feet.
- **ESSENTIAL OIL...** tea tree, eucalyptus, peppermint.
- (Divine, essential oil of peppermint, teatree and eucalyptus, Ra 24ct See Salt, Himalayan rock salt, Breathe Eze, Congest Ease available in the USA **www.thedontolman.com/store** and Australia **www.lynnienichols.com/shop**)

BODY *FOODS THAT HEAL*	MIND *POSSIBLE EMOTIONAL CAUSE*	SPIRIT *IMBALANCED CHAKRA*
---	---	---
SIGNATURE FOODS... apples, artichoke, broccoli, caraway seeds, raw honey, onions, peppermint, potatoes, radish, rosemary, turmeric, yams, carrots	• Are you feeling irritated by a certain person? • Are you disappointed/wanting more out of life? • Are you holding sadness or guilt from the past?	Throat Chakra- colour Sky Blue

RESPIRATORY SYSTEM
LEMON SALTED CASHEW BALLS

Ingredients: 1 cup cashews, the zest of 1 lemon, 1 drop essential lemon oil, a pinch of Himalayan rock salt, 1 cup medjool dates, 1 tbsp honey, ½ cup shredded coconut plus extra coconut for rolling

Method: In a processor blend the cashews until they are a chunky crumb texture. Add the lemon zest, lemon oil, salt, dates, honey and shredded coconut. Process until the mix forms a ball or it sticks together when you press a little between your fingers. If it's a little dry, add a few drops of water. Roll into balls, coat with desiccated coconut. Refrigerate

Makes approx. 8-10 balls

THROAT CANCER

***WHAT IS IT?...** **Throat Cancer** refers to a malignant tumour of the throat, voice box or tonsils.

***BODY – EPICURE*

- Get off all medication and supplements- herbs in the form of powders or teas are okay, but no pills or capsules!
- **Fastest...** Water fast for seven days **THEN**
- Do the five-week 35% food-grade hydrogen peroxide protocol combined with a cabala juice fast for 14–28 days ... if needed, can have raw vegan food also.
- Eat and juice a locally grown, fresh, raw organic vegan diet for highest nutritional force. At the same time, eat and juice daily—fresh, locally grown organic broccoli, cauliflower and asparagus (when in season).
- Suck on rock salt daily, the size of the end segment of your little finger.
- Eat one heaped teaspoon of organic raw honey, insalivate before swallowing.
- Drink one litre per 22 kilos bodyweight of pure water every day.
- Have daily a berry, asparaus smoothie, consisting of two cups berries and 12 stalks of asparagus (can add a banana to sweeten) plus water to desired consistency. Drink within 30 mins of making it. Can eat the foods instead if preferred.
- Sniff Breathe Eze up the nose, also spray in the mouth and swallow.
- Develop the darkest suntan you can by covering your body in Divine Body Butter or coconut oil and then exposing at least 70% of your body to the sun for one hour every day (30 mins each side).
- **ESSENTIAL OIL...** peppermint, myrrh, frankincense, cannabis, thyme, lemon, turmeric, clary sage.
- (Divine, Breath Ez, essential oil of peppermint, Ra 24ct See Salt, Himalayan rock salt available in the USA **www.thedontolman.com/store** and Australia **www.lynnienichols.com/shop**)

BODY *FOODS THAT HEAL*	MIND *POSSIBLE EMOTIONAL CAUSE*	SPIRIT *IMBALANCED CHAKRA*
SIGNATURE FOODS... apples, artichoke, broccoli, caraway seeds, raw honey, onions, peppermint, potatoes, radish, rosemary, turmeric, yams, carrots	• Are you having difficulty speaking your truth? • Are you feeling frustrated, unheard, misunderstood? • Are you swallowing sadness, which is creating feelings of depression and hopelessness?	Throat Chakra- colour Sky Blue

---

RESPIRATORY SYSTEM
LEMON LUNG DETOX JUICE

Ingredients: 1 large lemon including skin, 1 small head of broccoli, 6 stalks of asparagus, 1 tbsp honey

Method: Juice the lemon, broccoli and asparagus then add honey.

TONSILITIS

WHAT IS IT?... **Tonsilitis** is an inflammation caused by infection of the lymphatic tissue at the back of the throat, called the tonsils. Along with the adenoids, the tonsils are the first line of defence against viruses and bacteria.

BODY – EPICURE

- Get off all supplements and medication immediately.
- **Fastest...** Water fast for 7–10 days **OR...**
- Cabala juice fast for 7–21 days—it can take this long to clear.
- Drink hot water, lemon juice and honey.
- Lemon—put lemon on and in everythng, lemon and salt will clear this.
- Have a teaspoon full of raw organic honey, insalivate and then swallow; do this several times per day.
- Suck on rock salt, the size of the end segment of your little finger, daily and get plenty of salt in your diet.
- Use a nettie pot and a mix of water/tea tree oil to cleanse the nasal passage—this can also be done with Breathe Eze.

- Teatree oil—place two drops of oil on your finger and suck up into each nostril and into the throat then swallow.
- Sungazing morning and evenings in 13-second intervals; look at the sun until it reaches a 10-degree arc, or a clenched fist sitting on horizon as sun comes up, stop at top of fist. At night, start gazing as sun hits top of fist until it's gone.
- **ESSENTIAL OIL...** tea tree, peppermint, myrrh, frankincense.
- (Divine, essential oil of tea tree and lemon, Ra 24ct See Salt, Himalayan rock salt, Breathe Eze available in the USA **www.thedontolman.com/store** and Australia **www.lynnienichols.com/shop**)

BODY *FOODS THAT HEAL*	MIND *POSSIBLE EMOTIONAL CAUSE*	SPIRIT *IMBALANCED CHAKRA*
---	---	---
SIGNATURE FOODS... apples, artichoke, broccoli, caraway seeds, raw honey, onions, peppermint, potatoes, radish, rosemary, turmeric, yams, carrots	• Are you being judgemental of yourself or others? • Are you supressing fear? • Are you feeling supressed creatively?	Throat Chakra- colour Sky Blue

RESPIRATORY SYSTEM
THROAT SOOTHER

Ingredients: The juice and zest of 1 lemon, 4 tbsp honey, 1 drop eucalyptus essential oil, 1 tsp Himalayan rock salt

Method: Mix all ingredients together in a small bowl or cup and take a teaspoon of this every hour throughout the day.

WHOOPING COUGH

WHAT IS IT?... **Whooping Cough** is a respiratory bacterial disease that is contagious and characterised by uncontrollable coughing followed by a whoop.

BODY – EPICURE

- Get off all medication immediately—absolutely NO asthma sprays.
- Vitamin C will prevent and treat ... juice and eat one or two pieces of citrus fruit each day.
- Salt—give nature-made salty foods to the child to eat. Get them to suck on Himalayan rock salt daily; if they won't suck the salt, get them to lick the rock salt four or five times per day.
- Drink lots of water.
- Eat mashed potato with lemon juice and sea or Himalayan rock salt. Can also give them homemade potato chips fried in coconut oil, depending on the age.
- Drink three or four cups of hot water with the juice of a lemon and 1 teaspoon of raw honey.
- Use eucalyptus or teatree oil in a vapouriser or oil burner in the child's room.
- No airconditioning, sleep with fans on and/or windows open to electrify the air.
- Put Congest Ease on the chest, back and feet once or twice per day.
- **ESSENTIAL OIL...** orange, lemon, lime, eucalyptus, rosemary, bergamot.
- (Divine, essential oil of orange, eucalyptus and teatree, Ra 24ct See Salt, Himalayan rock salt, Congest Ease available in the USA **www.thedontolman.com/store** and Australia **www.lynnienichols.com/shop**)

BODY FOODS THAT HEAL	MIND POSSIBLE EMOTIONAL CAUSE	SPIRIT IMBALANCED CHAKRA
---	---	---
SIGNATURE FOODS... apples, artichoke, broccoli, caraway seeds, raw honey, onions, peppermint, potatoes, radish, rosemary, turmeric, yams, carrots	• Are you feeling controlled? • Are you feeling unheard or unseen?	Throat Chakra- colour Sky Blue / Heart Chakra- colour Emerald Green

RESPIRATORY SYSTEM
LEMON MASH

Ingredients: 1 large red-skinned organic potato, juice of 1 lemon, ½ tsp sea salt, 1 tbsp honey

Method: Cut the potato into thin slices and steam until soft. Leave the skin on if possible. Place the potato in a bowl with the lemon juice, salt and honey and mash well until smooth and creamy. (serves 1)

The 100th Monkey Effect...

The '100th monkey effect' is a term coined and first presented by Lyall Watson in his 1979 book Lifetide. The discovery is based on a research project using monkeys, on the island of Koshima in Japan.

In the 1950s the scientists on the island began dropping sweet potatoes on the ground to feed the monkeys. Whilst the monkeys liked the taste of the potato, they did not like the dirt and so after a while, one of the monkeys discovered that she could solve this problem by washing her potato in water. Other monkeys saw her doing this and adopted the very same behaviour. Pretty soon, more and more monkeys learned how to wash their potatoes and, after some time, it was observed that 100 monkeys had learned the new technique. Suddenly, all of the monkeys on the island knew how to wash their potatoes! It was as if they had reached a critical mass, which resulted in a species breakthrough. The most interesting part of the study is that this was not limited to the monkeys on the island of Koshima. Monkeys in other areas that had no physical contact with the educated monkeys suddenly adopted the same habit. The new knowledge seemed to spread purely from mind to mind across the islands, and some say even globally.

While this particular study has been well debated and allegedly discredited by academics, there are scholars even today that say there is observable truth to the finding! Another explanation of this phenomenon is found in the studies of morpho-genetic fields that have been introduced and thoroughly investigated by scholars like Rupert Sheldrake. The idea is that when a behaviour is repeated over and over it creates a sort of pattern that is increasingly strengthened over time. The pattern that is created becomes a part of a sort of memory bank if you will, and then the field is accessible to all. The more this is strengthened, the easier it makes it for others to adopt this particular behaviour, meaning that once something is learned it will get easier for the next group to learn the same thing, and in the end it becomes an instinctive skill. This explains why we all have certain skills at birth!

An example that is often referred to is the fact that many times throughout history the same things have been invented by different people in different parts of the planet at the same time—without their having any knowledge of each other at all. The telephone is but one common example where there, to this day, rests confusion about who is to be credited for this invention as several people seem to have thought of the same thing at the same time.

This field of information is known by many names. Carl G. Jung called it the 'collective unconscious'. Others call it the source field. The important factor here, though, is that it is accessible to all of us. Sheldrake has done research that backs up the existence of such a human energy field, whatever you want to call it. In the 1980s, he was part of an experiment where groups of people were shown puzzles in the form of hidden images. It was timed how long it took for the participants to solve the puzzles. Then the same puzzles were shown on television to millions of viewers where the answer was revealed. After this had taken place, new groups of people were shown the images that had no knowledge of the television show, yet ... nevertheless, the second groups managed to solve them much quicker, implying that learning indeed gets easier once more people have the skill.

It seems as though thoughts and actions create pathways that are strengthened through the numbers of those involved. These pathways are part of a field that we have access to via our minds and are used when we think. When the new pathways are then embraced by others, the energy field becomes strengthened so much, that they direct the energy in new patterns and this can override older and less appreciable patterns, meaning that when the shift of energy first takes place, when critical mass is reached, old die-hard habits tend to vanish. After all, energy will always travel the route of least resistance, just like water running down a hill. You can think of this field as a field of possibilities where anything can be created, and you are a part of it! **You are the creator or creatrix, male or female energy developing this field!**

The Idea of the 100th monkey effect has today become a popular strategy for social change. The idea is that when enough people focus on a new positive pattern of behaviour, as soon as the critical number is reached it causes a breakthrough after which the new pattern spreads from mind to mind through this morpho-genetic field, finally reaching everyone. This means that if enough people come to know something to be true, that it actually confirms that truth, and that if a certain amount of people hold their awareness on a desire for positive change, this will have a worldwide effect.

In theory it takes only a limited amount of people to change the world of human experience. So, when we look around us and family and friends don't want to hear the truths we embrace, we can at times begin to feel a sense of hopelessness about the situation, but the truth is there really is no reason for it. All you need to do is start with yourself. Be mindful about your own thoughts and emotions, and take responsibility for your actions.

A New Paradigm... Birds of a Feather

As I sat watching a flock of birds on the beach this morning, 'being' with the ebb and flow of the ocean tides ... not questioning, not worrying, not trying to work it out ... just going with the organic flow of life, a pang of sadness shot through my heart. Sadness at how far, as a human race, we have veered from truth! Amongst the terns I noticed a single seagull and couldn't help but smile knowing that for many years, I, like many others, have felt like that solitary gull, and yet today, just like the saying, 'birds of a feather flock together,' all around the world, people of similar vibration are gathering in order to 'be the change,' ecstatic to be cutting free from the 'old ways' of consumerism and materialism, awakened to the lies and deception, the false teachings that have been embedded into our psyche by our so-called education system, which in truth is nothing more than indoctrination via chant memorising! When have we ever been offered the opportunity to think, feel and question what those in power are saying/teaching without fear of ridicule or punishment? When have we ever been given a choice as to what 'feels' right or wrong, what feels like truth? From birth to seven years old we are like absorbent sponges on an ocean shore, taking in every drop of information washed over us, until, just like the sponge when the tide comes in, we are saturated with beliefs and programs that are a culmination of man-made rules, regulations, lies and possibly a little truth!

Just like the software of a computer, this indoctrination via chant memory has become the basis of our belief system, the subconscious programming of our mind that runs on autopilot 24 hours a day, seven days a week, attracting to us people and situations that affirm our fear based negative core beliefs, keeping us small and in constant need to try to control every aspect (or person) in our life in order to feel safe ... and, in this, losing all sense of what it is like to live intuitively, organically in the flow of life, just like that flock of birds on the beach and every other native animal.

Unknowingly, our minds have become sick (the real cause of disease) with negative beliefs about ourselves—the way we must look and act in order to be worthy of love, the material objects we must possess in order to be good enough and accepted by the masses, along with the deceptive belief that we are powerless victims of a cruel, cruel world, which, in truth, could not be further from the truth if only we realised the extent our true potential. We have been manipulated and trained, just like a domesticated animal, doing as we are told even if it does not feel right, for fear of consequences such as losing allowances or material wealth or much worse, all in the name of those in power having even more control and power over us as greed lines their pockets!

Well, those times are coming to an end, thank goodness; but in order for that to happen, it is said there will be a time of darkness such as what is taking place in the world right now. Just know that it must be this way in order to push those with their eyes shut tight to awaken and begin questioning the integrity and authenticity of their beliefs and governing systems, as the collective consciousness of our Souls begs to be free from the chains that have kept us slaves to our physicality for so long. Don't buy into the fear, this will only feed the chaos; instead, focus on all that you have to be grateful for. Give thanks to Mother's Angels of AFEW, the air that is the very breath of life, the sun that sends golden rays of galactic intelligence to every cell and molecule of your being and is the very substance of life on Earth, the earth that provides us with a place to call home and the water that nourishes every cell and cleanses our body and Soul. Allow gratitude to emanate out to the world as unconditional love and forgiveness, and in doing so you will begin to ebb and flow with the tides of life and fly freely with the winds of change, just as Nature intended.

From my Heart to Yours, I send vibrations of unconditional love.

Lynnie xx

The ENDOCRINE/REPRODUCTIVE SYSTEM

Consists of... all endocrine glands-pineal, pituitary, thyroid, parathyroid, adrenal, neuroendocrine, ovaries, testicles, genitals, womb/uterus

Chakra- Sacral (orange) / **Endocrine Gland and Function...** Ovaries and testicles are the primary reproductive organs, producing ova and sperm. The ovaries secrete estrogen and progesterone, which are vital for procreation.

Hold Emotional Molecules of trust, vitality, confidence, sexual power, anger, incompetence and distrust.

Foods That Support This System Are... apples, avocados, bananas, eggplant, figs, kiwifruit, mushrooms, nectarines, olives, plantains, passionfruit, peanuts, pears, pomegranates, nuts, seeds, grains, legumes

Support the Emotional / Physical Healing of This System with... INDIGO/BLUE and ORANGE foods.

Blue wholefoods support this system for longevity and promote feelings of fulfilment.

Orange wholefoods help with the release of blood disorders in this system whilst assisting the body to release emotions of loneliness and grief.

***Nugget... The ingredient in peanuts that causes arousal, called L-Arginine, is at the basis of the pharmaceutical drug Viagra? Truth is, men, all you have to do is pig out on those peanuts! In fact, for centuries, the Church of England banned men under a certain age from eating peanuts for this very reason.

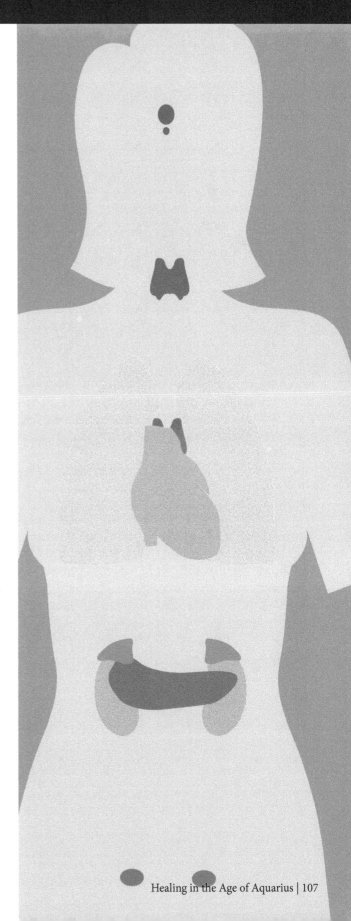

ADRENALS

BODY *FOODS THAT HEAL*	MIND *POSSIBLE EMOTIONAL CAUSE*	SPIRIT *IMBALANCED CHAKRA*
---	---	---
SIGNATURE FOODS... coffee bean	Are you feeling anxious, hopeless or empty? Are you lacking in self love? Are you feeling emotionally drained/exhausted?	Sacral Chakra- colour Orange / Base Chakra- **colour Red**

***NOTE... *There are only two types of sugar—fast and slow. Fast sugar is toxic to the human body and is found in artificial sweeteners such as aspartame as well as refined sugar! Slow sugars are found in fruits—the molecular size is so large it crosses the blood-brain barrier slowly; the brain tells the pancreas to produce glucagon, which is then moved to the adrenals where it heals the adrenals and creates adrenalin for energy. Fruit is the answer to healing any adrenal issues!*

ENDOCRINE SYSTEM/REPRODUCTIVE
ADRENAL BOOSTER

Ingredients: 2 apples, 2 pears, 4 nectarines, 2 large bananas, 4 dried figs, 3 kiwifruit, pulp of 4 passionfruit, insides of 2 pomegranates, ¼ cup peanuts, ¼ cup salted pistachios, ¼ cup macadamia nuts chopped

Method: Chop the apple and pear into bite-sized pieces – include the core/seeds and skins, place in a mixing bowl. Peel and dice the kiwifruit, deseed and dice the nectarines, slice the figs and add to the bowl. Scoop the insides of the pomegranates and add. In a dry pan, lightly toast the peanuts. Chop all nuts a little and put aside. Place the fruit mixture into serving bowls, add sliced banana, top with passionfruit pulp, chopped nut mix and serve. (serves 2)

BREASTS

BODY	MIND	SPIRIT
FOODS THAT HEAL	**POSSIBLE EMOTIONAL CAUSE**	**IMBALANCED CHAKRA**
---	---	---
SIGNATURE FOODS... all citrus fruits including oranges, tangerines, manderins, grapefruit, lemon and lime	Are you putting everbody else first and forgetting/refusing to nourish yourself? Do you have an overprotective mother attitude? drained/exhausted?	Sacral Chakra- colour Orange / Heart Chakra- colour Emerald Green

ENDOCRINE SYSTEM/REPRODUCTIVE
RAW CITRUS MOUSSE

Ingredients: orange, 1 mandarin, 1 tangarine

MOUSSE; 1 cup cashews, $1/3$ cup lime juice, $2/3$ cup orange juice, 2 drops citrus essential oil, 2 tbsp raw honey, $1/3$ cup coconut cream

Method: Soak the cashews for 1 hour in water then strain and place in a blender with all other mousse ingredients. Blend on high speed until very smooth and creamy

Dice the fruit into 1 cm pieces and mix together in a bowl. Place the fruit into a glass dessert bowl or cocktail glass and top with citrus mousse. Set in the fridge for 1hr. Garnish with fruit and a sprig of mint. (serves 2)

OVARIES

BODY *FOODS THAT HEAL*	MIND *POSSIBLE EMOTIONAL CAUSE*	SPIRIT *IMBALANCED CHAKRA*
---	---	---
SIGNATURE FOODS... olives, dates	Are you stifling your creativity? Are you rejecting your own sensuality/feminine nature? Are you supressing painful memories around males?	Sacral Chakra- colour Orange

ENDOCRINE SYSTEM/REPRODUCTIVE
BAKED EGGPLANT WITH OLIVE TAPANADE

Ingredients: 2 whole baby eggplants cut in half lengthways, 2 cups button mushrooms sliced, 2 avocados sliced, 2 cups of peanuts lightly toasted, ½ cup coconut oil, sea salt

OLIVE TAPANADE; **(see recipe under Dressings in back of book).**

Method: Slice the avocado and mushrooms. Lightly roast peanuts on a dry oven tray then chop. Cut the eggplants in halves lengthwise. With a sharp knife score the inside flesh of the eggplant being careful not to cut the skin. Drizzle the coconut oil over the scored flesh and season with a good dose of sea salt. Place in a moderate oven until inner flesh is extra soft and creamy. Spoon a thick layer of tapanade over the cooked eggplant, top with sliced mushrooms and avocado. Finish with a good sprinkle of toasted peanuts. (serves 2)

PINEAL

BODY *FOODS THAT HEAL*	MIND *POSSIBLE EMOTIONAL CAUSE*	SPIRIT *IMBALANCED CHAKRA*
---	---	---
SIGNATURE FOODS... pinenuts, rockmelon seeds, sesame seeds	Are you listening to and following your intuition? Are you feeling isolated and alone?	Sacral Chakra- colour Orange / Crown Chakra- **colour Violet**

***NUGGET... *Anciently, it was believed that the Neter (NTR) (the first indivisible cell at the time of conception) was housed and resided for the duration of our lifetime in the pineal gland (Cave of Brahma).*

ENDOCRINE SYSTEM/REPRODUCTIVE
ROCKMELON & PINE NUT SMOOTHIE

Ingredients: ¼ cup pine nuts, 2 cups diced rockmelon, ½ tbsp rockmelon seeds, 2 large banana

Method: Take the skin off the rockmelon and chop into small pieces. Place in the blender with the rockmelon seeds, pine nuts and banana. Mix on high speed until thick and creamy. (serves 1)

PITUITARY

BODY	MIND	SPIRIT
FOODS THAT HEAL	*POSSIBLE EMOTIONAL CAUSE*	*IMBALANCED CHAKRA*
---	---	---
SIGNATURE FOODS... peas, hazel nuts, pistachios	Are you feeling overwhelmed or confused by constant mind chatter?	Sacral Chakra- colour Orange / Third Eye Chakra- **colour Indigo**
	Are you feeling balance between body and mind?	

ENDOCRINE SYSTEM/REPRODUCTIVE
FERTILITY SMOOTHIE

Ingredients: 1 banana, 1 pear, 1 peach, 1 kiwifruit, 2 figs, ½ avocado, ½–1 cup water, 1 passionfruit

Method: Place all ingredients except the passionfruit in a blender and mix until smooth—add more water if necessary, to achieve desired thickness. Add the passionfruit and mix with a spoon before serving

PROSTATE

BODY *FOODS THAT HEAL*	**MIND** *POSSIBLE EMOTIONAL CAUSE*	**SPIRIT** *IMBALANCED CHAKRA*
---	---	---
SIGNATURE FOODS... Brazil nuts	Are fears or worries weakening your masculinity?	Sacral Chakra- colour Orange
	Are you feeling disappointed, not good enough? Have you given up?	

ENDOCRINE SYSTEM/REPRODUCTIVE
RAW ZUCCHINI STACK

Ingredients: 2 cups of rocket and 1 cup baby spinach leaves, 4 medium zucchini- sliced finely lengthways (use mandolin- about ½ cm thick), ½ punnet of cherry tomatoes sliced, 1 avocado sliced, tahini

GUACAMOLE; **(see recipe under Womb in Endocrine System)**

OLIVE TAPENADE; **(see recipe under Dressings in back of book)**

BASIL PESTO; **(see recipe under Dressings in back of book)**

RED CAPSICUM PESTO; **(see recipe under Dressings in back of book)**

Method: To prepare the zucchini stack, spread the rocket and baby spinach over the base of rectangular serving or casserole dish. Next, place a layer of sliced zucchini side by side, covering the rocket and base of dish. Spread a thick layer of olive tapenade over the zucchini. Add another layer of zucchini, top this with a generous layer of basil pesto or red capsicum pesto, followed by another layer of zucchini and then a thick layer of guacamole.

Place the sliced cherry tomatoes on top of the guacamole followed by a few slices of avocado for garnish. Drizzle tahini over the stack to finish. Using a sharp knife cut the zucchini stack into portions and serve immediately. (serves 6)

*For a non-vegan version, crumble organic feta or goat's cheese over the top of the stack

TESTICLES

BODY *FOODS THAT HEAL*	MIND *POSSIBLE EMOTIONAL CAUSE*	SPIRIT *IMBALANCED CHAKRA*
---	---	---
SIGNATURE FOODS... peanuts, almonds, passionfruit, figs	Are you uncomfortable with your masculinity? Are you holding on to feelings of shame, guilt or anger?	Sacral Chakra- colour Orange

***NOTE... *Asparagus will increase semen and sexual desire.*

ENDOCRINE SYSTEM/REPRODUCTIVE
BANANA SPLIT WITH CASHEW CREAM

Ingredients: 4 bananas cut in half lengthways, 2 cups peanuts chopped and toasted lightly, 6 passionfruit pulps, 4 kiwi fruit sliced

CASHEW CREAM **(see recipe under Dressings in back of book)**

Method: Place the banana halves side by side on a serving plate, top with sliced kiwi fruit and passionfruit. Add a big spoonful of cashew cream and a generous dose of toasted peanuts and serve immediately. (serves 4)

THYROID

BODY *FOODS THAT HEAL* --- **SIGNATURE FOODS...** mushrooms, nutritional yeast, seaweed	MIND *POSSIBLE EMOTIONAL CAUSE* --- Are you feeling victimised, 'It's not fair... What about me?' Are you feeling supressed or left out?	SPIRIT *IMBALANCED CHAKRA* --- Sacral Chakra- colour Orange / Throat Chakra- colour Sky Blue

***NUGGET... *Mushrooms are one of the highest sources of plant iodine and the perfect signature food for the thyroid. When you place mushrooms in the sun for 2 hrs–2 days prior to eating them, this also increases the vitamin D levels of the mushroom! The sun's rays on the skin of a mushroom has the same effect as it does on human skin.*

ENDOCRINE SYSTEM/REPRODUCTIVE
STUFFED BABA GHANOUSH MUSHROOMS

Ingredients: 4 large organic mushrooms.

BABA GHANOUSH; 1 eggplant diced, 1 tbsp tahini, 1 tbsp lemon juice, 2 clove garlic, sea salt to taste, ¼ cup pine nuts, 2 tsp sesame seeds, coconut oil

Method: Brush the mushrooms with coconut oil and place in a baking dish to lightly roast.

Baba Ghanoush; Roast the eggplant in coconut oil until very soft and creamy. Let cool slightly then place in a blender with the tahini, lemon juice, garlic, sesame seeds and pine nuts. Blend until a smooth consistency. Add sea salt until desired taste is achieved—approximately 1 tsp. Fill the roasted mushrooms with baba ghanoush and serve. (serves 2)

WOMB

BODY *FOODS THAT HEAL*	MIND *POSSIBLE EMOTIONAL CAUSE*	SPIRIT *IMBALANCED CHAKRA*
SIGNATURE FOODS... avocado, pear, eggplant, papaya	Are you blocking your creativity, holding on to past hurts or rejection? Are you neglecting to nurture yourself or holding on to mother issues?	Sacral Chakra- colour Orange

***NUGGET... *An avocado cut in half, seed left inside, looks just like a baby in the womb and, amazingly, it takes exactly nine months to grow an avocado from blossom to ripened fruit. This is a perfect signature match for the uterus/womb.*

ENDOCRINE SYSTEM/REPRODUCTIVE
MUMMA'S GUACAMOLE

Ingredients: 3 large, soft avocados, 1 medium-sized tomato diced, 1–2 cloves garlic finely diced, ½ red onion finely diced, ½-1 teaspoon Himalayan or sea salt to taste, black pepper to taste

Method: Scoop the flesh from the avocados and place in a mixing bowl. Mash well with a fork until smooth and creamy. Add the diced tomato, onion and garlic. Season to taste with salt and pepper. Serve with raw carrot, zucchini, green pear and celery sticks

DIS-EASES/DISORDERS OF *The* ENDOCRINE/REPRODUCTIVE SYSTEM

ADDISON'S DISEASE/CHRONIC ADRENAL INSUFFICIENCY/ HYPOCORTISOLISM

***WHAT IS IT?...** **Addison's disease** is the result of the adrenal glands not producing enough of the hormone cortisol and, in some cases, the hormone aldosterone.

***BODY – EPICURE*

- Get off all medication and supplements- herbs in the form of powders or teas are okay. You may have 72 hours of feeling toxicities leave the bloodstream.
- **Fastest...** Water fast for 7–10 days **OR...**
- Green juice fast for 21 days.
- For 28 days, eat and juice a locally grown, fresh, raw organic 100% fruit diet for highest functional capacity of the pancreas. Fruit is the answer to healing any adrenal issues!
- Have a lot of celery and good nature-made salt in the diet.
- Drink one glass of water every hour on the hour for 10 hours of each day for 30 days, or drink one litre of water per 22 kilos of bodyweight each day.
- Do a kidney purge—take ½ litre of sauerkraut juice, ½ litre of tomato juice and 13 drops essential oil of peppermint. Mix together and drink just before going to bed... Try not to get up again until the morning.
- Develop the darkest suntan you can by covering your body in Divine Body Butter or coconut oil and then exposing at least 70% of your body to the sun for one hour every day (30 mins each side).
- Walk for 30–45 minutes every day.
- First thing in the morning and one or two hours before bed, have a bath, as hot as you can tollerate, for 20 minutes with lavender oil. Add one or two cups of sea salt or epsom salts plus one cup of bicarb soda. Walk barefoot and relax after the soak.
- **ESSENTIAL OIL...** lavender, frankinsense, myhrr, basil, eucalyptus, geranium, peppermint for kidney flush.
- (Divine, essential oil of peppermint and lavender and Ra 24ct See Salt available in the USA **www.thedontolman. com/store** and Australia **www.lynnienichols.com/ shop**)

BODY *FOODS THAT HEAL*	MIND *POSSIBLE EMOTIONAL CAUSE*	SPIRIT *IMBALANCED CHAKRA*
---	---	---
SIGNATURE FOODS... apples, avocados, bananas, eggplant, figs, kiwifruit, mushrooms, nectarines, olives, plantains, passionfruit, peanuts, pears, pomegranates, nuts, seeds, grains, legumes	• Are you depriving yourself of nurturing and self-love? • Are you feeling anger/resentment toward yourself?	Throat Chakra- colour Sky Blue

***NOTE...** Salt is the fourth most critical nutrient to the human body. Every physiology, especially the brain and its electric force, which is kicked in by the adrenal cortex and its relationship to the adrenals, needs the electrolyte SALT.*

ENDOCRINE/REPRODUCTIVE SYSTEM
GREEN ADRENAL JUICE

Ingredients: 6 apples with core and skin, 1 large leaf kale, 1 cup spinach, pinch of sea salt
Method: Juice all vegetables and then add the salt. Drink immediately. (serves 1)

ANCIENT PERUVIAN ENERGY DRINK

Ingredients: 1–2 cups of black or green tea, 1 cup hemp seed milk, 1 tbsp dried macca root powder, 1 tsp organic honey
Method: Pour the tea into a blender; add the hemp seed milk, macca and honey. Blend thoroughly and drink.

ADRENAL FATIGUE

***WHAT IS IT?... **Adrenal fatigue** is a result of the adrenal glands not functioning at their optimum level, this can be caused by bad sleep and leads to a number of changes in hormones and neurotransmitters in the body.

***BODY – EPICURE

- Get off all medication and supplements- herbs in the form of powders or teas are okay, but no pills or capsules, especially fish oils.
- **Fastest...** Water fast for 14–20 days **OR...**
- 40 day cabala juice fast whilst snacking on Pulse.
- 28 days—eat and juice a locally grown, fresh, raw organic 100% fruit diet for highest functional capacity of the pancreas. Fruit is the answer to healing any adrenal issues!
- Have a lot of celery and good nature-made salt in the diet.
- Eat one or two cups of mushrooms each day – these can be raw or sueteed – place in the sun anywhere from two hours to several days prior to eating for highest concentration of phytolitic iodine and vitamin D.
- Do a kidney purge—take ½ litre of sauerkraut juice, ½ litre of tomato juice and 13 drops essential oil of peppermint. Mix together and drink just before going to bed... Try not to get up again until the morning.
- First thing in the morning and one or two hours before bed, have a bath, as hot as you can tollerate, for 20 minutes with lavender oil. Add one or two cups of sea salt or epsom salts plus one cup of bicarb soda. Walk barefoot and relax after the soak.
- Before getting out of bed each morning, assist adrenal activation by rotating feet and ankles, bending legs and pulling them up to the chest, rotating shoulders back and forward and neck right and left. This creates an elecric spark to the muscles and nerves and activates adrenal force back into the body.
- Walking daily in fresh electrified air for 30–45 minutes.
- Develop the darkest suntan you can by covering your body in Divine Body Butter or coconut oil and then exposing at least 70% of your body to the sun for one hour every day (30 mins each side).
- **ESSENTIAL OIL...** lavender, frankinsense, myhrr, basil, eucalyptus, geranium; peppermint for kidney flush.
- (Divine, essential oil of peppermint and lavender, Himalayan rock salt and Ra 24ct See Salt available in the USA **www.thedontolman.com/store** and Australia **www.lynnienichols.com/shop**)

BODY *FOODS THAT HEAL*	MIND *POSSIBLE EMOTIONAL CAUSE*	SPIRIT *IMBALANCED CHAKRA*
---	---	---
SIGNATURE FOODS... apples, avocados, bananas, eggplant, figs, kiwifruit, mushrooms, nectarines, olives, plantains, passionfruit, peanuts, pears, pomegranates, nuts, seeds, grains, legumes	• Are you neglecting yourself? • Are fear and anxiety keeping you stuck, unable to make a decision?	Sacral Chakra- colour Orange / Base Chakra- **colour Red**

***NOTE... *When we eat fruit, the brain tells the pancreas to produce glucagon, which is then moved to the adrenals where it heals the adrenals and creates adrenalin for energy.*

***NUGGET... *Anciently, the body was acknowleged as a tripartite, and the necessity of 'balance' was understood, therefore, eight hours per day were allocated to 'laying the body down', eight hours for 'family/pleasure' and eight hours for 'work'. When you lie down, the gravity flow and its shift of polarity to the entire earth has changed. Healing and repair can take place in this position. It is a period of regeneration and repar of the homeastatis of the autogenic self-healing system of the body and the brain. Adrenal Fatigue is casued by bad sleep and not being revitalised.*

ENDOCRINE/REPRODUCTIVE SYSTEM
ENDOCRINE FRUITS WITH GRANOLA AND PASSIONFRUIT CASHEW CREAM

Ingredients: 2 apples, 2 bananas, 5 nectarines, 2 pears, 2 pomegranates, 4 passionfruit, 1 tbsp honey

GRANOLA: ¼ cup each of chopped peanuts, almonds, pine nuts, brazil nuts, ⅛ cup sunflower seeds, 1 cup coarsely grated dried coconut, 1 tsp cinnamon, 1 cup raisins, ⅛ cup cacao nibs, pinch of Himalayan rock salt

Method: Mix all of the ingredients together and store in a glass jar in the fridge

Grate the apples, nectarines and pears and place in a bowl. Add the pomegranate pulp. Dice the banana and add to the mix just before serving. Place the mixture into serving bowls and top with the cinnamon granola and cashew cream

Cashew Cream; (see recipe under Dressings in back of book). Mix ½ cup cashew cream with the passionfruit. Drizzle over the granola to serve. (serves 2)

BREAST CANCER

***WHAT IS IT?...** **Breast cancer** is the malignant growth of abnormal cells of the breast tissue, most commonly occurring in women.

***BODY – EPICURE*

- Get off all medication and supplements- herbs in the form of powders or teas are okay, but no pills or capsules!
- **Fastest...** Water fast for 7–10 days **OR...**
- Do the five-week 35% food-grade hydrogen peroxide protocol combined with a cabala juice fast for 14-28 days. If needed, can have raw vegan food also.
- Eat and juice a locally grown, fresh, raw organic vegan diet for highest nutritional force, making sure that every day you eat one seeded fruit such as mango, avoado, peach, nectarine, olives, also eat strawberries.
- Eat and juice a lot of citrus—lemon, orange, grapefruit, mandarin etc. This is the signature food for the breast.
- Eat legumes, lentils, onions, garlic cooked slowly in a crockpot.
- Have one cup of lemon juiced with the peels every day, can mix with pure water.
- Suck on rock salt every day.
- Drink one litre per 22 kilos bodyweight of pure water every day.
- Have daily a berry, asparaus smoothie, consisting of two cups berries and 12 stalks of asparagus (can add a banana to sweeten) plus water to desired consistency. Drink within 45 minutes of making it. Can eat the foods instead if preferred.
- Walk for 45–60 mins each day bra-less, or jump on a rebounder to support the lymphatic stream.
- Develop the darkest suntan you can by covering your body in Divine Body Butter or coconut oil and then exposing at least 70% of your body to the sun for one hour every day (30 mins each side).
- **ESSENTIAL OIL...** citrus oils of orange, lime and lemon; lemongrass, frankincense, lavender, myhrr, peppermint, turmeric.
- (Divine, Himalayan rock salt, Ra 24ct gold salt, 35% food-grade hydrogen peroxide, essential oil of lemon and orange available in the USA **www.thedontolman.com/store** and Australia **www.lynnienichols.com/shop**)

BODY *FOODS THAT HEAL*	MIND *POSSIBLE EMOTIONAL CAUSE*	SPIRIT *IMBALANCED CHAKRA*
---	---	---
SIGNATURE FOODS... apples, avocados, bananas, eggplant, figs, kiwifruit, mushrooms, nectarines, olives, plantains, passionfruit, peanuts, pears, pomegranates, nuts, seeds, grains, legumes	• Are you putting everyone else first and neglecting your own needs/wants? • Do you have the belief that everyone else is more important than you are? • Are you holding deep-seated anger, hatred or resentment for yourself or others? • Are you holding on to grief/a deep painful secret that's eating away at you?	Sacral Chakra- **colour Orange** / Heart Chakra- colour Emerald Green

***NOTE...** *One of the biggest causes, apart from lack of vitamin D, is bra straps as they block the lymphatic flow. Avoid mamograms—it's published in medical journals that these cause cancer.*

***NUGGET...** *Pine needles are said to have 300 times more vitamin C than an orange*

***TESTIMONIAL...**
In 2013, I was diagnosed with cancer. I was obviously concerned and was uncertain as to which route to take. Shortly after that I was introduced to Don Tolman, and after a time, I began to follow his advice and chose not to adhere to my doctors'. In fact, they said I would die, but they were wrong. I not only survived stage 3 cancer, I thrived due to Don's counsel. But, as with life, things happen so you can imagine how shocked and upset I was when in August of 2016 I found a new lump under my arm. It was the size of a quarter.
I immediately got in contact with Don. His reaction was one I had become accustomed to, but it still surprised me because I was in a bit of a frenzy. Without so much as a hiccup and in a very nonchalant way, he gave me a number of protocols to follow. Underneath I was apprehensive and a little scared, but he had not steered me wrong previously, so I listened and immediately implemented the following steps: drain the lump with frequent lymphatic massage, eat a plant-based diet with lots of asparagus, broccoli, cauliflower, onions and garlic, walk at least a half hour a day, and drink lots of water. And within two weeks – THE LUMP WAS GONE! Don Tolman is the real deal! He knows what he knows, and it is the truth. If there

is anything I can say, it is this... Listen to his wisdom, let it resonate in your soul, and live to tell the story. This is not just my first or second personal testimonial about what Don has taught me, it is my third! Don is the bearer of truth in regards to what will and will not assist the human body in healing. I will forever be grateful for his continued support in my life.   Alicia

***TESTIMONIAL...

I thank Lyn every day for her friendship, support and guidance that she has bestowed on me, especially in the last few years. In February 2016, I was 55 years old and diagnosed with stage 3 breast cancer. It was in my milk duct on the left side. My first reaction was total shock as it had just been two years since my partner had been killed in a work accident and this was his anniversary, how could this be happening to me? Hadn't I been through enough? Besides, I'd had a mammogram in August 2015, which was fine. I made my appointments with the surgeon and oncologist at this stage. I'm totally against chemotherapy and radiation and had already made up my mind that I was not going down that path and so my research started for an alternative, more natural way. I reached out to Lyn for her help and immediately went on a 10-day water fast, followed by eating a raw vegetarian diet. I have Lyn's first book The Recipe, which has been my bible from day one, so much information, many inspirational stories and delicious recipes. I watched the series 'The Truth about Cancer' and found a natural oncologist on the Gold Coast. I did end up having a partial mastectomy and lymph nodes removed, which I regret now, as I've learnt so much in these last couple of years from Lyn, and Tyler and Don Tolman, but in the beginning, when you're fragile and emotional, it was very difficult standing my ground with the doctors and family while trying to find the right path to go down. I followed the surgery up with 10 rounds of IV Vit C, and 10 rounds of hyperthermia (heating the body up to no more than 40 degrees) and sent my bloods to Germany for a circulating tumour count. I adhered to a very strict sugar-free diet and did make the decision to take some tonics from my natural oncologist and naturopath. I did the above treatments again six months later and added emotional healing sessions, which had me crying for six days, releasing all that built-up pain and emotion, colonic hydrotherapy and lymphatic massaging (my lower lymphatics are very sluggish) and when my second lot of blood results returned from Germany with zero circulating tumour count ... I had beaten the cancer! Today, I still continue with my healthy lifestyle of predominately raw vegan. I still do juicing and water fasting followed by colon cleansing at least twice a year and I always will. I still work on my emotional well-being when I need it. I go to the gym every day and continue to play golf. I am in awe of the work that Lyn does. I highly recommend her and I'm forever grateful for her support and knowledge. Thanks Lyn, I love you... Coral

ENDOCRINE/REPRODUCTIVE SYSTEM
VITAMIN C HIT

Ingredients: 2 lemons with skin on, 5 oranges, 1 ruby-red grapefruit, 4 mandarin, 3 lime with skin on, 1 cup pine needles, 1 litre of water

Method: Boil 1 litre of water with the pine needles for 5 minutes and then let steep for a further 20 minutes. Strain and put liquid in the fridge to cool. Peel and deseed the orange, mandarin and lime. Juice all ingredients with a commercial juicer. Add to the pine tea. Drink throughout the day

CERVICAL CANCER

***WHAT IS IT?...** **Cervical cancer** is an out-of-control growth of abnormal cells on the lower part of the uterus that opens into the vagina, called the cervix.

***BODY – EPICURE*

- Get off all medication and supplements- herbs in the form of powders or teas are okay, but no pills or capsules!
- **Fastest...** Water fast for 7–10 days **OR...**
- Do the five-week 35% food-grade hydrogen peroxide protocol combined with a cabala juice fast for 14–28 days. If needed, can have raw vegan food also.
- Have daily one cup of lemon, juiced with peel on, can mix with pure water. Can add essential oil of lemon to food and water also.
- Eat and juice a locally grown, fresh, raw organic vegan diet for highest nutritional force, making sure that every day you eat one seeded fruit such as mango, avocado, peach, nectarine, olives etc, as well as pears and eggplant.
- Suck on rock salt every day.
- Drink one litre per 22 kilos bodyweight of pure water every day.
- Have daily a berry, asparaus smoothie, consisting of two cups berries and 12 stalks of asparagus (can add a banana to sweeten) plus water to desired consistency. Drink within 30 minutes of making it. Can eat the foods instead if preferred.
- Develop the darkest suntan you can by covering your body in Divine Body Butter or coconut oil and then exposing at least 70% of your body to the sun for one hour every day (30 mins each side).
- **ESSENTIAL OIL...** lemongrass, frankincense, lavender, myhrr, peppermint, turmeric.
- (Divine, Himalayan rock salt, Ra 24ct gold salt, 35% food-grade hydrogen peroxide, essential oil of lemon available in the USA **www.thedontolman.com/store** and Australia **www.lynnienichols.com/shop**)

BODY *FOODS THAT HEAL*	MIND *POSSIBLE EMOTIONAL CAUSE*	SPIRIT *IMBALANCED CHAKRA*
---	---	---
SIGNATURE FOODS... apples, avocados, bananas, eggplant, figs, kiwifruit, mushrooms, nectarines, olives, plantains, passionfruit, peanuts, pears, pomegranates, nuts, seeds, grains, legumes	• Are you holding deep-seated anger, hatred or resentment for yourself or others? • Are you holding on to grief/a deep painful secret that's eating away at you? • Are you holding on to negative concepts about sexuality/sensuality/this area of your body?	Sacral Chakra colour Orange

***NUGGET...** *Cancer means 'rot and decay'—tumours grow to contain toxicity in order to protect and assist you. Sunshine heals and remits cancers, it reduces and helps to shrink tumours.*

***TESTIMONIAL...** *At 32 years of age, Tash was diagnosed with a 2cm tumour on her cervix. The suggested medical solution was a radical hysterectomy which included the removal of her vagina, bladder and bowel, with a 10% chance she would die on the surgery table! The medical staff even strapped colostomy bags on her to show Tash how life was going to be. Thank goodness she had the strength and courage to say NO and continue to say NO, even though she was being relentlessly hassled to take this action! Instead, she changed her diet, began whole body and local hyperthermia, began taking cannabis oil, drank paw paw and sour sop leaf tea and embarked on some emotional healing to get to the root cause. Just a few weeks later, Tash received scan results that the lump had complexly gone and she was cancer free!*

ENDOCRINE/REPRODUCTIVE SYSTEM
PEARY NICE SALAD

Ingredients: 1 cup baby spinach leaves, 1 cup roasted peanuts, 1 large avocado, 1 cup pitted kalamata olives, 1 large green pear, 1 large eggplant, 1 heaped teaspoon of sea salt, 1 teaspoon of cumin, coconut oil

LEMON DRESSING; **(see recipe under Dressings in back of book)**

Method: Dice the eggplant into 2 cm squares then toss in coconut oil with cumin and salt, coat well. Bake in a moderate oven until very soft. Place in a salad bowl with the spinach, peanuts and olives. Dice the avocado into chunky pieces, cut the pear into matchsticks and add. Toss gently, dress and serve immediately. (serves 2)

CHLAMYDIA / GENITAL HERPES / GONNORHEA / SYPHILIS (STD's)

WHAT IS IT?... **Chlamydia** is a common sexually transmitted disease (STD) caused by the chlamydia trachomatis bacteria, which can be present in the vagina, cervix, urethra, rectum and throat of an infected person. Any type of sexual contact with an infected person can spread the infection.

Gonorrhea is a sexually transmitted disease (STD) that can cause infections in the rectum, genitals and throat in both men and women.

Syphillis is a sexually transmitted infection caused by the bacterium treponema pallidum.

BODY – EPICURE

- Get off all medication and supplements- herbs in the form of powders or teas are okay, but no pills or capsules!
- **Fastest...** Water fast for 7–10 days **OR...**
- 28-day cabala juice fast.
- Topically put fresh aloe vera gel on the area six or seven times per day. If this is not strong enough you can also use Golden Releaf or Healing Chrysm.
- Hydrogen peroxide—use a cotton bud and put 35% food-grade hydrogen peroxide directly onto the site, one sore at a time as it will sting. Can sometimes clear herpes in less than a week. It may come back once or twice, but do it again and eventually it will go for good.
- On dry areas, use a salt scrub of salt and coconut or olive oil or you can purchase Renew. Scrub gently then rinse and allow to evaporate dry.

- Suck on Himalayan rock salt daily, the size of the end section of your little finger.
- Drink one litre per 22 kilos bodyweight of pure water every day.
- Develop the darkest suntan you can by covering your body in Divine Body Butter or coconut oil and then exposing at least 70% of your body to the sun for one hour every day (30 mins each side).
- **ESSENTIAL OIL...** eucalyptus, geranium, tea tree, peppermint, oregano.
- (Divine, Golden Releaf, Healing Chrysm, Renew scrub, Himalayan rock salt, Ra 24ct gold salt, 35% food-grade hydrogen peroxide available in the USA **www.thedontolman.com/store** and Australia **www.lynnienichols.com/shop**)

BODY *FOODS THAT HEAL*	MIND *POSSIBLE EMOTIONAL CAUSE*	SPIRIT *IMBALANCED CHAKRA*
---	---	---
SIGNATURE FOODS... apples, avocados, bananas, eggplant, figs, kiwifruit, mushrooms, nectarines, olives, plantains, passionfruit, peanuts, pears, pomegranates, nuts, seeds, grains, legumes	• Are you giving your power away? • Is there a belief subconsiously that sex/genitals/sexuality are bad or dirty? • Are you feeling ashamed and that you deserve to be punished?	Sacral Chakra colour Orange

ENDOCRINE/REPRODUCTIVE SYSTEM
PLANTAIN WITH SMASHED AVO & OLIVES

Ingredients: 2 large plantain, 2 large avocados, 1 cup Kalamata olives, parsley for garnish, Himalayan salt

Method: In a bowl, gently smash the avocado with a fork and season with salt. Keep a few slices of avocado aside for garnishing. Slice the olives into thin rings and add to the mashed avocado, keeping ⅛ cup aside to garnish

Cut the plantain in halves lengthwise and gently fry in coconut oil. Lay the plantain side by side on a serving plate, spread with mashed avocado/olive mix. Garnish with sliced avocado, chopped parsley and olive rings. (serves 2)

DIABETES

WHAT IS IT?... **Diabetes** is a chronic condition marked by high blood sugar (glucose), caused by inadequate insulin production or by the body not being able to use insulin effectively, or, in some cases, both.

BODY – EPICURE

- Type 1 diabetes—begin to lessen insulin dose every few days by 5–10% until off completely.
- Type 2 diabetes can go off all medication immediately. **Fastest...**
- 28 days on cabala juice and mango or cherry Pulse
- THEN 7–10 days eating a diet of low glycemic fuit and vegetables such as: apples, berries, cherries, all citrus, pineapple, leafy greens especially spinach and all cruciferous veggies, broccoli, cauliflower, cabbage, Brussels sprouts, pears, peaches, bananas, mangoes and papayas, all red, yellow and orange foods especially sweet potatoes, extra virgin olive oil and organic coconut oil, avocados, hemp seeds, etc. THEN add to your diet any and all fresh non GMO fruits, veggies, nuts – especially almonds, walnuts, pecans and macadamias – seeds, wholegrains, beans, legumes, lentils, herbs, flax and ground flax, fresh made juices and smoothies... Stay vegetarian for six months.
- Eat spices such as basil, cayenne, cinnamon, ginger, thyme, turmeric.
- Support the pancreas by eating sweet potatoes (signature food) as well as other tubers such as yams, onion and garlic and berries, including watermelon and tomatoes.
- Eat foods that support the circulatory system.
- Drink one litre per 22 kilos bodyweight of pure water every day.
- Cleanse the colon regularly via gravity-fed colonics or self-administered enemas.
- Develop the darkest suntan you can by covering your body in Divine Body Butter or coconut oil and then exposing at least 70% of your body to the sun for one hour every day (30 mins each side).
- **ESSENTIAL OIL...** cinnamon, clove, coriander.
- Mango and Cherry Pulse, Divine, Himalayan rock salt, Ra 24ct gold salt, enema douche kit, essential oil of lemon and orange available in the USA **www.thedontolman. com/store** and Australia **www.lynnienichols.com/ shop**)

BODY *FOODS THAT HEAL*	MIND *POSSIBLE EMOTIONAL CAUSE*	SPIRIT *IMBALANCED CHAKRA*
---	---	---
SIGNATURE FOODS... apples, avocados, bananas, eggplant, figs, kiwifruit, mushrooms, nectarines, olives, plantains, passionfruit, peanuts, pears, pomegranates, nuts, seeds, grains, legumes	• Are you feeling like there's no sweetness in life? • Are you holding on to deep sorrow and yearning for what was or might have been? • Is perfectionism or fear of failure stopping you from achieving your desires?	Sacral Chakra colour Orange / Solar Plexus Chakra-

***TESTIMONIAL... *Watch the movie 'Simply Raw'*

ENDOCRINE/REPRODUCTIVE SYSTEM
SWEET POTATO SALAD

Ingredients: 4 large sweet potatoes peeled, 1 punnet of cherry tomatoes, 2 cups of baby spinach leaves, 2 large avocado, 2 large cloves of garlic, ½ large red onion, nature made salt

HERB DRESSING; **(see recipe under Dressings in back of book)**

Method: Cut the sweet potato into 2 cm cubes and bake with coconut oil and sea salt in a moderate oven until the potato is soft and golden. Let the potato cool and place in a bowl. Chop the tomatoes in halves, finely dice the garlic, slice the onion. Add all ingredients to the potato. Season with salt and drizzle with herb dressing. (serves 2)

DIABETIC DIARRHOEA

***WHAT IS IT?...* **Diabetic diarrhoea** is a common complaint, with up to 75% of patients visiting diabetes clinics reporting significant GI symptoms including diarrhoea.

***BODY – EPICURE*

- Type 1 diabetes—begin to lessen insulin dose every few days by 5–10% until off completely.
- Type 2 diabetes can go off all medication immediately. **Fastest...**
- Eat any and all foods that grow under the ground (tubers), especially sweet potato and regular potatoes, garlic, onion, and carrots.
- Eat a lot of blueberries, these can be fresh or organic dried.
- Have two cups of natural organic yoghurt each day to re-establish the flora and fauna of the gut.
- Drink one litre per 22 kilos bodyweight of pure water every day.
- Do a colon cleanse.
- Develop the darkest suntan you can by covering your body in Divine Body Butter or coconut oil and then exposing at least 70% of your body to the sun for one hour every day (30 mins each side).
- **ESSENTIAL OIL...** cinnamon, oregano, ginger, tea tree, clove, lavender.
- (Divine, Himalayan rock salt, Ra 24ct gold salt available in the USA **www.thedontolman.com/store** and Australia **www.lynnienichols.com/shop**)

BODY *FOODS THAT HEAL*	MIND *POSSIBLE EMOTIONAL CAUSE*	SPIRIT *IMBALANCED CHAKRA*
---	---	---
SIGNATURE FOODS... apples, avocados, bananas, eggplant, figs, kiwifruit, mushrooms, nectarines, olives, plantains, passionfruit, peanuts, pears, pomegranates, nuts, seeds, grains, legumes	• Are you feeling fearful/rejected? • Is the joy and sweetness literally running out of you? • Is the lack of joy in life causing you to let go of your dreams and desires?	Sacral Chakra colour Orange / Solar Plexus Chakra-

***TESTIMONIAL... *Many diabetics indulge in sugar-free lollies, which are full of artificial sweeteners such as aspartame. This can be the cause of diabetic diarrhoea.*

ENDOCRINE/REPRODUCTIVE SYSTEM
CURRIED YAM AND SWEET POTATO SOUP

Ingredients: 4 large sweet potatoes , 4 yam, 6 large cloves garlic, 4 large onions, 2 cups natural yoghurt, 1 tbsp sea salt, 1 tbsp curry powder, ⅛ cup coconut oil, ½ cup parsley, cracked black pepper

Method: Peel and dice the yam into cubes then steam until soft. Set aside. Dice the garlic and onions and fry in coconut oil until golden. Peel and chop the sweet potato into small cubes, add to the pan with the onion, garlic and coconut oil and allow to fry gently for a few minutes. Add a little water and continue to stir-fry for a further 10 minutes. Add the curry powder and 8 cups of water and bring to the boil. Turn down to low heat and simmer for 30 minutes until the sweet potato is very soft.

Allow to cool slightly then place in a blender on high speed until smooth and creamy. Place back in the saucepan, add the steamed yam and heat. Add extra water if desired. Taste and add extra salt if necessary. Serve in soup bowls, garnished with a dollop of natural organic yoghurt, pepper and chopped parsley. (serves 4)

ENDOMETRIOSIS

***WHAT IS IT?...** **Endometriosis** is a condition that affects women and is caused by the endometrial tissue growing outside of the womb, which often causes pain around menstruation.

***BODY – EPICURE*

- Get off all medication and supplements- herbs in the form of powders or teas are okay, but no pills or capsules!
- **Fastest...** Water fast for 7–10 days **OR...**
- Cabala juice fast for 28 days to reset the body rhythms.
- Eat and juice locally grown, fresh, raw organic fruits and vegetables—no animal for at least 12 months.
- Eat free-range organic eggs and ruby-red grapefruit to help get rid of any blood clots.
- Eat eggplant, pears, mangoes, green garlic stuffed olives and avocado with oilive oil and sea salt several times each week.
- Organic natural yoghurt—1 tablespoon inserted into the vagina each evening before bed. Use only organic pads and tampons.
- One to three days before the menstrual cycle begins, eat dark organic chocolate or drink cacao.
- Salt water douche—each morning using one heaped teaspoon of sea salt in one litre of water.
- Drink one litre per 22 kilos bodyweight of pure water every day.
- Develop the darkest suntan you can by covering your body in Divine Body Butter or coconut oil and then exposing at least 70% of your body to the sun for one hour every day (30 mins each side).
- **ESSENTIAL OIL...** rose, lavender, clary sage.
- (Divine, Himalayan rock salt, Ra 24ct gold salt, available in the USA **www.thedontolman.com/store** and Australia **www.lynnienichols.com/shop**)

BODY	MIND	SPIRIT
FOODS THAT HEAL	*POSSIBLE EMOTIONAL CAUSE*	*IMBALANCED CHAKRA*
---	---	---
SIGNATURE FOODS... apples, avocados, bananas, eggplant, figs, kiwifruit, mushrooms, nectarines, olives, plantains, passionfruit, peanuts, pears, pomegranates, nuts, seeds, grains, legumes	• Are you feeling insecure, inadequate, not good enough, lacking in self-love? • Are you afraid to change your programming/beliefs? • Are you feeling rejected by men?	Sacral Chakra colour Orange

***NUGGET...** *The cacao bean is part of the cannabis family (delta 9 cannabinoids chemical), which reduces menstrual pain and emotions.*

ENDOCRINE/REPRODUCTIVE SYSTEM
CREAMY OMELETTE WITH ROAST EGGPLANT

Ingredients: 4 free range organic eggs, ½ cup of coconut cream, 8 green garlic stuffed olives, 1 large clove garlic, ½ cup spring onion or chives, ¼ cup chopped parsley, ⅛ cup chopped chives for garnish, 1 avocado, 1 small eggplant, coconut oil for baking.

Method: Cut the eggplant into long 1 cm-thick slices, season generously with sea or rock salt and coconut oil, bake in a moderate oven until very soft and sloppy. Peel and dice the garlic, chop the spring onions/chives and parsley, slice the olives into rings. Whisk the eggs in a mixing bowl with the coconut cream. Add the garlic, onions, parsley and olives. Season with salt and pepper.

Heat some coconut oil in a frypan and pour the omelette mix into the pan. Turn down to low/medium heat and cook until the bottom of the omelette is golden and the top of the omelette begins to bubble. Use an egg flip to turn the omelette over and brown the other side. Place on a serving plate, lay the hot, soft eggplant on one half of the omelette, top this with slices of avocado and Himalayan salt, then fold the remaining half over. Garnish with chopped parsley, avocado slices and chives. (serves 1)

GRAVES DISEASE/ HYPER/HYPO THYROIDISM
and HYPER/HYPO PARATHYROIDISM

***WHAT IS IT?...** **Graves disease** is an autoimmune condition that causes the thyroid gland to become overactive, hyperthyroidism, producing too much hormone and creating symptoms such as protrusion of the eyes and swelling of the neck.

Hyperthyroidism is an overactive thyroid gland, which causes increased heartbeat rate and, as a result, faster metabolism. The most common cause of hyperthyroidism is Graves' disease, which is more prevalent in women than men.

Hypo Thyroidism is an underactive thyroid gland that does not make enough hormone, and, as a result, the body makes less energy and metabolism becomes sluggish.

Hyperparathyroidism is caused by the overactivity of one or more of the four parathyroid glands, which are located in the neck, creating an overproduction of parathyroid hormone, which becomes destructive to many of the body's tissues.

Hypoparathyroidism occurs when the parathyroid glands don't produce enough parathyroid hormone, which results in muscular spasms due to deficiencies of calcium and phosphorus compounds in the blood.

***BODY – EPICURE*

- Get off all medication and supplements- herbs in the form of powders or teas are okay, but no pills or capsules!
- **Fastest...** Water fast for 7–10 days **OR...**
- Cabala juice fast for 21 days as well as eating two cups of raw and sauteed mushrooms in lemon juice every day for 90 days.
- Eat and juice locally grown, fresh, raw organic fruits and vegetables that support the endocrine system as well as cruciferous foods such as broccoli, Brussels sprouts, cabbage and kale; also eat reutabagas, peaches and turnips.
- Eat one or two cups of raw and cooked mushrooms (saute' with lemon juice) every day—button and portabello mushrooms have the highest concentration of phytolitic iodine, which will balance hperthyroidism. Put them in the sun for two hours to several days prior to eating to enhance the iodine and vitamin D levels.
- Ferments—eat and drink ferments such as sauerkraut, kefirs, natural organic yoghurts, foods in brine, kombucha, tempeh, blue cheese, etc.
- Do the water protocol- one glass of water every hour on the hour for at least eight hours of the day or drink one litre per 22 kilos bodyweight of pure water.
- Walk for 45 mins each day while fasting.
- Develop the darkest suntan you can by covering your body in Divine Body Butter or coconut oil and then exposing at least 70% of your body to the sun for one hour every day (30 mins each side).
- FOR EYES... Make a saline solution for eyedrops, this needs to be the same salinity as tears—can purchase Eye of Horus. Heat honey in a glass jar and then put one or two drops in each eye before bed.
- Develop the darkest suntan you can by covering your body in Divine Body Butter or coconut oil and then exposing at least 70% of your body to the sun for one hour every day (30 mins each side).
- **ESSENTIAL OIL...** hyper; frankincense, lemongrass, rosemary, myrtle, geranium; hypo; rosemary.
- (Divine, Himalayan rock salt, Ra 24ct gold salt available in the USA **www.thedontolman.com/store** and Australia **www.lynnienichols.com/shop**)

BODY *FOODS THAT HEAL*	MIND *POSSIBLE EMOTIONAL CAUSE*	SPIRIT *IMBALANCED CHAKRA*
---	---	---
SIGNATURE FOODS... apples, avocados, bananas, eggplant, figs, kiwifruit, mushrooms, nectarines, olives, plantains, passionfruit, peanuts, pears, pomegranates, nuts, seeds, grains, legumes	• Are you feeling 'What about me, when's it going to be my turn?' • Are you putting everyone else first and then feeling neglected/angry/resentful?	Sacral Chakra colour Orange / Throat Chakra- colour Sky Blue

***NOTE...** Common button and portabello mushrooms have the highest concentration of phytolitic idodine, which will balance hperthyroidism.

***NUGGET...** Put mushrooms in the sun for two hours to several days prior to eating to enhance the iodine and vitamin D levels.

***TESTIMONIAL...** Don assisted a lady in Australia to regrow her thyroid gland. Unfortunately, fear got the better of her and she had surgery to remove it a second time. Again, she sought the help of Don and guess what? Yep, she grew it back a second time! According to Don, it takes 9-13 months of eating 1 cup of mushrooms daily. They are the highest in iodine the thyroid and body needs. Mushrooms target the thyroid specifically.

ENDOCRINE SYSTEM
CRUCIFEROUS & TEMPEH STIR-FRY

Ingredients: 1 medium head of broccoli, 4 Brussels sprouts, ¼ large green cabbage, ¼ large red cabbage, 4 large kale leaves, 1 packet of tempeh, 1 cm turmeric, 1 inch ginger, 1 cup spring onions, 2 tsp sea salt, 1 heaped tsp miso paste (optional; peach for garnish)

Method: Dice the broccoli into small 1 cm pieces; cut the Brussels sprouts into quarters; finely shred the red and green cabbage and the kale. Peel and finely dice the ginger and tumeric. Chop the spring onions into 2 cm lengths. Cut the tempeh into 2cm cubes- leaving a few long slices for garnish

Gently fry the tempeh in coconut oil until golden, season with salt and pepper then set aside. Place all other ingredients into the pan with miso, 1 tsp salt and a drizzle of water and stir-fry for a few minutes, leaving slightly crunchy. Mix through the tempeh; season with pepper and more salt if desired. Garnish with tempeh and/or slices of peach (serves 2)

HASHIMOTO'S DISEASE

WHAT IS IT?... **Hashimoto's disease** is an autoimmune disease where the cells of the immune system attack the thyroid gland, resulting in inflammation of the thyroid and an underactive thyroid, hypothyroidism.

BODY – EPICURE

- Get off all medication and supplements- herbs in the form of powders or teas are okay.
- **Fastest...** Water fast for 7–10 days **OR...**
- Cabala juice fast for 21 days as well as eating two cups of raw and sauteed mushrooms in lemon juice every day for 90 days.
- Eat and juice locally grown, fresh, raw organic fruits and vegetables that support the endocrine system as well as cruciferous foods such as broccoli, Brussels sprouts, cabbage and kale; also eat reutabagas, peaches and turnips.
- Eat one or two cups of raw and cooked mushrooms (sauté with lemon juice) every day—button and portabello mushrooms have the highest concentration of phytolitic iodine, which will balance hperthyroidism. Put them in the sun for two hours to several days prior to eating to enhance the iodine and vitamin D levels.
- Ferments—eat and drink ferments such as sauerkraut, kefirs, natural organic yoghurts, foods in brine, kombucha, tempeh, blue cheese, etc.
- Do the water protocol—one glass of water every hour on the hour for at least eight hours of the day or drink one litre per 22 kilos bodyweight of pure water.
- Walk for 45 mins each day while fasting.
- Develop the darkest suntan you can by covering your body in Divine Body Butter or coconut oil and then exposing at least 70% of your body to the sun for one hour every day (30 mins each side).
- **ESSENTIAL OIL...** rosemary.
- (Divine, Himalayan rock salt, Ra 24ct gold salt, 35% food-grade hydrogen peroxide, essential oil of lemon and orange available in the USA **www.thedontolman.com/store** and Australia **www.lynnienichols.com/shop**)

BODY *FOODS THAT HEAL*	MIND *POSSIBLE EMOTIONAL CAUSE*	SPIRIT *IMBALANCED CHAKRA*
SIGNATURE FOODS... apples, avocados, bananas, eggplant, figs, kiwifruit, mushrooms, nectarines, olives, plantains, passionfruit, peanuts, pears, pomegranates, nuts, seeds, grains, legumes	• Are you feeling 'What about me, when's it going to be my turn?' • Are you putting everyone else first and then feeling neglected/angry/resentful?	Sacral Chakra colour Orange / Throat Chakra- colour Sky Blue

NOTE... *A cabala fast will target and shrink the swelling, while mushrooms target the thyroid itself.*

ENDOCRINE/REPRODUCTIVE SYSTEM
MUSHROOMS WITH CABBAGE & BLUECHEESE

Ingredients: 4 large portobello mushrooms, ¼ large green cabbage, 1 packet of non-animal-rennet blue cheese, pinch of sea salt

Method: Bake mushrooms in the sun for 2hrs to enhance the vitamin D, then peel and brush with a generous amount of coconut oil and place on a baking tray in a moderate oven for 10 minutes. Shred the cabbage and steam for 2 minutes then place in a mixing bowl with the salt and blue cheese. Place mushrooms on a serving plate and top with a large spoonful of the cabbage mix. (serves 2)

HYPER & HYPO GLYCEMIA / IMPAIRED GLUCOSE INTOLLERANCE (IGT)

***WHAT IS IT?...** **Hypoglycemia** is low blood sugar, common in people with diabetes but can also occur in people who do not have diabetes.

Hyperglycemia is caused when the body doesn't make or use the hormone insulin efficiently. This is common in people with diabetes.

***BODY – EPICURE*

- **Fastest...** Water fast for 7–10 days **OR...**
- 28 days on raw fruit and vegetables, 70–80% fruit or 30 days on mango or cherry Pulse.
- Support the pancreas by eating sweet potatoes, which are the signature food; also eat yams, berries including watermelon and tomatoes.
- Eat foods that support the circulatory system.
- Drink one litre per 22 kilos bodyweight of pure water every day.

- Develop the darkest suntan you can by covering your body in Divine Body Butter or coconut oil and then exposing at least 70% of your body to the sun for one hour every day (30 mins each side).
- **ESSENTIAL OIL...** cinnamon, coriander, ylang ylang.
- (Divine, Mango and Cherry Pulse, Himalayan rock salt, Ra 24ct gold salt available in the USA **www.thedontolman.com/store** and Australia **www.lynnienichols.com/shop**)

BODY	MIND	SPIRIT
FOODS THAT HEAL	**POSSIBLE EMOTIONAL CAUSE**	**IMBALANCED CHAKRA**
---	---	---
SIGNATURE FOODS... apples, avocados, bananas, eggplant, figs, kiwifruit, mushrooms, nectarines, olives, plantains, passionfruit, peanuts, pears, pomegranates, nuts, seeds, grains, legumes	• Are you feeling like there's no sweetness in life? • Are you holding on to deep sorrow and yearning for what was or might have been? • Is your perfetionism or fear of failure stopping you from achieving your desires?	Sacral Chakra colour Orange / Solar Plexus Chakra-

ENDOCRINE SYSTEM
GLUCOSE HIT

Ingredients: 4 cups watermelon, 4 tomatoes, 2 cups strawberries

Method: Juice in a commercial juicer and drink immediately. (serves 2)

MENOPAUSE

***WHAT IS IT?...* **Menopause** is a normal process that all women experience as they go through the change of life where menstruation stops and, with this, the ability to reproduce. Menopause and pre-menopause are the change in estrogen production. Lack of estrogen affects the hypothalamus of the brain, which regulates the body's temperature. When the ovaries produce less estrogen, the hypothalamus thinks the body is overheating and creates a cooling response. Symptoms before or during the menopause process include hot flushes, emotional mood swings, night sweats, and brain fog.

***BODY – EPICURE*

- **Fastest...** Water fast for 7–10 days **OR...**
- Cabala juice fast for 14–28 days
- Eat and juice a locally grown, fresh, raw organic vegetarian diet for highest nutritional force, making sure that every day you eat foods with one seed, which support the endocrine system.
- Cook beans, legumes, lentils onion and garlic in a crockpot and eat this regularly.
- Eat lots of celery, bokchoy, rhubarb and other stalk plants which have 21–30% phytolitic plant sodium to support bone strength during menopause.
- Have fermented food and drinks such as yoghyrt, kefirs, sauerkraut, kombucha, tempeh, blue cheese, olives in brine, etc.
- Eat two good-sized cucumbers every day.
- Drink 1 tbs apple cider vinegar and ¼ tsp bicarb in a tall glass with warm water on an empty stomach 3 x day 20–30 mins before each meal.
- Suck on rock salt every day.
- Drink one litre per 22 kilos bodyweight of pure water every day.
- SLEEP-Valerium root assists with better sleep. Lavender oil mixed with water, sprayed onto pillows and bedding just before bed. Hot chamomile tea.
- HOT FLUSHES—When you feel a hot flush coming on, put three or four drops of peppermint oil in your hands and rub them together until they are warm. Cup your hands over the nose and mouth and breathe in; then move hands away and breathe out. Do this for two or three minutes. Also, drink two or three cups of peppermint tea each day. Have hot salt water baths with 1 tsp lavender oil for 20 minutes just before bed, follow this with a cold shower for one minute.
- MOODS—Raw organic dark chocolate is healthy and mood lifting. Eat orange and yellow foods together such as pineapple and orange, mango and banana, etc. Peppermint oil placed on the temples and behind the neck. Lavender oil on temples and behind the neck. Deep breathing exercises to oxygenate the brain/blood. Sunshine, walking, yoga/meditation including beautiful relaxing music and mindfulness will help to calm and balance the emotions. Drink peppermint tea.
- Develop the darkest suntan you can by covering your body in Divine Body Butter or coconut oil and then exposing at least 70% of your body to the sun for one hour every day (30 mins each side).
- Sungazing morning and evenings in 13-second intervals; look at the sun until it reaches a 10-degree arc, or a clenched fist sitting on horizon as sun comes up, stop at top of fist. At night, start gazing as sun hits top of fist until it's gone.
- **ESSENTIAL OIL...** peppermint, lavender.
- (Divine, Himalayan rock salt, Ra 24ct See Salt, essential oil of peppermint and lavender available in the USA **www.thedontolman.com/store** and Australia **www.lynnienichols.com/shop**)

BODY *FOODS THAT HEAL*	MIND *POSSIBLE EMOTIONAL CAUSE*	SPIRIT *IMBALANCED CHAKRA*
---	---	---
SIGNATURE FOODS... apples, avocados, bananas, eggplant, figs, kiwifruit, mushrooms, nectarines, olives, plantains, passionfruit, peanuts, pears, pomegranates, nuts, seeds, grains, legumes	• Are you afraid of aging, feeling unlovable, unable to love yourself and your body?	Sacral Chakra colour Orange / Third Eye Chakra- **colour Violet**

***NOTE...** Hot flushes is expansion and contraction at a cellular level. Salt in the ocean ionises into calcium and does the same in the human body. 70% of the earth is water, 90% of that water is salt water. When sunlight shines through salt water, it ionises into calcium. If you have plenty of salt you cannot suffer from weak bones*

***NUGGET... *Ancient Life Rituals for times of emotional lows/menopausal moods*
1. *Pinkie Promise- get a ring to fit the pinkie finger of the right hand (this is where the phrase pinkie promise came from). Each time you look at that ring, you will be reminded to ask each day and seek in order to download pure intelligent moments that give the epicure to this loss of zest, gratitude for life.*
2. *The term Knock on Wood was understood to positively affect the head and the brain. Go out in nature and find a bit of wood that attracts you. Take it home and, before you go to bed, put it above the heart/sternum, knock on it three times and ask for the answer to what you need to do in order to regain gratitude and zest for life.*

Extra Info on Night Sweats... Eating the wrong kinds of foods and drinks before bedtime can create night sweats in men and women. These foods include: refined sugars, artificial sweeteners, hydrogenated fats, highly refined foods, spicy foods, hard alcohol, caffeine after 11:00 a.m., smoking and even second-hand smoke.

Protocol: Ginger is a natural source of phytoestrogens, which means it can balance your hormones and keep night sweats and mood swings at bay. It also has anti-inflammatory properties that clear inflammation. Mix one or two inches of grated ginger with a cup of hot water and steep for 5–10 minutes. Add honey and drink immediately. Consume 3 x per day.

Pomegranates contain phytoestrogens, polyphenols, ellagitannins, and anthocyanins—all of which are powerful antioxidants that help balance hormones. Drink one cup of fresh juice 1–2 x daily.

Aloe Vera has phytonutrients and phytoestrogens that help to balance hormones, relieve stress and improve sleep (thanks to the plant's sedative properties). The anti-inflammatory properties of aloe vera help in reducing inflammation. Consume one cup daily.

Ginseng exhibits estrogenic properties and, when taken regularly, can help with night sweats. Drink ginseng tea 2–3 x per day for several weeks.

Flaxseed is packed with omega-3 fatty acids, fibre and lignans, which are beneficial in treating menopausal symptoms such as night sweats and hot flashes. Mix one tablespoon of powdered flaxseed with a glass of warm water or nut milk, and honey and drink one cup daily.

ENDOCRINE/REPRODUCTIVE SYSTEM
MUSHROOM AND LENTIL HOTPOT

Ingredients: 1 cup red lentils and 1 cup kidney beans soaked for 2hrs, 4 large onions, 6 large cloves of garlic, 1 tsp tumeric, 1 tbsp sea salt, 4 cups sliced mushrooms, 2 inches ginger diced, 1 tbsp curry powder, 1 tsp garam masala, 5 cups of water, 2 tbsp coconut oil for frying

Method: Peel and dice the onion, garlic, ginger and turmeric and fry for 2 minutes in the coconut oil. Transfer this mix to a crockpot or large saucepan, along with all other ingredients and cook on low heat until the legumes are well cooked and the hotpot becomes thick. Add more water and extra salt if necessary. (serves 4)

MENORRHAGIA

***WHAT IS IT?...** **Menorrhagia** is the term used for heavy bleeding during periods, which can be caused by: blood thinners, birth control pills, IUDs and other medical pharma cut, burn and poison treatments. No one should ever have a hysterectomy!

***BODY – EPICURE*

- Cold compress- will cause contraction of the blood vessels, reducing the flow of blood. Put a few ice cubes in a thin towel and place it over your abdomen for 15 to 20 minutes. Repeat every four hours until symptoms have disappeared.
- Apply a hot water bottle to your lower abdomen or back for pain/cramps.
- Drink a few cups of chamomile, sage or green tea daily.
- Get regular exercise.
- Warm baths will relax muscles and ease pain and tension.
- Massage your lower back with warm coconut or olive oil to relieve pain.
- As lack of sleep can worsen the problem, get at least seven to eight hours of sound sleep.
- Do not lift heavy weight during menstruation.
- **Blackstrap Molasses-** is rich in iron and aids in the production of red blood cells, reducing blood clots and soothing the muscles of the uterine walls to reduce pain. Add one or two teaspoons of blackstrap molasses to a cup of warm water or organic coffee and drink 1 x per day. Or, add ½ tablespoon of blackstrap molasses to a glass of lemongrass tea and drink 1 x in morning and 1 x at night.
- **Apple Cider Vinegar-** works as a tonic to flush toxins and maintain hormonal balance, helping to treat symptoms such as cramping, headaches, irritability and fatigue. Mix one or two teaspoons of raw, unfiltered apple cider vinegar in a glass of water and drink 3 x per day during menstruation.
- **Red Raspberry-** leaves contain tannins that help strengthen the uterine muscles and reduce abdominal pain. Add one tablespoon of dried red raspberry leaves to a cup of hot water, steep for 10 minutes then drink up to 3 x per day, beginning one week before your cycle is due and throughout your period.
- **Cayenne-** helps balance blood flow and helps maintain hormonal balance. Add ½ teaspoon of cayenne powder and some honey to a glass of warm water and drink 2-3 x per day during your cycle.
- **Coriander seeds-** can help stop heavy menstrual cycles, improve uterine functioning and balance female hormones. Add one teaspoon of coriander seeds to two cups of water and boil until the quantity reduces by half, strain and add honey. Drink while warm 2-3 x daily during your monthly cycle.
- **Cinnamon-** is effective in reducing heavy menstrual bleeding by stimulating blood flow away from the uterus. It also helps to relieve cramps. Add one teaspoon of cinnamon powder to a cup of hot water, let sit for a few minutes, add honey and drink 2 x per day. Alternatively, take three drops of cinnamon bark tincture, 2 x per day, or 15-30 drops of cinnamon essential oil diluted in ¼ cup of water, up to 3 x per day. Follow any of these remedies during your period only.
- **Comfrey-** controls heavy bleeding by helping to constrict blood vessels, thereby reducing heavy bleeding. Put two teaspoons of comfrey leaves in a cup of hot water and steep for 20 minutes. Strain and drink 1 x per day during heavy bleeding.
- **Iron-** helps prevent iron-deficiency, anaemia. Eat dark green vegetables, legumes, pumpkin seeds, egg yolks, raisins, and prunes.
- **Magnesium-** balances progesterone and estrogen. Magnesium deficiency can cause heavy menstruation; therefore, eating magnesium-rich foods such as oats, nuts and seeds, avocado, dark chocolate, pumpkin, squash and watermelon will help control the profuse bleeding.
- **ESSENTIAL OIL...** helichrysum, myhrr, geranium, lavender.

BODY	MIND	SPIRIT
FOODS THAT HEAL	*POSSIBLE EMOTIONAL CAUSE*	*IMBALANCED CHAKRA*
---	---	---
SIGNATURE FOODS... apples, avocados, bananas, eggplant, figs, kiwifruit, mushrooms, nectarines, olives, plantains, passionfruit, peanuts, pears, pomegranates, nuts, seeds, grains, legumes	• Are you rejecting your divine feminine nature? • Are you rejecting your sexuality/ sensuality? • Are you feeling fearful or guilty around sexuality?	Sacral Chakra colour Orange

CINNAMON SEEDED CHOCOLATE BRITTLE

Ingredients: ¾ cup cocao powder, ⅓ cup chopped almonds, ⅓ cup chopped cashews, ⅓ cup chopped walnuts, 1 tsp cinnamon, 2½ tbs honey, 1 cup raisins, 1 cup coconut oil, ½ cup peanut butter (or any nut butter), ¼ cup sunflower seeds, ¼ cup pepitas, pinch of Himalayan salt

Method: Combine all ingredients together in a bowl. On a large flat tray, place banana leaf or greaseproof paper. Pour the chocolate mix onto the banana leaf, spreading evenly so that it creates a thin layer. Place in the fridge or freezer to set for one hr. Break the chocolate into pieces and store in an air-tight container in the fridge or freezer

OVARIAN CANCER

***WHAT IS IT?...* **Ovarian cancer** refers to a growth of cancerous cells in the ovary, 90% of the time arising on the outer lining, epithelium, of the ovary. The other 10% of cases begin at the egg-producing cells and the tissues within the ovary.

***BODY – EPICURE*

- Get off all medication and supplements- herbs in the form of powders or teas are okay, but no pills or capsules!
- **Fastest...** Water fast for 7–10 days **OR...**
- Do the five-week 35% food-grade hydrogen peroxide protocol combined with a cabala juice fast for 14–28 days. If needed, can have raw vegan food also.
- Have daily one cup of lemon, juiced with peel on, can mix with pure water.
- Eat and juice a locally grown, fresh, raw organic vegan diet for highest nutritional force, making sure that every day you eat one seeded fruits such as mango, avocado, peach, nectarine and especially olives, which are the signature food for the ovaries.
- Suck on rock salt every day.
- Drink one litre per 22 kilos bodyweight of pure water every day.
- Have daily a berry, asparaus smoothie, consisting of two cups berries and 12 stalks of asparagus (can add a banana to sweeten) plus water to desired consistency. Drink within 45 minutes of making it. Can eat the foods instead if preferred.
- Develop the darkest suntan you can by covering your body in Divine Body Butter or coconut oil and then exposing at least 70% of your body to the sun for one hour every day (30 mins each side).
- **ESSENTIAL OIL...** lemon, lemongrass, frankincense, lavender, myhrr, turmeric.
- (Divine, Himalayan rock salt, Ra 24ct gold salt, 35% food-grade hydrogen peroxide, essential oil of lemon available in the USA **www.thedontolman.com/store** and Australia **www.lynnienichols.com/shop**)

BODY *FOODS THAT HEAL*	MIND *POSSIBLE EMOTIONAL CAUSE*	SPIRIT *IMBALANCED CHAKRA*
---	---	---
SIGNATURE FOODS... apples, avocados, bananas, eggplant, figs, kiwifruit, mushrooms, nectarines, olives, plantains, passionfruit, peanuts, pears, pomegranates, nuts, seeds, grains, legumes	• Are you holding deep-seated anger, hatred or resentment for yourself or others? • Are you holding on to grief/a deep painful secret that's eating away at you? • Are you holding on to negative concepts about sexuality/ sensuality/this area of your body? • Are you blocking your creativity by holding on to past hurts? • Are you holding on to past hurts from men/rejecting your own femininity? • Are you feeling unloved and alone?	Sacral Chakra colour Orange

***TESTIMONIAL...** *Kate was a 22-year-old nurse who had been diagnosed with advanced ovarian cancer, which had metastasised into her stomach, intestines and lungs. She'd been told by her doctor that it was too late for chemotherapy or radiation and that her prognosis was one month or so to live, if she was lucky! When Kate and I first spoke on the phone, she was quite sceptical as to how a retreat could help her and, being a nurse, had no concept whatsoever of how emotional healing would assist in ridding her body of cancer! However, with nothing to lose she attended the retreat, detoxifying her physical body by eating a predominately raw vegetarian diet and drinking vegetable juices, whilst at the same time healing her mind and spirit via the different therapies on offer. Kate's emotional healing sessions were very powerful and extremely traumatic, pulling up memories from the past that had been supressed for many years, some as far back as childhood, eating away at her without any conscious awareness on her behalf. As she accessed the blocked cellular memories during her healings she was astounded by the sheer force of the emotions that arose, crying uncontrollably for hours on end as the pain and trauma that had been hidden away for so long was released, frightening her initially as her warrior demeanour fell away and a vulnerable little girl began to truly heal. After leaving the retreat, Kate continued at home to detoxify her body both physically and emotionally, staying positive with the knowledge that her body could heal from a cold, therefore it could* *heal from cancer. Kate and I kept in touch throughout her healing journey. Her positivity rarely wavered; in fact, I remember her telling me the story of how a customer commented that she'd taken a day off work, asking if she'd been sick, to which she replied, 'No, just cancer!' Nine months after I initially met and spent time with Kate, I was invited to her wedding where she stood up at the time of her speeches and announced to everyone attending that not only was she marrying her best friend that day, but after nine months of battling advanced ovarian cancer, she was now cancer-free!*

Four years later, Kate is still cancer-free and in her own words...I don't know that I'd be here today if I hadn't been to the retreat. During my week with Lyn, I started on an alkaline diet, drank too many cups a day of Jason Winters tea and MMS, which I have no doubt helped me immensely with my fight, but by far the biggest thing, though, was the emotional healing sessions. I had a lot of emotional baggage that I'd hidden away; I knew about it, but I didn't know how to deal with it and never thought it would turn into something so sinister. During my week with Lyn, I started healing over a few sessions and learnt how to continue with that healing after I returned home. I've been able to face my demons and fight this cancer where it actually started. Thanks to Lyn and the amazing work she does at the retreat, not only was I well enough to marry my best friend last month, I also got to announce on the same day that I'm now in remission...

ENDOCRINE/REPRODUCTIVE SYSTEM
AVOCADO TAPENADE CUPS WITH MANGO

Ingredients: 1 avocado cut in half and deseeded, flesh of ½ mango

TAPENADE; **(see recipe in back of book)**

Method: Dice the mango into small pieces. Fill the avocado halves with olive tapenade and top with the diced mango. (serves 1)

PANCREATITIS

***WHAT IS IT?...* **Pancreatitis** is characterised by inflammation of the pancreas, which is the abdominal gland situated behind the stomach that secretes hormones as well as digestive enzymes. Gallstones and heavy alcohol are often the cause of this.

***BODY – EPICURE*

- Get off all medication and supplements- herbs in the form of powders or teas are okay, but no pills or capsules!
- **Fastest...** Water fast for 7–10 days **OR...**
- Do the five-week 35% food-grade hydrogen peroxide protocol combined with a cabala juice fast for 21–28 days.
- Then eat a fruit diet for two or three weeks—all and any fruit including tomatoes, avocado, olives, which are also fruit.
- Support the pancreas by eating sweet potatoes which are the signature food for the pancreas.
- Have daily one cup of lemon, juiced with peel on, can mix with pure water.

- Suck on rock salt every day.
- Drink one litre per 22 kilos bodyweight of pure water every day.
- Develop the darkest suntan you can by covering your body in Divine Body Butter or coconut oil and then exposing at least 70% of your body to the sun for one hour every day (30 mins each side).
- **ESSENTIAL OIL...** basil, coriander, frankincense, fenugreek, citrus.
- (Divine, Himalayan rock salt, Ra 24ct gold salt, 35% food-grade hydrogen peroxide, essential oil of lemon and orange available in the USA **www.thedontolman.com/store** and Australia **www.lynnienichols.com/shop**)

BODY	MIND	SPIRIT
FOODS THAT HEAL	*POSSIBLE EMOTIONAL CAUSE*	*IMBALANCED CHAKRA*
---	---	---
SIGNATURE FOODS... apples, avocados, bananas, eggplant, figs, kiwifruit, mushrooms, nectarines, olives, plantains, passionfruit, peanuts, pears, pomegranates, nuts, seeds, grains, legumes	• Are you feeling ashamed of something you have done in the past? • Are you feeling angry/rejected? • Are you unable to find the sweetness in life?	Sacral Chakra colour Orange / Solar Plexus Chakra-

ENDOCRINE SYSTEM
SWEET POTATO CHIPS & 3 DIPS

Ingredients: CHIPS: 4 large sweet potato, sea or rock salt, 1 cup coconut oil

GUACAMOLE: **(see recipe under Womb in Endocrine System)**

OLIVE TAPENADE: **(see recipe under Dressings in back of book)**

CHILLI TOMATO SALSA: 1 large tomato, 1 cup sundried tomatoes, 1 tsp sea salt, 1 clove garlic, ½ red onion, 1 large chilli (can add 2 tbsp organic natural yoghurt if desired)

Method: To make the salsa, place all ingredients in a processer and pulse once or twice until finely chopped. Non vegan- add yoghurt just before serving

Peel the sweet potatoes and cut into 1 cm strips. Steam lightly, then shallow fry in coconut oil until golden brown. Season with salt and pepper and serve with the guacamole, olive tapenade and chilli tomato salsa. (serves 2)

POLYCYSTIC OVARIAN SYNDROME (PCOS)

***WHAT IS IT?...** **Polycystic Ovarian Syndrome (PCOS)** is a hormonal condition in which the levels of estrogen and progesterone are out of balance, leading to symptoms such as irregular menstrual cycles, acne, reduced fertility, obesity, excessive facial and body hair and the growth of ovarian cysts.

***BODY – EPICURE*

- Get off all medication and supplements- herbs in the form of powders or teas are okay, but no pills or capsules!
- **Fastest...** Water fast for 7–10 days **OR...**
- Cabala juice fast for 28 days to reset the body rhythms. Or can do water and Pulse for up to 90 days.
- Eat and juice locally grown, fresh, raw organic fruits and vegetables—especially one-seeded foods such as mango, peach, apricot, nectarine etc, no animal for at least 12 months. Can have free-range organic eggs.
- Eat eggplant, pears, mangoes, green garlic stuffed olives and avocado with oilive oil and sea salt several times each week.
- Eat mushrooms that have been placed in the sun for two hours to several days.
- Organic natural yoghurt—one tablespoon inserted into the vagina each evening before bed. Use only organic pads and tampons.
- Salt water douche—each morning using one heaped teaspoon of sea salt in one litre of water.
- Drink one litre per 22 kilos bodyweight of pure water, every day.
- Drink one cup of freshly squeezed lemon juice with peel on every day. You can dilute this with water to drink.
- Develop the darkest suntan you can by covering your body in Divine Body Butter or coconut oil and then exposing at least 70% of your body to the sun for one hour every day (30 mins each side).
- **ESSENTIAL OIL...** mentha spicata (spearmint), clary sage, thyme, sandalwood.
- (Divine, Himalayan rock salt, Ra 24ct See Salt available in the USA **www.thedontolman.com/store** and Australia **www.lynnienichols.com/shop**)

BODY *FOODS THAT HEAL*	MIND *POSSIBLE EMOTIONAL CAUSE*	SPIRIT *IMBALANCED CHAKRA*
---	---	---
SIGNATURE FOODS... apples, avocados, bananas, eggplant, figs, kiwifruit, mushrooms, nectarines, olives, plantains, passionfruit, peanuts, pears, pomegranates, nuts, seeds, grains, legumes	• Are you blocking your creativity by holding on to past hurts? • Are you rejecting your femininity by holding on to past hurts from men? • Are you feeling unloved and alone?	Sacral Chakra colour Orange / Solar Plexus Chakra-

ENDOCRINE SYSTEM
ONE-SEEDED FRUIT GLASS WITH SALTED AVOCADO & CASHEW CREAM

Ingredients: 2 mango, 4 peach, 4 apricot, 4 nectarine, 1 large avocado, ½ cup cashews, Himalayan salt, 2 tbsp honey, cashew cream (see recipe in back of book)

Method: Cut the flesh from all of the one-seeded fruits. Dice into small pieces and mix together in a bowl. Place the avocado and salt in a separate bowl and mash with a fork until smooth and creamy.   Fill $1/3$ of a serving glass with the salted avocado then top the glass with mixed fruits. Finish with a generous dose of cashew cream garnished with crunchy toffee cashews

Toffee Cashews; Place the cashews in a dry pan on low heat with a pinch of Himalayan salt and toast until lightly golden. Turn off the heat and let cool slightly, then add a drizzle of honey. Set aside until cool and crunchy. (serves 2)

PROSTATE ENLARGEMENT / PROSTATE CANCER / BENIGN PROSTATIC HYPERPLASIA (BPH)

***WHAT IS IT?...** **Benign prostatic hyperplasia (BPH)** is an enlarged prostate gland, which is a walnut-sized male reproductive gland that carries sperm and makes most of the semen. The prostate gland is located beneath the bladder and surrounds the tube that carries urine, called the urethra. As the prostate becomes enlarged it can partly block the urethra causing problems with urination.

Prostate cancer is the growth of abnormal cells in the prostate gland.

***BODY – EPICURE*

- Get off all medication and supplements- herbs in the form of powders or teas are okay, but no pills or capsules!
- **Fastest...** Water fast for 7–10 days **OR...**
- Do the five-week 35% food-grade hydrogen peroxide protocol combined with a cranberry juice fast for 14-21 days. If needed, can have raw vegan food also.
- Daily have one cup of pure lemon juiced with the peel on, you can mix with pure water.
- Eat and juice a locally grown, fresh, raw organic vegan diet for highest nutritional force.
- Eat one cup of Brazil nuts each day.
- Every morning eat two cups of rolled oats soaked overnight in the juice of one lemon and one tablespoon of flaxseed, one tablespoon of wheatgerm—you can have with apple juice or nut milk if desired.
- Suck on rock salt every day.
- Drink one litre per 22 kilos bodyweight of pure water every day.
- Have daily a berry, asparaus smoothie, consisting of two cups berries and 12 stalks of asparagus (can add a banana to sweeten) plus water to desired consistency. Drink within 45 minutes of making it. Can eat the foods instead if preferred.
- Do kegel exercises at least six times per day for two or three minutes each time.
- Develop the darkest suntan you can by covering your body in Divine Body Butter or coconut oil and then exposing at least 70% of your body to the sun for one hour every day (30 mins each side).
- Do a colon cleanse to remove toxic plaque.
- **ESSENTIAL OIL...** lemon, saw palmetto, pumpkin seed oil, fennel, geranium, myrtle, lavender, peppermint.
- (Divine, Himalayan rock salt, Ra 24ct gold salt, 35% food-grade hydrogen peroxide, essential oil of lemon and orange available in the USA **www.thedontolman.com/store** and Australia **www.lynnienichols.com/shop**)

BODY *FOODS THAT HEAL*	MIND *POSSIBLE EMOTIONAL CAUSE*	SPIRIT *IMBALANCED CHAKRA*
---	---	---
SIGNATURE FOODS... apples, avocados, bananas, eggplant, figs, kiwifruit, mushrooms, nectarines, olives, plantains, passionfruit, peanuts, pears, pomegranates, nuts, seeds, grains, legumes	• Are your fears jeopardising your masculinity? • Are you feeling judgemental of others? • Is there an underlying sense of pressure or guilt around sex or sexuality? • Are you burdened by financial/work pressures?	Sacral Chakra colour Orange

***TESTIMONIAL...

July 14, 2001

Dear Mr Tolman,

"I was told today by my Doctor to go home and get my affairs in order, that after three years of fighting prostate cancer it had won and there was no more he could do to help me.

I am writing you with tears that are making it hard to see. I love my wife and children and I am not ready to leave them.

I heard you on a radio interview and wrote down your contact information. I don't mean to bother you. I can imagine you are very busy. If you have any ideas and the time, could you be so kind as to respond in a way that is convenient to you?"

Sincerely Jim

Dear Jim,

"There is so much I would love to share with you about the complexity of the chemical make-up in the matrix of whole foods and the synergism of one whole food to the next. Maybe some time in the future. Spinach, for instance, has upon analysis been found to contain over 12,000 phytolitic chemical constituents of which only 104 have been named and recorded with some understanding. What I'm suggesting is that you try nature's chemotherapy, which is a treatment of whole foods. The following 28-day dietary program will feed the brain, the blood and the endocrine system the highest synergized nutritional chemistry known to medical science as applied specifically to the latest oncological studies applied to colon, prostate and breast cancers. Dr Mitchell Gaynor, director of New York's Strang Cancer Prevention Center and Chief Chair at New York City Hospital is also a professor of hematology and molecular biology at Cornell Medical School is a friend. In Newsweek Magazine November 30th 1998, Dr Gaynor was highlighted on the cover and with a ten-page section presenting the new science of whole foods and its relationship to cancer. You can find it on the web at www.newsweek.com. It's as if today's science is now confirming an ageless wisdom of the past. Dr Gaynor declares 'We have seen the future of cancer research and the future is whole foods.'

I am not a medical doctor, but I work with patients of medical doctors all over the United States, Australia, New Zealand and Japan. With this in mind I give you the following diet that has helped hundreds with prostate cancer to help their doctors help them. An interesting observation of classical period physicians of ancient Rome was that the earth grows foods under the ground, on the ground and above the ground in trees. They noticed the human body has three levels also consisting of; a basement, from the navel down; a main floor, from the navel up to the throat; and upper rooms, from the throat to the top of the head. An intuitive gnosis lead them to understand that meals could be prepared that the bodies

cellular intelligence would recognize and bring into play the various systems in the needed levels of the body in generating healing and harmony from a state of chaos. They noticed a sliced carrot looks like the patterns of the eye, that a walnut has the pattern of the brain, that a cluster of grapes is in the shape of the heart and that each individual grape looks like a blood cell. Today's medical research into whole foods shows the profound accuracy of nature's mimicry applied to these patterns. This was called the doctrine of signatures in past ages. I have made an in depth study of signatures and its application to today's nutritional science.

It is with 40 years of observation and application to human lives I share the 28-day life giving foundational dietary experience with you. Godspeed to your recovery, Jim. If you have any questions or need assistance in any way, emotionally or otherwise please call, write, or email me. Thanx for your interest"

Don Tolman

28-Day Health Recovery

Each day for the first seven days, you eat no less than eight ounces of Brazil nuts, one large head of broccoli (raw), one large head of broccoli (steamed), lemon juice, salt and cayenne pepper can be the only condiments mixed in olive oil (extra virgin). Eat at least ½ cup of this oil mix each day. One ounce of whole or fresh ground flax seed mixed into one large bowl of oatmeal eaten without milk but sweetened to taste with maple syrup (100 percent real maple syrup, no additives). With this, snack on a variety of red, green and purple grapes throughout the day (two or more pounds). Your only beverage is pure spring water.

On the morning of the eighth day, all food and water is stopped. In its place you drink a minimum of two quarts of fresh made Cabala juice and as much as you desire. No water! No food! Just drink Cabala juice for 14 days. The juice has to be made fresh daily! Carrots, three apples, a whole lemon and 1/3 of a beet.

On the morning of the 21st day, you indulge in the same menu of the first seven days, to the end of the 28. From this point, it would be a healthy lifestyle to maintain a diet of 80 percent raw whole foods from the Physicians Committee for Responsible Medicine's new Four Food Groups Chart that include fruits, vegetables, nuts-seeds-grains and legumes. The other 20 percent of the healthy diet would include cooked whole foods, especially heavy multi-grain bread, real whole butter and tubers like yams, potatoes and onions.

July 14, 2005

Dear Mr Tolman,

"As you already know from my previous letters and emails, it has been four years since you sent your letter to me. I'm in the best health of my life. I can honestly say I have never felt better, even as a young man. My prostate has renewed itself and my doctor lets me talk to some of his other patients in order to share your whole food, walking, water, clean air and sunshine method of self-care. It makes so much sense to be personally responsible for your health. Disease, thanks to you, no longer scares me. I wish with all my heart the whole world could at least hear your message, from your own mouth, you are a master of simplicity and voice. May the heavens bless you in all you do."

A friend and now a Farmacist
Jim

ENDOCRINE/REPRODUCTIVE SYSTEM
LEMON & BRAZIL NUT BIRCHER MUESLI

Ingredients: 1 cup rolled oats, juice of 1 lemon, 1 tbsp honey, 1 tbsp flaxseed, 1 tbsp wheatgerm, ½ tsp cinnamon, ½ cup Brazil nut milk

BRAZIL NUT MILK; 1 cup Brazil nuts and 2 cups water

Method: Place the rolled oats, honey and lemon juice in a bowl to soak overnight. Make the Brazil nut milk by placing Brazil nuts and water in a high-speed blender until completely liquid. Pour into a nutmilk bag and squeeze out the milk. Mix the nut pulp into the muesli along with the wheatgerm and flaxseed. Sprinkle with cinnamon and serve with the nut milk. (serves 1)

UTERINE FIBROIDS

WHAT IS IT?... **Uterine fibroids** are non-cancerous growths that develop in the uterine wall. They can be solitary or there may be many, and they range in size from tiny to larger than a rockmelon.

BODY – EPICURE

- Get off all medication and supplements- herbs in the form of powders or teas are okay, but no pills or capsules!
- **Fastest...** Water fast for 7–10 days **OR...**
- Cabala juice fast for 28 days to reset the body rhythms.
- Eat and juice locally grown, fresh, raw organic fruits and vegetables—no animal for at least 12 months.
- Eat free-range organic eggs and ruby-red grapefruit to help get rid of any blood clots.
- Eat one or two cups of mushrooms that have been placed in the sun for two hours prior to eating.
- Eat eggplant, pears, mangoes, green garlic stuffed olives and avocado with olive oil and sea salt several times each week.
- Organic natural yoghurt—one tablespoon inserted into the vagina each evening before bed. Use only organic pads and tampons.
- One to three days before the menstrual cycle begins, eat dark organic chocolate.
- Apply warm castor oil packs administered to the area.
- Salt water douche—each morning using one heaped teaspoon of sea salt in one litre of water.
- Drink one litre per 22 kilos bodyweight of pure water every day.
- Develop the darkest suntan you can by covering your body in Divine Body Butter or coconut oil and then exposing at least 70% of your body to the sun for one hour every day (30 mins each side).
- **ESSENTIAL OIL...** clary sage, thyme, frankincense.
- (Divine, Himalayan rock salt, Ra 24ct gold salt, 35% food-grade hydrogen peroxide, essential oil of lemon and orange available in the USA **www.thedontolman.com/store** and Australia **www.lynnienichols.com/shop**)

BODY *FOODS THAT HEAL*	MIND *POSSIBLE EMOTIONAL CAUSE*	SPIRIT *IMBALANCED CHAKRA*
---	---	---
SIGNATURE FOODS... apples, avocados, bananas, eggplant, figs, kiwifruit, mushrooms, nectarines, olives, plantains, passionfruit, peanuts, pears, pomegranates, nuts, seeds, grains, legumes	• Are you feeling insecure, inadequate, not good enough, lacking in self-love? • Are you afraid to change your programming/beliefs? • Are you feeling rejected by men?	Sacral Chakra colour Orange

ENDOCRINE/REPRODUCTIVE SYSTEM
PEPPERMINT CHOCOLATE MOUSSE

Ingredients: 2 avocado, 1 cup medjool dates, 1 tbsp honey, 2 cups coconut cream, ¾ cup cacao, 2 drops peppermint oil, few mint leaves

Method: Place all ingredients into a blender and process until very smooth and creamy. Serve in a cocktail glass and garnish with fresh mint leaves. (serves 2)

FERTILITY PROTOCOL

Women...

Eat olives (anciently meaning, 'all lives') and all fruits with one seed including dates (dates were anciently called as such because of the dating period and getting pregnant).

Eat lots of mushrooms to get the thyroid/hormones working.

Drink one cup of lemon juice daily, this targets the liver, which assists the function of the neuroendocrine glands and assists the entire neuroendocrine flow.

Sungaze morning and evening... The bio-photons of light engage cells of the neuroendocrine system—all 10,000 cells of the body run off light!

Go on a diet of water and pulse for 90 days.

Let go of emotional stress and all supplements.

Raw dairy and/or ferments daily—these are high in photolytic calcium, as are lots of leafy greens.

Iron is one of the most important things to help fertility. High-iron foods are beans, lentils, quinoa and leafy greens (iron + salt + water = calcium).

Only eat high-complex carbohydrates in wholegrains, veggies and fruit—avoid refined carbohydrates as these diminish the functional capacity of the endocrine system.

Eat lots of omega 3s—fatty acids help to regulate the reproductive hormones of men and women and help to relieve stress... Flaxseeds, pumpkin seeds, nuts, free range eggs and wild yams are all good sources. Wild yams stimulate the ovum. Populations eating lots of these have a high rate of conception/high rate of twins and triplets.

Antioxidants in berries kick up the functional capacity of the reproductive system—they target the eggs and sperm.

Organic free-range eggs help with menstrual flow, and raw dairy, nuts, eggs, wholegrains and legumes all help with ovum and sperm mobility.

Mercury in fish and seafood blocks the ability to get pregnant—highest in mercury are the very large fish such as swordfish, king mackerel, tuna, shark, and salmon.

Avoid trans-fats—these kill fertility! Eat nuts, olive oil, safflower, sunflower, cold-pressed extra virgin oils.

Acupuncture, reflexology, chiropractic and emotional healing are all great natural fertility treatments as they remove blockages in energy flow.

Folic acid in fruit picks up sperm production in men and ovum function in women and helps to avoid birth defects.

Herbal teas – red clover, Siberian ginseng, stinging nettle, and black kohosh – are all beneficial for fertility purposes.

Men...

Stress and over exercise can decrease testosterone in men; instead, relax, have a massage, and have fun.

Avoid hot saunas and spas as these temporarily lower the number and quality of sperm.

Eat peanuts and asparagus to increase sperm volume, also figs and sunflower seeds.

Asparagus speeds up the swimming of sperm and creates four to five times more volume; eat daily for three weeks before ejaculation.

Smoking commercial tobacco and drinking hard alcohol lowers fertility... Instead, have organic beer or wine.

Sex...

Men should let the volume of sperm build up over the weeks prior to the woman's fertile time by not ejaculating. Once the fertile time arrives, intercourse should take place doggie style, with the woman's head down and buttocks in the air so that the gravitational flow allows the sperm to flow downward. The woman should stay like this for approximately 15 minutes or so afterward.

Seed Cycling for Women:

Every menstruator is different. I will use some standard numbers to illustrate the different phases of the menstrual cycle. These numbers may be completely different for you. For example: if you ovulate on day 18 of your cycle, your follicular phase will be 18 days, while your luteal phase might be shorter. Please find out for yourself how it is for you.

Follicular Phase Characteristics:

estrogen-dominant phase, starts on the first day of your period, lasts until one day before ovulation, usually days 1–14 of your cycle.

Seeds to support this phase:

daily, 1 TBS of flaxseeds, 1 TBS of pumpkin seeds. Why do they make your hormones happy? They are rich in omega 3 fatty acids, flax seeds contain lignans (they block excess estrogen), pumpkin seeds are high in zinc (this supports progesterone levels to rise in the second part of your cycle).

Luteal Phase Characteristics:

the second part of your cycle, progesterone dominant phase, starts on the day of your ovulation and lasts until one day before your next period, usually days 15–28 of your cycle.

Seeds to support this phase:

daily, 1 TBS of sesame seeds, 1 TBS of sunflower seeds. Why do they make your hormones happy? They are rich in omega 6 fatty acids, sesame seeds contain lignans (they block excess estrogen), sunflower seeds support the liver in its detoxification process to remain hormonal balance in the body (the mineral helping here is selenium).

Following the Moon Cycle...

To create a similar pattern with an irregular or even absent monthly bleeding, it is suggested to start with flax and pumpkin seeds on the first day of the new moon and switch to sesame and sunflower seeds about two weeks later, on the full moon. The reason we choose this pattern is that in earlier days, when there was no artificial light, women used to start bleeding at the dark of the moon and ovulated around the full moon. You can switch to following your own cycle once your menstruation has returned or become more regular.

Seed Preparation and Consummation...

Make sure you buy whole, organic raw seeds and grind them just prior to eating each day so the seeds do not oxidise and go rancid. The nutrients from ground seeds are more easily absorbed in the body. To maintain freshness, you can grind the seeds in the morning and place in a glass jar with lid in the fridge for afternoon consumption. Ideas to consume your seeds: blend them in a smoothie, add to oatmeal, add to soups and salads.

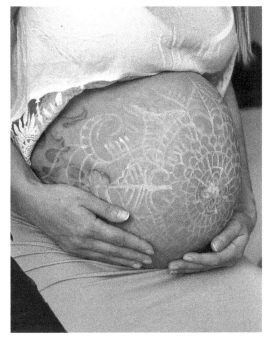

Outcome...

Be aware that it normally takes up to three to four cycles before you notice any big results in hormonal balancing; however, you might notice differences earlier than this. Be patient with your body (especially if you have just got off hormonal birth control) and be persistent in the seed cycling. Please note, this is no magic potion. If your hormones are disrupted aggressively, or you have bigger things going on like endometriosis or PCOS, seed cycling alone will not solve your problem.

Type 1 and Type 2 Diabetes

Just so you know, diabetes didn't exist until refined sugar was invented. Venice, Italy was the marketer and chemical owner of the process that started in the 1500s. Healers in Egypt noticed that bees and ants were all of a sudden drinking the urine of some people. The healers tasted the urine and it tasted sweet (called mellitus). In that day 'siphon' was called diabetes or drainage... 'Diabetes mellitus' was the body draining toxic fake sugars. A book called Sugar Blues exposed this decades ago.

You cause diabetes by what you eat, when you eat and where you eat. Baby formulas and manufactured baby food created diabetes in children and young people. Diabetes today is a 300+-billion-dollar annual industry. In just one year they increased the amount of people having diabetes 300% by doubling the glycaemic measures that qualify you to be on pharma insulin.

Widely prescribed drugs for type 2 diabetes (a non-disease condition), such as Actos and Avandia, work by increasing your body's insulin sensitivity. These drugs can create heart problems, they can increase your risk of heart failure, and they lead to accumulation of fluids on the legs, ankles and lungs. In some extreme cases, they lead to liver failure. They've also been known to cause weight gain... It's frustrating to me that so many people expose themselves to these potentially deadly effects to treat something that's influenced by lifestyle, diet and toxic chemicals, refined sugars and artificial sweeteners. Animal insulin comes from dead animals including cows, pigs and humans... Insulin is what causes amputations and blindness, not the diabetes (this truth has been exposed multiple times and then deleted and removed from investigative literature). In general, typically the medical/pharma employees/doctors/nurses/sales reps/etc. are taught that people with diabetes either have a total lack of insulin (type 1 diabetes) or they have too little insulin or cannot use insulin effectively (type 2 diabetes).

Stop eating lifeless, food-less foods that give no nutrition or any health benefits. Start eating foods that will work together to manage your glucose levels—like spreading real butter (not margarine that's 98% plastic) on wholegrains, not toxic flours and fake cereals, etc. Healthy fats and plant proteins can make some of your favourite 'taboo' foods work for you rather than against you—no drugs necessary. Avoid acesulfame, aspartame, saccharin, white stevia, sucralose... They all have over 20 marketing chemical names... Instead, go with raw organic honey, pure organic maple syrup, and pure green stevia...

The answer is found in non-GMO, organic fruits, veggies, tubers (sweet potatoes, garlic and onions) nuts, seeds, beans, legumes, lentils, herbs, spices, non-refined plant oils and wholegrains, flax and ground flax and walnuts. There is an ancient mix of plant foods that some called, **'The Most Sacred Olympic Meal'** that appears to work miracles! Even the King James version of the Bible called it, **'Pulse'** of the Cosmos.

Fruits with what they call low glycaemic levels slowly digest to avoid spikes in blood sugar. Some doctors and investigative studies know that it's true and that these fruits heal type 1 and type 2 diabetes. They include apples, berries, cherries, all citrus, pineapple, leafy greens especially spinach and all cruciferous veggies, broccoli, cauliflower, cabbage, Brussels sprouts, pears, peaches, bananas, mangoes and papayas, all red, yellow and orange foods especially sweet potatoes, extra virgin olive oil and organic coconut oil, avocados, hemp seeds, etc. Other fruit trees today called nuts also heal diabetes: almonds, walnuts, pecans and macadamias. You can make them into nut butters and put them onto the fruits listed. Spices like basil, cayenne, cinnamon, ginger, thyme, turmeric, green tea, organic wine, and unfiltered, no-additive, no-preservative beer. Some healers used kawakawa leaf and honey in hot/warm water for diabetes.

Type 1 diabetes (formerly called juvenile-onset or insulin-dependent diabetes) accounts for 5–10 out of 100 people who are told they have diabetes. In type 1 diabetes, they are told that the body's immune system destroys the cells that release insulin, eventually eliminating insulin production from the body. Also, they say that without insulin cells cannot absorb sugar (glucose), which they need to produce energy.

Type 2 diabetes (formerly called adult-onset or non-insulin-dependent diabetes) can develop at any age. It is most commonly given as a diagnosis during adulthood. But type 2 diabetes in children as a diagnostic is rising. Type 2 diabetes accounts for the vast majority of people who have diabetes ... 90 to 95 out of 100 people. In type 2 diabetes, they say that the body isn't able to use insulin the right way. They call this insulin resistance. As type 2 diabetes gets worse, the pancreas may make less and less insulin and this is called insulin deficiency.

How are Type 1 and Type 2 Alike? Both types of diabetes greatly increase a person's risk for a range of serious complications because of the side effects of medications and insulin use. Although doctors are trained to say that monitoring and managing the disease can prevent complications, diabetes and its meds and insulin remain the leading cause of blindness and kidney failure. It also continues to be a critical risk factor for heart disease, stroke, foot or leg amputations and more.

The Difference in Healing Protocols... It has been my experience in working with many type 2 diabetics, who are no longer diabetic, that if they have the courage and are not full of medically induced fear, they can just stop the meds and insulin immediately and do the following to heal themselves of the symptoms of this diagnosed disease. If they have it within themselves to simply **drink an ancient juice recipe and eat an ancient meal as a snack through the day and do this for 28 days,** they will no longer be diabetic. The first three to five days are the hardest because it's uncomfortable to detox and cleanse and reset the physiological function of the body's organs to an elevated level of performance. You may feel weak and tired, but all of that leaves and energy returns, like I said, typically within three to five days, for some seven days. After the 28 days, eat a diet of low glycaemic foods for 7–10 days. Then add to your diet any and all fresh fruits, veggies, nuts, seeds, wholegrains, fresh-made juices, and fruit smoothies, and stay vegetarian for at least six months. You might even consider during this process giving yourself an enema once in a while or going to a gravity-fed colonic clinic just to make sure you remove toxins from the intestinal canal.

It's best to get rid of the mental need to test your blood sugar levels during this. As the body heals and resets it could read as being all over the place. Don't let this bother you, it's part of the cellular process of reconstruction and cellular physiological organ function. Health is simple. Nature's complex so we don't have to be. Just embrace Nature and you'll be rewarded with health and healing for doing so.

Go Bananas...

Just like apples do, a banana a day also keeps the doctor away!

Ancient records show that banana cultivation in Egypt and New Guinea goes back 8,000 years, even appearing in Egyptian Hieroglyphics. Bananas, just like apples, are one of Nature's nutritional powerhouses, consisting of many vitamins, minerals and proteins. Anciently it was recorded that bananas originated from the planet Venus ('Goddess of Love', also called 'Earth's Twin Sister') and came to our world on solar winds. Bananas grow on huge plants (not trees) and botanically they are actually a berry! The banana is the largest plant in the world and belongs to the same family as the orchid and lily. A single banana is called 'a finger and they grow in 'hands' of around 10–20. The word banana actually comes from the Arabic word for hand, which is banan. Today's nutritional studies show that just one banana has loads of Vitamin C, Potassium, Phosphorus, Proteins, Manganese, Vitamin A, all of the B Vitamins including Riboflavin, Niacin, B6, & Folic Acid, Calcium, Magnesium, Iron and Zinc and contain Nature's healthy sugars and fibres.

Bananas deliver quick energy. This is why it's the number-one fruit among athletes. They can help to overcome and prevent a huge range of illnesses and ailments including lowering blood pressure, which protects against heart disease and strokes. Bananas soothe intestinal disorders and can assist with regular bowel movements. They are great for those with depression due to containing tryptophan, a type of protein that the body converts into serotonin, which then relaxes the body and lifts your moods.

Hold on to that Peel!

Don't be so quick to throw that banana peel away, they are medicinal and even anaesthetic! Did you know that rubbing the inside of banana peel onto an insect or mosquito bite can reduce itching, swelling and irritation? It can clear rashes. If you tape a piece of banana peel over a splinter, the enzymes help to draw the splinter out. Get rid of headaches by rubbing banana peel onto the forehead. Food science has found the name of the banana to be 'musa sapientum', meaning 'Fruit of the Wise.' Eating as many yellow bananas as you can is a wise thing to do. The colour yellow is healing and protective, this is why the yellow Sun is so healing mentally, emotionally, physically and even socially.

Cowboy Don

The DIGESTIVE / EXCRETORY SYSTEM

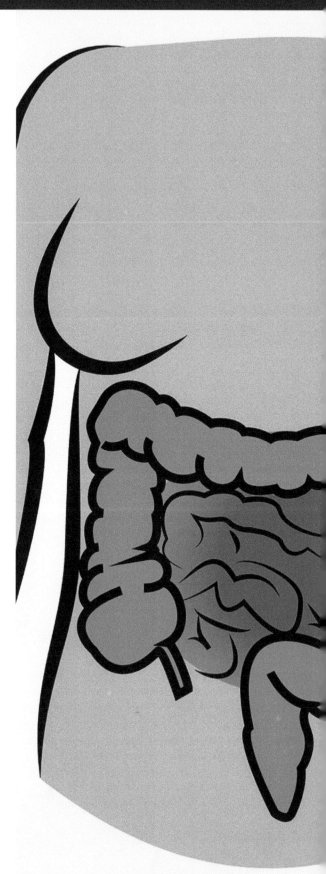

Consists of... skin, mouth/salivary glands, oesophagus, liver, stomach, gallbladder, pancreas, colon, small intestine, kidney, bladder, appendix and rectum

Chakra- Solar Plexus (yellow) /Endocrine Gland and Function... Neuroendocrine glands of the Pancreas are located deep in the abdomen, behind the stomach. The glands secrete insulin, glucagon, somatostatin and other chemicals. This controls blood glucose (blood sugar) and overall glucose metabolism and helps to control other endocrine cells of the digestive tract.

Holds Emotional Molecules of... acceptance, self-esteem/pride, self-control, arrogance, and grief are stored in this system.

Foods That Support This System Are... apples, beer, black pepper, cucumbers, flaxseeds, green beans, lentils, okra, plums, psyllium, quinoa, sweet potatoes, sauerkraut, leafy greens, fermented foods

Support the Emotional/Physical Healing of This System with... GREEN and RED foods.

Green wholefoods support this system with the release of toxicity and promote a feeling of personal power.

Red wholefoods are hugely beneficial in this system as they help release disease whilst assisting the release of the low vibratory emotions of shame, guilt and dishonesty.

***NOTE... The digestive system is the most critical system when it comes to maintaining health. Our ancestors were aware of this and that is why importance was placed on regular internal cleansing.

APPENDIX

BODY *FOODS THAT HEAL*	MIND *POSSIBLE EMOTIONAL CAUSE*	SPIRIT *IMBALANCED CHAKRA*
---	---	---
SIGNATURE FOODS... Digestive/ Excretory System... apples, beer, black pepper, cucumbers, flaxseeds, green beans, lentils, okra, plums, psyllium, quinoa, sweet potato, sauerkraut, leafy greens, fermented food	Are you allowing fear to block the flow of joy? Are you feeling powerless?	Solar Plexus Chakra- / Sacral Chakra colour Orange

DIGESTIVE/EXCRETORY SYSTEM
DIGESTIVE HOTPOT

Ingredients: 2 cups of split red lentils soaked for a couple of hours, 3 brown onions diced, 3 cloves of garlic diced, 2 tsp ginger peeled and diced, 1 tsp chilli diced finely, 1 heaped tsp garam masala, 2 cups of chopped green beans, 6 cups of water, 2 large sweet potatoes, baked and then mashed, coconut oil for baking and frying, 1 tsp sea salt, extra salt and pepper for seasoning

Method: Peel, chop and bake the sweet potato in a good dose of coconut oil. Fry the onion, ginger and garlic for a few minutes in a pan with a little coconut oil before adding the red lentils, salt and water. Bring to the boil, then turn down and simmer for approximately 30 minutes until the lentils are soft. Move this mixture into a casserole dish, add the garam masala, fresh chilli and green beans. Add a little more salt here if necessary. Top with mashed sweet potato seasoned with black pepper. Drizzle with coconut oil and bake in a moderate oven for 10–15 minutes until heated through. (serves 4)

BLADDER

BODY *FOODS THAT HEAL*	MIND *POSSIBLE EMOTIONAL CAUSE*	SPIRIT *IMBALANCED CHAKRA*
---	---	---
SIGNATURE FOODS... cranberries	Are you feeling pissed off about something? Are you afraid to let go of old beliefs and ideas?	Solar Plexus Chakra- / Sacral Chakra colour Orange

DIGESTIVE/EXCRETORY SYSTEM
CRANBERRY QUINOA IN CUCUMBER BLADDERS

Ingredients: ¼ cup cold cooked quinoa, 1 large sweet potato diced and baked in coconut oil, 1 cup dried organic cranberries, 1 cup bean sprouts, sprinkle of flaxseeds, 1 tsp fresh ginger diced finely, ½ cup coriander, large cucumbers cut in halves lengthwise with centres hollowed out, 1 tsp sea salt

DRESSING; ¼ cup olive oil & ¼ cup balsamic vinegar combined, 1 tbsp raw honey

Method: Place the hollowed cucumbers on a serving dish. Toss all other ingredients together in a mixing bowl including the cucumber seeds. Add dressing then spoon the quinoa mix into the hollowed cucumbers just before serving.

COLON/BOWEL

BODY	MIND	SPIRIT
FOODS THAT HEAL	*POSSIBLE EMOTIONAL CAUSE*	*IMBALANCED CHAKRA*
---	---	---
SIGNATURE FOODS... green beans, tamarind, black pepper	Are you feeling insecure, fearful of letting go of past beliefs?	Solar Plexus Chakra- / Base Chakra- **colour Red**
	Are you feeling stubborn and controlling, wishing others would change?	

DIGESTIVE/EXCRETORY SYSTEM
SPICY LENTIL SOUP

Ingredients: 2 cups red lentils, 4 brown onions diced, 6 cloves garlic chopped finely, 5 cm fresh ginger chopped, 1 heaped tbsp cumin, 1 tbsp curry powder, ¼ tsp cinnamon, 2 tsp paprika, 1 tbsp sea salt, 9 cups water

Method: Fry onions and garlic in coconut oil for a few minutes until onion softens. Add chilli, ginger, cumin, curry, cinnamon, paprika and stir for a further 2 minutes. Add lentils and stir for another couple of minutes before adding water and sea salt. Bring to boil then simmer for ½ hour until lentils are soft. Taste test, add more salt if necessary. (serves 4)

GALLBLADDER

BODY *FOODS THAT HEAL*	**MIND** *POSSIBLE EMOTIONAL CAUSE*	**SPIRIT** *IMBALANCED CHAKRA*
---	---	---
SIGNATURE FOODS... radish, rye	Are you lacking in power, will or attention? Are you feeling not good enough, a failure, second best or unimportant?	Solar Plexus Chakra-

***NOTE...** If the gallbladder has been removed, support the immune system by eating any and all foods grown under the ground, especially sweet potato, onions, garlic and carrots. You can also place 1 tbsp fenugreek seeds in a glass of water and drink this each day. Fresh, dried and frozen blueberries target diarrhoea caused by not having a gallbladder.*

DIGESTIVE/EXCRETORY SYSTEM
SWEET POTATO & RADISH MASH ON RYE TOAST

Ingredients: 2 cups red lentils, 4 brown onions diced, 6 cloves garlic chopped finely, 5 cm fresh ginger chopped, 1 Ingredients: 2 pieces of organic rye bread, 1 large sweet potato, 2 red finely diced radish, ½ cup olive oil, 1 tbsp fresh chopped rosemary, sea salt and pepper

Method: Peel and bake the sweet potato in coconut oil until soft and caramelised then place in a bowl and season with salt and pepper. Smash with a fork until smooth then add the finely diced radish. Toast the rye and top with a good serve of the mash. Mix the olive oil and rosemary, drizzle over the sweet potato to serve. (serves 1)

KIDNEYS

BODY *FOODS THAT HEAL*	MIND *POSSIBLE EMOTIONAL CAUSE*	SPIRIT *IMBALANCED CHAKRA*
---	---	---
SIGNATURE FOODS... kidney bean, red bean	Are you holding on to feelings of shame and disappointment, a belief that you are a failure? Are you feeling criticised and overreacting?	Solar Plexus Chakra- / Base Chakra- **colour Red**

***NOTE... *Kidney stone purge: Mix ½ litre of sauerkraut juice, ½ litre tomato juice and 13 drops of peppermint oil. Drink before noon.*

DIGESTIVE/EXCRETORY SYSTEM
KIDNEY BOOST CONCARNE

Ingredients: 450 g organic kidney beans pre-cooked, 2 onions peeled and diced, 2 cloves of garlic diced finely, finely diced chilli to taste, 4 tomatoes diced finely, ½–1 tsp sea salt, 1 tbsp coconut oil, 2 cups wild rice

Method: To prepare the wild rice, soak in water for three days, changing the water morning and night. Drain well. Combine tomato, onion, garlic and chilli to the cooked kidney beans. Season with sea salt and serve on a bed of rice. For nachos, spoon the kidney bean mix over a plate of organic cornchips and serve

*** For a non-vegan version, top the nachos with some organic goat's cheese or feta cheese before serving

LIVER

BODY **FOODS THAT HEAL**	MIND **POSSIBLE EMOTIONAL CAUSE**	SPIRIT **IMBALANCED CHAKRA**
SIGNATURE FOODS... yellow foods such as squash and yellow wax bean, butternut pumpkin, leeks	Are you feeling angry, frustrated, guilty or fearful?	Solar Plexus Chakra-
LEMON JUICE- One cup per day for 90 days will assist the liver to heal	Are you blaming others for the lack of joy and love in your life?	

***NOTE...** *LIVER FLUSH—drink one litre of grapefruit juice and one cup of organic virgin olive oil blended together 30 minutes prior to going to bed. Typically the next day you will pass gallstones and bile in the stool. You may need to do this two or three days in a row.*

***NUGGET...** Did you know that every 90 days you have a brand-new liver? When healing the liver, the anions in one cup of lemon juice per day will create bile, allowing the liver to go into mitosis and replace itself to heal.*

DIGESTIVE/EXCRETORY SYSTEM
LIVER-LOVING SPICED LEMON & EGGPLANT SALAD

Ingredients: 1 med/large eggplant cut into 2 cm cubes, 2 tsp cumin, 1 tsp paprika, 2 tsp sea salt, $1/3$ cup coconut oil, peel of 1 lemon diced finely, juice of 1 lemon, 1 punnet of cherry tomatoes halved, 2 cups flat leaf parsley chopped, 1 clove garlic diced finely, 1 cup baby spinach leaves

Method: In a mixing bowl place the diced eggplant, spices, sea salt and half of the coconut oil. Toss well until eggplant is coated evenly. Pour onto a baking tray with the rest of the coconut oil and bake in a moderate oven, turning occasionally until eggplant is soft—approximately 15–20 minutes. Peel the lemon before juicing then dice the peel finely. Toss this in a salad bowl with the tomatoes, parsley, finely diced garlic and spinach. Remove the eggplant from the oven, let cool for a few minutes before tossing through the salad mix. Toss the lemon juice through the salad and serve immediately.

***For a non-vegan version, cut halloumi cheese into 2 cm strips and gently fry until golden brown. Cut into 2 cm pieces and toss through the salad; serve immediately while halloumi and eggplant are still warm. (serves 2)

PANCREAS

BODY *FOODS THAT HEAL*	MIND *POSSIBLE EMOTIONAL CAUSE*	SPIRIT *IMBALANCED CHAKRA*
---	---	---
SIGNATURE FOODS... sweet potato, buckwheat, cinnamon, dates, green peas and beans	Has life lost all sweetness? Are you feeling frustrated, angry, rejected, helpless or hopeless?	Solar Plexus Chakra-

***NOTE... *Sugar affects the pancreas! However, there are two types of sugars, fast and slow. Fast sugars are toxic, they are small in molecular structure and cross the blood-brain barrier very quickly causing chaos to the brain. This causes the pancreas to produce insulin. Fast sugars cause diabetes. Slow sugars are large in molecular structure and cross the blood-brain barrier slowly, the pancreas then produces glucogen. The adrenals use glucogen and turn it into adrenalin. This is where our energy comes from. Fruits and sweet vegetables are slow sugars; therefore they are extremely healthy and needed by the body!*

DIGESTIVE/EXCRETORY SYSTEM
MINTED CINNAMON POTATO

Ingredients: 2 large sweet potato, ½ tsp cinnamon, ½ cup fresh mint leaves

Method: Peel and dice the sweet potato into 2 cm chunks. Bake in a moderate oven with coconut oil until golden brown and caramelised. Sprinkle with cinnamon, add torn mint leaves then serve while hot

Herb Cider Dressing; **(see recipe under Dressings in back of book)**

Serves 2

STOMACH

BODY
FOODS THAT HEAL

SIGNATURE FOODS... ginger

MIND
POSSIBLE EMOTIONAL CAUSE

Are you having trouble digesting
new ideas or information?

Are you dreading change, feeling
fear, anxiety and worry?

SPIRIT
IMBALANCED CHAKRA

Solar Plexus Chakra-

DIGESTIVE/EXCRETORY SYSTEM
LENTIL PATTIES WITH CHILLI MANGO SAUCE

Ingredients: 1 large sweet potato roasted in coconut oil until soft and then mashed with a fork (approx 1.5 cups mashed), 1 cup red lentils rinsed then placed in 2.5 cups water, 10 cm leek diced finely or 1 large onion diced finely, 1 cup walnuts chopped in food processor and left a little chunky, 1 cup rolled oats chopped finely in a food processor, 3 cloves garlic diced, 1 heaped tsp curry powder, 1.5 heaped tsp cumin, 2 inches fresh ginger diced, 1 heaped tsp sea salt

CHILLI MANGO SAUCE; Flesh of 1 large mango, 1 chilli

Method: Place lentils and water in a saucepan and bring to the boil. Reduce heat and simmer for approximately 15 minutes until tender. Drain and set aside to cool. Combine all ingredients together in a bowl and mix well. Using your hands, make into patties. Gently fry in coconut oil, on medium to low heat, until golden on both sides.

Place the mango in a blender on high speed until a smooth sauce consistency. Finely dice the chilli. Mix the two together, then drizzle over the patties to serve. (serves 4)

RECTUM

BODY FOODS THAT HEAL	MIND POSSIBLE EMOTIONAL CAUSE	SPIRIT IMBALANCED CHAKRA
---	---	---
SIGNATURE FOODS... Colon- green bean, tamarind, black pepper	Are you holding on to crap from the past in the way of experiences, beliefs, fears or emotions? Are you angry about having to 'let go' of something? Are you feeling guilty, not good enough, unforgiveable?	Solar Plexus Chakra- / Base Chakra- **colour Red**

DIGESTIVE/EXCRETORY SYSTEM
SPICY GINGER BEANS

Ingredients: 500 g green beans trimmed and cut into 2 cm lengths, 4 shallots cut into 2 cm lengths, 2 large cloves of garlic diced finely, 2 inches of fresh ginger peeled and diced, 2 tbsp coconut oil, salt and black pepper to season, olive oil

Method: Place all ingredients together with coconut oil in a stainless-steel fry pan and stir-fry for 2 minutes, beans should still be crunchy. Place in a serving bowl with a good dose of olive oil. Season with Himalayan or sea salt and pepper. Serve immediately

***For a non-vegan version, toss in organic butter instead of olive oil

ACNE

***WHAT IS IT?...** **Acne** is a disease prevalent among adolescents and is characterised by red pimples that are caused by inflamed or infected sebaceous glands, which are the oil glands that secrete sebum and carry dead skin cells, via the follicle, out of the body.

***BODY – EPICURE*

- Get off all medication and supplements- herbs in the form of powders or teas are okay.
- Fastest... Water fast for 7–10 days OR...
- Cabala juice fast 14–28 days
- Eat and juice a locally grown, fresh, raw organic vegetarian diet for highest nutritional force and gentle detox.
- Walking daily for 30 to 45 minutes to get the lymphatic system working.
- Sunshine—put fresh squeezed lemon juice on the skin the go in the sun for 30–40 minutes, letting the sun bleach through the anions of the juice, rinse. Before bed, put apple cider vinegar on the acne.
- Put witch hazel oil on face then cover and let it dry—do this for seven days then put apple cider vinegar on the face for seven days and then follow this with aloe vera on the face for seven days.
- Use good clays from dams/hot springs—get bentonite and diatomaceous clay and do a facial with this; let the clay dry and then rinse.
- Make a skin mask from ground-up avocado and garlic, put on the skin and let dry for a few hours then rinse.
- Cucumber cut and rubbed all over the face will cool the skin and draw out toxicities.
- **ESSENTIAL OIL...** witch hazel rubbed directly onto the skin.
- (Developmental Clarity-Diatomaceous/Bentonite Clay available in the USA **www.thedontolman.com/store** and Australia **www.lynnienichols.com/shop**)

BODY *FOODS THAT HEAL*	MIND *POSSIBLE EMOTIONAL CAUSE*	SPIRIT *IMBALANCED CHAKRA*
---	---	---
SIGNATURE FOODS... apples, beer, black pepper, cucumbers, flaxseeds, green beans, lentils, okra, plums, psyllium, quinoa, sweet potatoes, sauerkraut, leafy greens, fermented foods	• Are you rejecting or hating yourself? • Are you not good enough, unworthy of love? • Are you oversensitive to others' opinions?	Solar Plexus Chakra- / Throat Chakra- colour Sky Blue

***NOTE...** *One of the main causes of acne is synthetic chocolate—exchange this for good healthy organic dark chocolate. Acutane, prescribed for acne, is one of the leading causes of making young people sterile.*

ACNE SCARRING... Make a poultice out of squashed onion and put all over the scarring, leave on for a few hours at a time. Witch hazel oil can also assist with scarring.

DIGESTIVE/EXCRETORY SYSTEM
SALTED CASHEW CHOCOLATE

Ingredients: 1 cup raw cashews, 1 cup raisins, 2 tbsp raw honey, ¾ cup organic cocao, pinch of Himalayan salt, ½ cup nut butter (organic peanut butter, almond butter etc), ½ cup organic cold pressed coconut oil

Method: Place all ingredients together in a bowl and mix well. Line the base of a small casserole dish with banana leaf (or greaseproof paper) and pour the liquid chocolate in. Place in the fridge or freezer to set for 1 hour. Cut into squares and it is ready to devour ☺

AVOCADO AND GARLIC FACE MASK

Ingredients: Cucumber, avocado and garlic

Method: Cut the cucumber into thin slices. Place the avocado and garlic in a blender and pulse to a smooth consistency. Rub the avocado mask all over the face and leave for a few hours. Rinse off and place slices of fresh cucumber over the face for half an hour to cool the skin and draw out additional toxicities.

APPENDICITIS

***WHAT IS IT?...** **Appendicitis** is inflammation of the appendix, which is connected to the large intestine on the lower right side of the abdomen. Pain from appendicitis may begin in the middle of the abdomen.

***BODY – EPICURE*

- Get off all medication and supplements- herbs in the form of powders or teas are okay, but no pills or capsules! **Fastest...**
- When you feel appendix pain, do a self-administered daily enema or have a gravity-fed colonic and the pain will go away. Continue to do this over the next few days. (Enema douche kits available www.lynnienichols.com/shop)
- Salt covenant—drink one litre of water with two heaped teaspoons of sea salt first thing each morning to flush the digestive tract and colon.
- Eat ferments such as sauerkraut, olives in salt brine, tempeh, kombucha, organic kefirs and yoghurt.
- Do a colon cleanse with bentonite clay and herbs for cleaning of the digestive tract/colon and to rid toxic plaque buildup.
- FOR PARASITES- Snack on ½ cup of raw pumpkin seeds each day. Eat one or two cloves of raw garlic each day and 1 onion a day—can be red, white or brown.

Parasites can't handle a lot of fibre so eat two large carrots every day, late afternoon. Eat figs daily, fresh or dried. Parasites hate coconut oil so make a mix of coconut oil/one clove garlic and oregano, aniseed or clove oil (parasites hate all of these so it doesn't matter which you use) and drink a dose of this daily for as long as necessary. Can also mix one teaspoon of black walnut oil with a few drops of aniseed, clove or oregano oil together with organic natural yoghurt and have a spoonful of this daily. Drink fresh juice of lemon, lime, grapefruit and orange—parasites cannot stand citrus.
- Develop the darkest suntan you can by covering your body in Divine Body Butter or coconut oil and then exposing at least 70% of your body to the sun for one hour every day (30 mins each side).
- **ESSENTIAL OIL...** aniseed, clove, black walnut, oregano.
- (Divine, colon cleanses, Ra 24ct See Salt, Himalayan rock salt available in the USA **www.thedontolman.com/store** and Australia **www.lynnienichols.com/shop**)

BODY *FOODS THAT HEAL*	MIND *POSSIBLE EMOTIONAL CAUSE*	SPIRIT *IMBALANCED CHAKRA*
---	---	---
SIGNATURE FOODS... apples, beer, black pepper, cucumbers, flaxseeds, green beans, lentils, okra, plums, psyllium, quinoa, sweet potatoes, sauerkraut, leafy greens, fermented foods	• Are you in a state of constant fear? • Are you desperately wanting something that you fear you cannot have?	Solar Plexus Chakra- / Sacral Chakra- Colour Orange

***NOTE...** *Our appendixes protect us from parasitic overcome. They have a purpose and we need them!*

DIGESTIVE/EXCRETORY SYSTEM
LEMON GINGER KOMBUCHA

Ingredients: Kombucha scobie, 2 cups of kombucha tea from the mother, 2 litres of pure water, ¾ cup raw organic sugar, 7 organic lemon and ginger teabags

Method: Boil the water and add the sugar, stirring with a clean stainless-steel spoon until the sugar has dissolved. Take the tags off the teabags and float them in the boiling mixture for 1hr. Once the tea has cooled, take out the teabags and pour the liquid into a glass or ceramic urn with a tap on the bottom for easy bottling. Cover the top with some cheesecloth so the scobie can breathe and leave for 10–12 days in a warm area

NOTE: There is no exact fermenting time. Generally, the warmer the climate, the quicker the fermentation process will be. Ten days is a minimum fermentation time to ensure the sugar has been turned to beneficial probiotic.

B12 DEFICIENCY

***WHAT IS IT?...** **Vitamin B12 deficiency** is a condition that may be experienced if the body is not absorbing correctly or if part of the stomach has been removed during weightloss surgery.

***BODY – EPICURE*

Fastest...

- Eat fruit, free-range organic eggs, fresh squeezed juices and lots of grains, which are the fruits of grasses and contain the highest concentration of B vitamins.
- Do a colon cleanse to remove toxicity and plaque, which can affect the body's ability to absorb nutrients properly.
- (Divine, colon cleanses, Ra 24ct See Salt available in the USA **www.thedontolman.com/store** and Australia **www.lynnienichols.com/shop**)

| **BODY** | **SPIRIT** |
FOODS THAT HEAL	*IMBALANCED CHAKRA*
SIGNATURE FOODS... apples, beer, black pepper, cucumbers, flaxseeds, green beans, lentils, okra, plums, psyllium, quinoa, sweet potatoes, sauerkraut, leafy greens, fermented foods	Solar Plexus Chakra- / Sacral Chakra- Colour Orange

---

***NOTE...** Grains are the fruits of grasses and contain the highest concentration of B vitamins. Your body makes B12 when fruits eaten move into the first three feet of the digestive tract—the fermentation that takes place generates B12. Gorillas are 99% fruitarian—they have no B12 deficiencies!*

DIGESTIVE/EXCRETORY SYSTEM
B12 BREAKFAST WITH AVOCADO SALSA

Ingredients: 2 free-range organic eggs, 1–2 pieces of thick organic multigrain bread, 1 avocado, 1 large tomato, 1 clove garlic, sea salt, ⅛ cup nutritional yeast

Method: Dice the avocado, garlic and tomato and mix together in a bowl. Season with Himalayan salt and pepper. Toast the bread and poach the eggs, timing it so that both are ready at the same time. Spoon a big serve of salsa onto the toast, add the eggs, the nutritional yeast, salt and pepper. Garnish with a little salsa and serve. (serves 1)

BLADDER INFECTION/CYSTITIS

***WHAT IS IT?...** **Bladder Infection** is inflammation of the urinary bladder caused by infection and results in frequent painful urination.

Cystitis is the most common urinary tract infection, often caused by the E.coli bacterium, and causes inflammation of the bladder.

Both can be a result of sexual hygiene.

***BODY – EPICURE*

- **Fastest...** Water fast for 7–10 days **OR...**
- Do the five-week 35% food-grade hydrogen peroxide protocol combined with a cranberry juice fast for 14–21 days.
- Eat organic cranberries, fresh or dried, as well as cranberry Pulse.
- Drink one litre per 22 kilos bodyweight of pure water every day.
- Organic natural yoghurt—1 tablespoon inserted into the vagina each evening before bed. Use only organic pads and tampons.
- Salt water douche—each morning using one heaped teaspoon of sea salt in one litre of warm water.
- Develop the darkest suntan you can by covering your body in Divine Body Butter or coconut oil and then exposing at least 70% of your body to the sun for one hour every day (30 mins each side).
- Do kegel exercises by tightening the muscles, holding for 10–15 seconds and then letting go for one minute, repeating four or five times. (Women can use a jade egg to strengthen the pelvic floor muscles—available www.lynnienichols.com)
- PREVENTION: It is beneficial for the woman to urinate and cleanse after sexual intercourse.
- **ESSENTIAL OIL...** clove, oregano, cinnamon, lavender.
- (Divine, Cranberry Pulse, 35% food grade hydrogen peroxide, colon cleanses, Ra 24ct See Salt available in the USA **www.thedontolman.com/store** and Australia **www.lynnienichols.com/shop**)

BODY *FOODS THAT HEAL*	MIND *POSSIBLE EMOTIONAL CAUSE*	SPIRIT *IMBALANCED CHAKRA*
---	---	---
SIGNATURE FOODS... apples, beer, black pepper, cucumbers, flaxseeds, green beans, lentils, okra, plums, psyllium, quinoa, sweet potatoes, sauerkraut, leafy greens, fermented foods	• Are you feeling peed off about something or someone? • Are you afraid to let go of old, outdated beliefs/past experiences?	Solar Plexus Chakra- / Sacral Chakra- **Colour Orange**

***NOTE...** *Sexual hygiene in men is critical.*

DIGESTIVE/EXCRETORY SYSTEM
PEAR, BANANA AND CRANBERRY SMOOTHIE

Ingredients: 2 pear, 2 banana, 2 cup cranberries, 1 ½ cups water

Method: Chop all ingredients and place in a blender on high speed until smooth and creamy. Add more water if desired. (serves 1–2)

BOILS

***WHAT IS IT?...** **Boils, also known as skin abscesses, furuncles and carbuncles,** are inflamed/infected hair follicles that become very painful and fill with pus as they push up through the skin's surface.

***BODY – EPICURE*

- Get off all medication and supplements- herbs in the form of powders or teas are okay, but no pills or capsules!
- Fastest... Water fast for 7 days OR...
- Cabala juice fast 14 days.
- Take hot salt water baths with one or two cups bicarb soda and one or two cups salt.
- Rub apple cider vinegar onto the boil, wait for an hour until dry and then rub a mix of ½ teatree, ½ eucalyptus oil onto the boil.
- Drink one or two tablespoons of apple cider vinegar and blackstrap mollasses daily.
- Drink one cup of lemon, freshly juiced with the peels on, every day.
- As the sun goes down, eat orange foods, especially carrots.
- Use an astringent such as witch hazel oil, or alcohol topically—can use the gua sha mix of triple distilled vodka and bicarbonate of soda. Mix to a paste and rub over the skin. This will help the hair to shed out through the epidermal layers.
- Suck on Himalayan rock salt daily, the size of the end segment of your little finger.
- Do salt scrubs—can use lemon ReNew salt scrub to assist healing of the liver/skin.
- Wear loose clothing only, especially if the boils are in the pelvic region.
- Drink one litre per 22 kilos bodyweight of pure water every day.
- Develop the darkest suntan you can by covering your body in Divine Body Butter or coconut oil and then exposing at least 70% of your body to the sun for one hour every day (30 mins each side).
- **ESSENTIAL OIL...** witch hazel oil rubbed onto the boil.
- (Divine, lemon ReNew salt scrub, Ra 24ct See Salt, Himalayan rock salt available in the USA **www.thedontolman.com/store** and Australia **www.lynnienichols.com/shop**)

BODY *FOODS THAT HEAL*	MIND *POSSIBLE EMOTIONAL CAUSE*	SPIRIT *IMBALANCED CHAKRA*
---	---	---
SIGNATURE FOODS... apples, beer, black pepper, cucumbers, flaxseeds, green beans, lentils, okra, plums, psyllium, quinoa, sweet potatoes, sauerkraut, leafy greens, fermented foods	• Are you seething with anger to boiling point? • Are emotions boiling to the surface, coming to a head?	Solar Plexus Chakra- / Throat Chakra- colour Sky Blue

DIGESTIVE/EXCRETORY SYSTEM
CLEANSING ASTRINGENT SCRUB

Ingredients: Aluminium-free bicarbonate soda, alcohol such as vodka, fine sea salt

Method: Make a paste out of the ingredients. Gently rub over the infected area to cleanse and exfoliate. Rinse and gently pat dry. (This is a great cleanser/exfoliant for the entire body)

BOWEL CANCER / COLON CANCER... RECTAL CANCER... COLORECTAL CANCER

***WHAT IS IT?...** **Bowel/Colon cancer** is a group of malignant cancer cells originating in any part of the large bowel (colon).

Rectal cancer is a disease in which a group of abnormal cancerous cells form in the last few inches of the large intestine, closest to the anus, which is called the rectum. Symptoms include abnormal bowel movements and blood in the stools.

Colorectal cancer is where the cancer occurs in both the colon and rectum.

***BODY – EPICURE**

- Get off all medication and supplements- herbs in the form of powders or teas are okay, but no pills or capsules!
- **Fastest...** Water fast for 7–10 days **OR...**
- Do the five-week 35% food-grade hydrogen peroxide protocol combined with a cabala juice fast for 21–28 days... You can eat raw carrots, celery and apples if you feel the need. Have self-administered or gravity-fed colonics during the fast.
- Drink lemon juiced with the peel on every day.
- Eat and juice a locally grown, fresh, raw organic fruit diet for highest nutritional force.
- Have fruit smoothies with ½–1 cup of organic olive oil added.
- Suck on rock salt every day.
- Drink one litre per 22 kilos bodyweight of pure water every day.
- Have daily a berry, asparaus smoothie, consisting of two cups berries and 12 stalks of asparagus (can add a banana to sweeten) plus water to desired consistency.

Drink within 45 minutes of making it. Can eat the foods instead if preferred.
- Salt covenant—drink one litre of water with two heaped teaspoons of sea salt first thing each morning to flush the digestive tract and colon.
- Joule of Thor—have one shotglass every day.
- Do a colon cleanse with bentonite clay and herbs for cleaning of the digestive tract/colon and to rid toxic plaque buildup.
- Develop the darkest suntan you can by covering your body in Divine Body Butter or coconut oil and then exposing at least 70% of your body to the sun for one hour every day (30 mins each side).
- **ESSENTIAL OIL...** lemon, thyme, rosemary, oregano.
- (Divine, Pulse, Joul of Thor, colon cleanses, Ra 24ct See Salt, Himalayan rock salt available in the USA
- **www.thedontolman.com/store** and Australia **www.lynnienichols.com/shop**)

BODY	MIND	SPIRIT
FOODS THAT HEAL	**POSSIBLE EMOTIONAL CAUSE**	**IMBALANCED CHAKRA**
---	---	---
SIGNATURE FOODS... apples, beer, black pepper, cucumbers, flaxseeds, green beans, lentils, okra, plums, psyllium, quinoa, sweet potatoes, sauerkraut, leafy greens, fermented foods	• Are you refusing to release past experiences that no longer serve you? • What crap from the past is eating away at you? • Are you feeling guilty, not good enough, a failure? • Are you feeling as though you need to be punished?	Solar Plexus Chakra- / Base Chakra- **colour Red**

***TESTIMONIAL... DEB'S INSPIRATIONAL STORY**

Due to her diagnosis of bowel cancer, Deb had endured five operations and much emotional trauma, arriving for her seven-day retreat feeling fearful that she would never again have the ability to experience her passion of running and with strict dietary requirements and the need to stay in close vicinity of a bathroom. By day four of her retreat, however, it was obvious that Deb had begun to heal both emotionally and physically, as for the first time in months her diarrhoea had subsided and she was able to confidently embark on a two-hour excursion through the rainforest. During Deb's emotional healing sessions, the innate wisdom of her body drew her to the physical pain she had felt constantly for months on end, and with this, the memories, sadness and grief that accompanied the physical manifestation. As she expressed the emotions that she had unknowingly supressed for many years, ALL of the physical pain disappeared from her body, and she was left in a state of bliss so beautiful she was mesmerised. This is the level of the soul, where ego and mind drop away and all that remains is the Source of who we truly are, the pure divinity and innocence of a newborn child, a sense of peace, love, joy and freedom.

Several weeks after Deb's retreat, in her words... I have gone from strength to strength since I last saw you. My diet is probably around 95% raw and I am finding this so easy to digest and absolutely all pain has gone. In addition, I seem to have loads more energy and feel full of vitality ... it's great, so many people have told me how well I look ... that makes me feel so good. I have been walking three times a week, about 5 km each time, I do two yoga sessions a week and one fun zumba session. My confidence levels are high, the future looks brilliant and this is due to the healing week with you, Lyn. I have recommended you to everyone! Thank you for fixing me, I wish you health and happiness always, love Deb...

And a couple of weeks later, in Deb's words... Just a quick good news update, I had my six-monthly specialist appointment, blood tests, exams, etc. My blood cancer markers are under five, which means no active cancer cells detected ... hooray. The specialist is amazed at how well I look and how well I am doing.

And just four months after Deb attended the retreat, she is back doing what she is passionate about. In her words... I ran a 5 km run a couple of weeks ago in a time of 27.30mins! I even amazed myself! I am feeling very happy and so much stronger.

And just six months after the retreat in Deb's words... It was today one year ago that I was diagnosed with cancer; it is a good day for reflection and celebration ... what a journey it's been. Thank you for all your support, encouragement and healing therapies, without which I would not be where I am today.

DIGESTIVE/EXCRETORY SYSTEM
FIBRE SALAD WITH LEMON ZEST

Ingredients: 3 apples, 3 stalks of celery, 1 medium carrot, zest of 1 lemon, pepper

LEMON DRESSING; **(see recipe under Dressings in back of book)**

Method: Grate the carrot and apple with core and skin and place in a bowl. Add finely sliced celery and lemon zest. Season with black pepper. Add dressing and serve (serves 2)

CROHN'S/ULCERATIVE COLITIS/INFLAMMATORY BOWEL DISEASE (IBS)

***WHAT IS IT?...* **Crohn's disease** is a long-standing condition that causes the lining of the digestive system to become inflamed and can affect any part of the digestive system. Most commonly Crohn's affects the small intestine (ileum) or the large intestine (colon).

Ulcerative Colitis is a disease of the large intestine (colon) where the colon lining becomes inflamed and develops ulcers that produce mucous and pus, causing rectal bleeding, diarrhoea and cramping abdominal pain.

Irritable Bowel Syndrome (IBS) is a common gut condition causing abdominal pain, bloating, diarrhoea, cramping and constipation for months on end.

Inflammatory Bowel Disease (IBD) is a term used to describe ulcerative colitis and Crohn's disease.

***BODY – EPICURE*

- **Fastest...** Water fast for 7–10 days **OR...**
- Cabala juice fast for 21–28 days. Do the salt covenant each day whilst fasting and a colon cleanse with herbs and bentonite clay at the end of the fast.
- Eat a raw food diet or Pulse for 30 days—add natural oils such as avocado.
- Eat an avocado each day—cut in half and filled with organic virgin olive oil and sea salt.
- Eat musligens such as soaked flax seeds, ocre, chia, aloe vera—½ cup daily for 28 days.
- Have a fruit smoothie with ½–1 cup of oil each day.
- Eat and drink ferments such as organic kefirs and yoghurts, foods preserved in salt brine, sauerkraut, tempeh, kombucha.
- Eat a diet high in natural oils and vitamin E foods such as wholegrains, sunflower seeds, avocado, garlic, nuts, and ginger.
- Drink one litre per 22 kilos bodyweight of pure water every day.
- Walk every day for 45–60 minutes in the fresh air.
- Salt covenant—drink one litre of water with two heaped teaspoons of sea salt first thing each morning to flush the digestive tract and colon.
- Joule of Thor—have one shotglass every day.
- Do a colon cleanse with bentonite clay and herbs for cleaning of the digestive tract/colon and to rid toxic plaque buildup.
- Develop the darkest suntan you can by covering your body in Divine Body Butter or coconut oil and then exposing at least 70% of your body to the sun for one hour every day (30 mins each side).
- **ESSENTIAL OIL...** copaiba, patchouli, peppermint.
- (Divine, Pulse, Joule of Thor, colon cleanses, Ra 24ct See Salt, Himalayan rock salt available in the USA **www.thedontolman.com/store** and Australia **www.lynnienichols.com/shop**)

BODY *FOODS THAT HEAL*	MIND *POSSIBLE EMOTIONAL CAUSE*	SPIRIT *IMBALANCED CHAKRA*
---	---	---
SIGNATURE FOODS... apples, beer, black pepper, cucumbers, flaxseeds, green beans, lentils, okra, plums, psyllium, quinoa, sweet potatoes, sauerkraut, leafy greens, fermented foods	• Are you holding on to the past, fearful of making change? • Are you being judgemental, controlling, self-righteous? • Are you lacking self-love, being harsh on yourself? • What shit are you holding on to, literally/what are you unable to eliminate from your past?	Solar Plexus Chakra- / Base Chakra- **colour Red**

DIGESTIVE/EXCRETORY SYSTEM
VANILLA CHIA & CHOCOLATE MOUSSE

Ingredients: Chia: ¼ cup chia seeds, 2 cups coconut cream, 1 tbsp raw honey, ½ tsp vanilla paste, ⅛ cup chocolate nibs

MOUSSE; ½ cup soaked cashews, 1 avocado, 2 tbsp raw honey, 2 cups coconut cream, ¾ cup cacao, ½ tsp vanilla paste

Method: Chia: pour the seeds into a 500 ml glass jar, add vanilla, honey and ¼ cup water. Stir consistently until the mix begins to thicken. Top the jar with coconut cream and mix well. Put aside for a few hours or overnight until the chia swells and becomes jelly-like

Mousse: Place all ingredients in a blender on high speed until smooth and creamy

In a serving glass, place a 2 cm layer of chia. Follow this with a similar amount of chocolate mousse, and continue alternating until the glass is full. Garnish with crushed chocolate nibs and a sprig of mint. (serves 4)

CHRONIC KIDNEY DISEASE (CKD)/CHRONIC RENAL DISEASE

***WHAT IS IT?...** **Chronic kidney disease** is a loss of kidney function, each stage relating to the level of kidney function and damage

***BODY – EPICURE*

- **Fastest...** Water fast for 7–10 days **OR...**
- Do a cabala juice fast for 14–21 days.
- KIDNEY PURGE–Drink ½ litre of tomato juice mixed with ½ litre of sauerkraut juice (get from jar of sauerkraut), add 13 drops of peppermint oil and drink before bed (don't get up until the morning if possible).
- Drink one litre of unsweetened, preservative-free cranberry juice every day.
- Eat a fruit diet for 60–90 days including nuts and grains, especially Brazil and macadamia nuts.
- Eat organic cranberries, fresh or dried, as well as cranberry Pulse.
- Eat legumes—in a crockpot cook up all and any legumes (especially kidney beans), lentils, broccoli, asparagus and eat one or two bowls of this each day.

- Salt—have lots of salt and celery in the diet.
- Salt covenant—Drink one litre of water with two heaped teaspoons of sea salt first thing each morning.
- Drink one litre per 22 kilos bodyweight of pure water every day.
- Develop the darkest suntan you can by covering your body in Divine Body Butter or coconut oil and then exposing at least 70% of your body to the sun for one hour every day (30 mins each side).
- **ESSENTIAL OIL...** lemon, orange, lime, grapefruit, peppermint.
- (Divine, Cranberry Pulse, colon cleanses, Ra 24ct See Salt, Himalayan rock salt, essential oil of peppermint available IN THE USA **www.thedontolman.com/store** and Australia **www.lynnienichols.com/shop**)

BODY	MIND	SPIRIT
FOODS THAT HEAL	**POSSIBLE EMOTIONAL CAUSE**	**IMBALANCED CHAKRA**
---	---	---
SIGNATURE FOODS... apples, beer, black pepper, cucumbers, flaxseeds, green beans, lentils, okra, plums, psyllium, quinoa, sweet potatoes, sauerkraut, leafy greens, fermented foods	• Are you ctiticising yourself or feeing criticised by others? • Are you acting like a victim/poor me/feeling like you can't change a situation? • Are you feeling ashamed or disappointed?	Solar Plexus Chakra- / Base Chakra- **colour Red**

***NUGGET...** **KIDNEY PURGE-** drink ½ litre of tomato juice mixed with ½ litre of sauerkraut juice (get from jar of sauerkraut), add 13 drops of peppermint oil and drink before bed.

DIGESTIVE/EXCRETORY SYSTEM
MEXICAN SALAD

Ingredients: 800 g of organic kidney beans, 3 tomatoes diced, 1 red onion finely diced, ½ cup coriander chopped, 2 avocados diced, 2 cloves of garlic finely diced, ½ cos lettuce shredded finely, 3 tablespoons lemon juice and zest of 1 lemon, ½ bag of organic corn chips, sea salt

Cashew Mayonnaise **(see recipe under Dressings in back of book)**

Method: Combine the diced tomato, onion, garlic, coriander and kidney beans together in a bowl. Season with sea salt and pepper to taste. Dice the avocado and combine with lemon juice and zest. Create layers in a glass serving bowl beginning with finely shredded lettuce, then bean mix, and lastly, the diced avocado/lemon. Drizzle a generous dose of cashew mayonnaise over the top, followed by a sprinkle of coriander. Top with a thick layer of crushed corn chips

Non-Vegan; add crumbled organic feta cheese just prior to the crushed corn chips.

CIRRHOSIS OF THE LIVER & FATTY LIVER DISEASE

***WHAT IS IT?...** **Cirrhosis** is a condition where healthy liver tissue is replaced by scar tissue that blocks the flow of blood through the liver and, in turn, affects the processing of nutrients, hormones, etc. Cirrhosis is often caused by excessive alcohol consumption, hepatitis C and B and fatty liver caused by diabetes and obesity.

Fatty liver disease is also known as hepatic steatosis and is where fat builds up in the liver, causing inflammation. Fatty liver can be caused by different factors including excess alcohol consumption and a prolonged bad diet high in carbohydrates and calories.

***BODY – EPICURE*

- **Fastest...** Water fast for 7–10 days **OR...**
- Cabala juice fast for 14–21 days.
- Drink one cup of freshly juiced, with peels on, lemon juice, every single day. You can add water to this to dilute but must be one whole cup of lemon.
- LIVER FLUSH—Drink one litre of grapefruit juice and one cup of organic virgin olive oil blended together, 30 minutes prior to going to bed. Typically the next day you will pass gallstones and bile in the stool. You may need to do this two or three days in a row.
- No refined carbohydrates and sugars, sugary drinks and processed foods as these will only damage the liver further.
- No hard alcohol.
- Fruit diet—eat and juice locally grown, fresh, raw organic fruits for 30 days, just fruit, juices and water.
- Yellow—eat all and any yellow foods, such as grapes, apples, squash, bananas, lemons, tomatoes, capsicum.
- Eat a Well-Balanced Diet—If you are having trouble eating or you are experiencing digestive problems, stick to small, simple meals and water throughout the day. Eat plenty of fresh fruits and vegetables; avocados and coconut oil have healthy fats that are needed. Other foods that help are sweet potatoes, bananas, ginger root, and turmeric.
- Zinc is necessary for normal liver function and zinc foods are powerful antioxidants that boost immune function, which is important for healing hepatitis C. Foods high in zinc include black-eyed peas, soybeans, lima beans, mushrooms, pumpkin and pumpkin seeds, brightly coloured fruits and vegetables, kelp and organic non-GMO wholegrains.
- Probiotics help to support the liver because the beneficial bacteria in the gut promote the health and functioning of the liver. Probiotic foods include organic yogurt, kefir, organic no-animal-rennet white cheeses, sauerkraut and other fermented veggies, kombucha, garlic stuffed olives and any other saline ferments.
- Black Seed Oil for its antioxidant, anti-inflammatory, anti-cancer and immune-stimulating effects. A key compound of black seed oil, thymoquinone, protects the liver from damage through several mechanisms like scavenging free radicals and elevating glutathione levels.
- Sunshine/Vitamin D—research shows that it's common for people with chronic hepatitis C to have a lack of vitamin D because it needs to be stored in the liver and fatty tissues. Develop the darkest suntan you can by covering your body in Divine Body Butter or coconut oil and then exposing at least 70% of your body to the sun for one hour every day (30 mins each side). Also, eat mushrooms that have been set out in the sun for an hour as they have a high amount of vitamin D—eat them raw or cooked.
- Gentle exercise daily can help to relieve symptoms such as tiredness and low energy. Outdoor yoga or walking in the fresh air is beneficial for boosting energy levels and benefiting your mind and emotions.
- Drink one litre per 22 kilos bodyweight of pure water, every day—you can add pure lemon oil to this.
- Take colloidal silver with fulvic acid.
- **ESSENTIAL OIL...** lemon, cypress, geranium, german chamomile.
- (Divine, Pulse, Ra 24ct See Salt, Nature's Silver Bullet (colloidal silver with fulvic acid), pure essential oils, Himalayan rock salt available in teh USA **www.thedontolman.com/store** and Australia **www.lynnienichols.com/shop**)

BODY	MIND	SPIRIT
FOODS THAT HEAL	*POSSIBLE EMOTIONAL CAUSE*	*IMBALANCED CHAKRA*
---	---	---
SIGNATURE FOODS... apples, beer, black pepper, cucumbers, flaxseeds, green beans, lentils, okra, plums, psyllium, quinoa, sweet potatoes, sauerkraut, leafy greens, fermented foods	• Are you feeling hurt and unable to forgive? • Are you feeling like a victim and is this causing you to be angry and judgemental? • Is anger/hatred eating away at you?	Solar Plexus Chakra-

HOT HEALING LIVER HIT

Ingredients: 1 piece Ezekiel sprouted bread, organic butter, habernano and jalopeno peppers, 2 cloves garlic, 1 tsp sunflower/safflower oil

Method: Spread the butter on the bread, toasting first if preferred. Layer some peppers and the grated garlic on top. Drizzle with sunflower/safflower oil (If peppers are too hot you can use grated ginger instead)

LIVER DETOX JUICE

Ingredients: 1 medium beet, 6 celery stalks, 1 cup fresh cilantro, 1 full lemon with skin, 1 inch of ginger

Method: Juice and drink immediately,

COELIAC DISEASE

***WHAT IS IT?...** **Coeliac disease** is an immune condition where the small intestine is extra sensitive and reactive to gluten, a protein found in wheat, rye and barley

***BODY – EPICURE*

- **Fastest...** Water fast for 7–10 days **OR...**
- Do a cabala juice fast for 10–14 days and at the same time do the salt covenant by drinking one litre of water with two heaped teaspoons of sea salt first thing in the morning.
- Eat and juice locally grown, fresh, raw organic fruits and vegetables for 30 days.
- Eat Pulse and natural oils such as avocado, nuts, good organic olive oil, coconut oil, etc.
- Drink one litre per 22 kilos bodyweight of pure water every day.
- Do a colon cleanse with bentonite clay and herbs for cleaning of the digestive tract/colon and to rid toxic plaque buildup.
- Do self-administered daily colonics (Enema douche travel kits available **www.lynnienichols.com/shop**)
- Joule of Thor—have one shotglass every day.
- Develop the darkest suntan you can by covering your body in Divine Body Butter or coconut oil and then exposing at least 70% of your body to the sun for one hour every day (30 mins each side).
- **ESSENTIAL OIL...** peppermint, lemon, ginger, grapefruit.
- (Divine, Pulse, colon cleanses, Joule of Thor, Ra 24ct See Salt, Himalayan rock salt available in the USA **www.thedontolman.com/store** and Australia **www.lynnienichols.com/shop**)

BODY FOODS THAT HEAL	MIND POSSIBLE EMOTIONAL CAUSE	SPIRIT IMBALANCED CHAKRA
---	---	---
SIGNATURE FOODS... apples, beer, black pepper, cucumbers, flaxseeds, green beans, lentils, okra, plums, psyllium, quinoa, sweet potatoes, sauerkraut, leafy greens, fermented foods	• Are you feeling hurt, criticised, overly sensitive to others' words and opinions? • Are you focusing on the negative instead of all there is to be grateful for?	Solar Plexus Chakra-

***NOTE...** *Honey is great for any allergic reaction.*

DIGESTIVE/EXCRETORY SYSTEM
CRUNCHY CHOC MOUSSE

Ingredients: 2 avocado, ½ cup coconut cream, ¼ curp raw honey, 1 tbsp coconut oil, ½ cup cocao powder, ½ tsp vanilla paste, pinch Himalayan salt, ½ cup chopped macadamia, ½ cup chopped cashews, 2 strawberries, 2 sprigs mint

Method: Place a can of organic coconut cream in the fridge overnight. Skim the solid coconut cream off the top and discard the remaining milky liquid. Process all ingredients, except the nuts, in a blender until smooth and creamy. Add the nuts and serve in a dessert glass garnished with sliced strawberry and a sprig of mint. (serves 2)

CONSTIPATION

WHAT IS IT?... **Constipation i**s an infrequent passing of stools, or difficulty emptying the bowels due to hardened feces.

BODY – EPICURE

- **Fastest...** Water fast for 7–10 days **OR...**
- Do a cabala juice fast for 10–14 days and at the same time do the salt covenant by drinking one litre of water with two heaped teaspoons of sea salt first thing in the morning OR...
- Eat and juice locally grown, fresh, raw organic fruits and vegetables for 30 days.
- Eat Pulse and natural oils such as avocado, nuts, good organic olive oil, coconut oil, etc.
- Have fermented foods such as sauerkraut, olives in brine, tempeh, kefir, kombucha, natural organic yoghurt, blue cheese, kim-chi, fermented veggies, good organic beer and red wine.
- Snack on carrots, celery, apples and other high fiber foods every day.
- Drink one litre per 22 kilos bodyweight of pure water every day.
- Massage the abdomen with a digestive stimulant essential oil.
- Salt covenant—drink one litre of water with two heaped teaspoons of sea salt first thing each morning to flush the digestive tract and colon.
- Do a colon cleanse with bentonite clay and herbs for cleaning of the digestive tract/colon and to rid toxic plaque buildup.
- Do daily self-administered colonics with an enema bag. (Enema douche travel kits available **www.lynnienichols.com/shop**)
- Develop the darkest suntan you can by covering your body in Divine Body Butter or coconut oil and then exposing at least 70% of your body to the sun for one hour every day (30 mins each side).
- **ESSENTIAL OIL...** fennel, peppermint.
- (Divine, Pulse, colon cleanses, Ra 24ct See Salt, Himalayan rock salt available USA **www.thedontolman.com/store** and Australia **www.lynnienichols.com/shop**)

BODY *FOODS THAT HEAL*	MIND *POSSIBLE EMOTIONAL CAUSE*	SPIRIT *IMBALANCED CHAKRA*
---	---	---
SIGNATURE FOODS... apples, beer, black pepper, cucumbers, flaxseeds, green beans, lentils, okra, plums, psyllium, quinoa, sweet potatoes, sauerkraut, leafy greens, fermented foods	• Are you holding in what you really want to say instead of expressing yourself? • Are you stuck holding on to crap from the past/ not releasing old ideas and experiences?	Root Chakra- **colour Red** / Solar Plexus Chakra-

DIGESTIVE/EXCRETORY SYSTEM
SALAD OF APPLE AND BLUE CHEESE

Ingredients: 4 apples, ½ –1 packet of non-animal rennet blue cheese, 1 large avocado, 1 cup walnuts

LEMON DRESSING; **(see recipe under Dressings in back of book)**

Method: Dice the apple, including seeds, and avocado into cubes and place in a salad bowl. Add the crumbled blue cheese and walnuts and gently toss. Drizzle with lemon dressing. (serves 2)

CRYPTOSPORIDIOSIS/GASTROENTERITIS/INFECTIOUS DIARRHOEA

***WHAT IS IT?...* **Cryptosporidosis** is a diarrhoea condition caused by microscopic parasites called cryptosporidium, which live in the intestine of animals and humans. The disease and parasite are both commonly known as 'crypto'.

Gastroenteritis is inflammation of the stomach and small intestine (gastrointestinal tract). Symptoms include diarrhoea (watery bowel movements), abdominal pain and vomiting, which is often caused by bacteria or parasites.

***BODY – EPICURE*

- **Fastest...** Water fast for 7–10 days **OR...**
- Cabala juice fast for 14–28 days.
- Eat foods high in starch and any and all foods that grow under the ground (tubers), especially sweet potato and regular potatoes—can have these raw, fried, mashed or baked. Also eat garlic, onion, carrots and bananas.
- Eat a lot of blueberries, these can be fresh or organic dried.
- Two cups of natural organic yoghurt and other ferments such as sauerkraut, fermented veggies, kombucha, keffer each day to re-establish the flora and fauna of the gut.
- Drink one litre per 22 kilos bodyweight of pure water every day.
- Suck on Himalayan rock salt, the size of the last segment of your little finger, daily.
- Salt covenant—Drink one litre of water with two heaped teaspoons of sea salt first thing each morning to flush the digestive tract and colon and do self-administered daily colonics. (Enema douche travel kits available **www.lynnienichols.com/shop**)
- Do a colon cleanse with bentonite clay and herbs for cleaning of the digestive tract/colon and to rid toxic plaque buildup.
- Develop the darkest suntan you can by covering your body in Divine Body Butter or coconut oil and then exposing at least 70% of your body to the sun for one hour every day (30 mins each side).
- **ESSENTIAL OIL...** oregano, ginger, peppermint, fennel, lemon, lavender.
- (Divine, Pulse, colon cleanses, Ra 24ct See Salt, Himalayan rock salt available in the USA **www.thedontolman.com/store** and Australia **www.lynnienichols.com/shop**)

BODY *FOODS THAT HEAL*	MIND *POSSIBLE EMOTIONAL CAUSE*	SPIRIT *IMBALANCED CHAKRA*
---	---	---
SIGNATURE FOODS... apples, beer, black pepper, cucumbers, flaxseeds, green beans, lentils, okra, plums, psyllium, quinoa, sweet potatoes, sauerkraut, leafy greens, fermented foods	• Who's bugging you, who's giving you the shits, literally? • Are you letting go of something you really want? • Are your emotions overwhelming, making you want to run from life? • Are you rejecting yourself or life in general?	Solar Plexus Chakra-

DIGESTIVE/EXCRETORY SYSTEM
TUBER MASH WITH FERMENT

Ingredients: 2 large sweet potatoes, 2 large regular potatoes, 1 large clove garlic diced finely, ½ onion diced finely, 1 cup natural organic yoghurt, sea or rock salt, black pepper

Method: Dice and steam the regular potatoes until soft. Slice the sweet potatoes and bake in coconut oil in the oven until caramelised. Finely dice the garlic and onion. Place all cooked potatoes in a mixing boxl and mash. Add the garlic, onion and natural yoghurt and mix well. Season with salt and black pepper. (serves 4)

DERMATITIS/PSORIASIS

WHAT IS IT?... **Dermatitis** is the term used for skin irritation/inflammation caused by an external substance, resulting in itchy, sore red skin that often cracks and becomes weepy and swollen.

Psoriasis is an inflammatory skin condition caused by an excess of skin cells being produced and then dying off at once, creating a very thick, dry, scaly layer on the skin's surface, which can crack and become weepy. Most commonly, this condition affects the elbows, scalp and knees but can affect the whole body including the soles of the feet and palms of the hands.

BODY – EPICURE

- **Fastest...** Water fast for 7–10 days **OR...**
- Cabala juice fast for 14–21 days whilst doing the five-week hydrogen peroxide protocol to oxygenate all 10,000 trillion cells of the body.
- One cup of freshly juiced, with peels on, lemon juice, every single day. You can add water to this to dilute but must be one whole cup of lemon.
- LIVER FLUSH—Drink one litre of grapefruit juice and one cup of organic virgin olive oil blended together 30 minutes prior to going to bed. Typically the next day you will pass gallstones and bile in the stool. You may need to do this two or three days in a row.
- Fruit smoothie daily with ½–1 cup of organic virgin olive oil added to this for 28 days.
- Eat and juice locally grown, fresh, raw organic vegan diet and include lots of olives, avocado and nuts for natural oils. Also include anything hot such as garlic, onions, peppers, ginger, etc.
- Yellow—eat all and any yellow foods.
- Salt scrub—scrub the body daily with a mix of good oils and salt (you can purchase Renew Body Scrub); once you have rinsed off, pat dry and apply a body butter such as Divine.
- Put lemon juice on the skin and go into the sun.
- Drink one litre per 22 kilos bodyweight of pure water, every day, you can add pure lemon oil to this.
- Sunshine—Develop the darkest suntan you can by covering your body in Divine Body Butter or coconut oil and then exposing at least 70% of your body to the sun for one hour every day (30 mins each side).
- **ESSENTIAL OIL...** lemon, tea tree, lavender, bergamot, chamomile.
- (Divine, Renew Body Scrub, Pulse, Ra 24ct See Salt, Himalayan rock salt available in the USA **www.thedontolman.com/store** and Australia **www.lynnienichols.com/shop**)

BODY	MIND	SPIRIT
FOODS THAT HEAL	*POSSIBLE EMOTIONAL CAUSE*	*IMBALANCED CHAKRA*
---	---	---
SIGNATURE FOODS... apples, beer, black pepper, cucumbers, flaxseeds, green beans, lentils, okra, plums, psyllium, quinoa, sweet potatoes, sauerkraut, leafy greens, fermented foods	• Are you suppressing your feelings? • Are you numbing yourself for fear of being hurt/rejected?	Solar Plexus Chakra-

NOTE... *The skin is the largest organ of elimination; when the other organs of the excretory system, such as the liver, are not eliminating optimally, the body will push toxicity out via the skin.*

DIGESTIVE/EXCRETORY SYSTEM
CHILLI AVO NUT BUTTER

Ingredients: 1 cup organic almond butter, 1 large avocado, chilli, Himalayan salt

Method: Place the nut paste, avocado and finely diced chilli in a bowl. Smash it all together with a fork and season with salt. Use the butter as a spread on sandwiches or toast and top with whatever you wish.

ECZEMA

WHAT IS IT?... **Eczema** is a condition where the skin becomes rough and inflamed, sometimes cracking and bleeding. Many people experience eczema as unbearably itchy, causing them to scratch until bleeding.

BODY – EPICURE

- **Fastest...** Water fast for 7–10 days **OR...**
- Cabala juice fast for 14–21 days whilst doing the five-week hydrogen peroxide protocol to oxygenate all 10,000 trillion cells of the body.
- One cup of freshly juiced, with peels on, lemon juice, every single day. You can add water to this to dilute but must be one whole cup of lemon.
- LIVER FLUSH—Drink one litre of grapefruit juice and one cup of organic virgin olive oil blended together 30 minutes prior to going to bed. Typically the next day you will pass gallstones and bile in the stool. You may need to do this two or three days in a row.
- Fruit smoothie daily with ½–1 cup of organic virgin olive oil added to this for 28 days.
- Eat and juice locally grown, fresh, raw organic vegan diet and include lots of olives, avocado and nuts for natural oils. Also include anything hot such as garlic, onions, peppers, ginger, etc.
- Yellow—eat all and any yellow foods.
- Salt scrub—scrub the body daily with a mix of good oils and salt (you can purchase Renew Body Scrub); once you have rinsed off, pat dry and apply a body butter such as Divine. Apply the body butter two or three times per day.
- May sting a little—put lemon juice on the skin and go into the sun.
- Drink one litre per 22 kilos bodyweight of pure water, every day—you can add pure lemon oil to this.
- Vitamin D /Sunshine—Develop the darkest suntan you can by covering your body in Divine Body Butter or coconut oil and then exposing at least 70% of your body to the sun for one hour every day (30 mins each side). Also, place button or portabella mushrooms in the sun for one hour and eat daily for high volumes of vitamin D.
- Non-alcohol witch hazel is an astringent that can help and lavender oil baths are soothing.
- Apple Cider Vinegar—apply two or three times a day. Drink two or three cups of clean warm water and 2 tbsp of ACV daily.
- **CHILDREN**—It's imperative to rid the diet of all artificial colours, flavours, chemical additives, artificial anti-oxidants, preservatives etc. Gently detox the body via green juices and gravity-fed colonics.
- Note: High toxicity levels in a child's body can result in oversensitivity to the natural chemicals found in fruits and vegetables called salicylates, resulting in eczema.
- **ESSENTIAL OIL...** lavender, witch hazel, lemon.
- (Divine, Pulse, 35% food-grade hydrogen peroxide, colon cleanses, Ra 24ct See Salt, Himalayan rock salt, pure essential oils available in the USA **www.thedontolman.com/store** and Australia **www.lynnienichols.com/shop**)

BODY	MIND	SPIRIT
FOODS THAT HEAL	**POSSIBLE EMOTIONAL CAUSE**	**IMBALANCED CHAKRA**
---	---	---
SIGNATURE FOODS... apples, beer, black pepper, cucumbers, flaxseeds, green beans, lentils, okra, plums, psyllium, quinoa, sweet potatoes, sauerkraut, leafy greens, fermented foods	• Are you unaccepted by others? • Are you feeling irritated/angry/ erupting in bouts of anger? • Are you holding your feelings inside, itching to speak your truth?	Solar Plexus Chakra- Crown Chakra- **colour Violet**

NOTE... *The liver and the skin are directly connected so cleansing and supporting the liver will be hugely beneficial to healing all skin conditions.*

High toxicity levels in a child's body can result in oversensitivity to the natural chemicals found in fruits and vegetables called salicylates, resulting in eczema. If your child is sensitive to green juices/smoothies, try a gentle detox using the foods below:

Red or Golden Delicious apples peeled, pears- only the pear-shaped variety such as Packham, white or brown thickly peeled potatoes, lettuce, cabbage-white and red, celery, Brussels sprouts, asparagus, green beans, fresh beetroot, chives, chocos, organic sweet corn, garlic, peas, butternut pumpkin, turnips (also called rutabaga/swede), spring onions, white organic rice, preservative-free wholegrain bread, absolutely organic milk, butter, cream and sour cream.

*** TESTIMONIAL... *Read Jesse's story in my introduction*

DIGESTIVE/EXCRETORY SYSTEM
YELLOW SMOOTHIE WITH OILS

Ingredients: 2 large bananas, 1 small pineapple, 2 yellow capsicum, 1 cup yellow cherry tomatoes, ½ cup mild flavoured olive oil, ⅛ cup water.

Method: Chop all ingredients and place in a blender with the oil on high speed until smooth and creamy. Add the water until desired consistency. (serves 2)

GALLSTONES

WHAT IS IT?... **Gallstones** are hard stone-like deposits found in the gallbladder, made up of undissolved bile cholesterol and bilirubin created by the liver and stored in the gallbladder.

BODY – EPICURE

- **Fastest...** Water fast for 7–10 days **OR...**
- Cabala juice fast for 14–21 days.
- Drink one cup of freshly juiced, with peels on, lemon juice, every single day. You can add water to this to dilute but must be one whole cup of lemon.
- LIVER FLUSH—Drink one litre of grapefruit juice and one cup of organic virgin olive oil blended together 30 minutes prior to going to bed. Typically the next day you will pass gallstones and bile in the stool. You may need to do this two or three days in a row.
- Fruit diet—eat and juice locally grown, fresh, raw organic fruits for 30 days, just fruit, juices and water.
- Yellow—eat all and any yellow foods.
- Drink one litre per 22 kilos bodyweight of pure water, every day—you can add pure lemon oil to this.
- Sunshine—Develop the darkest suntan you can by covering your body in Divine Body Butter or coconut oil and then exposing at least 70% of your body to the sun for one hour every day (30 mins each side).
- **ESSENTIAL OIL...** lemon, lime, peppermint.
- (Divine, Pulse, Ra 24ct See Salt, pure essential oils, Himalayan rock salt available in the USA **www.thedontolman.com/store** and Australia **www.lynnienichols.com/shop**)

BODY *FOODS THAT HEAL*	MIND *POSSIBLE EMOTIONAL CAUSE*	SPIRIT *IMBALANCED CHAKRA*
---	---	---
SIGNATURE FOODS... apples, beer, black pepper, cucumbers, flaxseeds, green beans, lentils, okra, plums, psyllium, quinoa, sweet potatoes, sauerkraut, leafy greens, fermented foods	• Are you feeling bitter/resentful, unable to forgive, critical and controlling of others? • Are you blaming others for your hurt? • Is anger/resentment stopping you from being your authentic self and making you want to control others?	Solar Plexus Chakra-

DIGESTIVE/EXCRETORY SYSTEM
GALLBLADDER FLUSH

Ingredients: 1 litre of grapefruit juice, 1 cup of organic virgin olive oil

Method: Blend 1 litre of grapefruit juice and 1 cup of organic virgin olive oil together and drink 30 minutes prior to going to bed. Typically the next day you will pass gallstones and bile in the stool. You may need to do this two or three days in a row.

GASTROPARESIS

***WHAT IS IT?...** **Gastroparesis** is a condition caused by abnormally weak stomach muscles, resulting in a delay in the emptying of food from the stomach into the intestine and causing symptoms such as bloating, nausea, vomiting, and heartburn.

***BODY – EPICURE*

- **Fastest...** Water fast for 7–10 days **OR...**
- Cabala juice fast for 14–28 days.
- Eat foods high in starch and any and all foods that grow under the ground, (tubers) especially sweet potato and regular potatoes—can have these raw, fried, mashed or baked. Also eat garlic, onion, carrots and bananas.
- Eat a lot of blueberries, these can be fresh or organic dried.
- Eat two cups of natural organic yoghurt each day and other ferments such as sauerkraut, kombucha, keffir, olives in brine to re-establish the flora and fauna of the gut.
- Eat sharp cheddar cheese at the onset of heartburn/reflux.
- Drink one litre per 22 kilos bodyweight of pure water every day.
- Do a colon cleanse with bentonite clay and herbs for cleaning of the digestive tract/colon and to rid toxic plaque buildup.
- Salt covenant—drink one litre of warm water with two heaped teaspoons of sea salt first thing each morning to flush the digestive tract and colon.
- Do self-administered daily colonics. (Enema douche travel kits available www.lynnienichols.com/shop)
- Develop the darkest suntan you can by covering your body in Divine Body Butter or coconut oil and then exposing at least 70% of your body to the sun for one hour every day (30 mins each side).
- **ESSENTIAL OIL...** ginger, lemon, fennel, peppermint, lavender.
- (Divine, Pulse, colon cleanses, Ra 24ct See Salt, Himalayan rock salt available in the USA **www.thedontolman.com/store** and Australia **www.lynnienichols.com/shop**)

BODY *FOODS THAT HEAL*	MIND *POSSIBLE EMOTIONAL CAUSE*	SPIRIT *IMBALANCED CHAKRA*
---	---	---
SIGNATURE FOODS... apples, beer, black pepper, cucumbers, flaxseeds, green beans, lentils, okra, plums, psyllium, quinoa, sweet potatoes, sauerkraut, leafy greens, fermented foods	• Are you constantly experiencing feelings of fear, worry, uncertainty? • Are you living in a state of negativity instead of focusing on the positive? • Are you afraid of the new?	Solar Plexus Chakra-

DIGESTIVE/EXCRETORY SYSTEM
CURRIED SWEET POTAO SOUP WITH BANANA SWIRL

Ingredients: 4 large sweet potatoes, 6 large cloves of garlic, 4 large brown onions, 4 large carrots, 1 medium banana, 1 tbsp curry, 1 tsp sea salt, ½ cup organic natural yoghurt, 6 cups water

Method: Scrub the sweet potatoes and carrots and cut into small chunks, toss in a bowl with coconut oil then place on a baking tray in moderate oven until soft and caramelised. In a large pan, fry the onion and garlic in coconut oil for a couple of minutes. Add the curry powder, vegetables, salt and 6 cups of water and bring to the boil, simmer for 15 minutes.

Allow to cool slightly before placing in a blender on high speed until smooth and creamy, return to the pan for re-heating. Whizz the banana and natural yoghurt together in a blender until smooth then pour into a squeeze bottle. Place the hot soup into serving bowls and garnish with a banana swirl. (serves 2)

GERD (GASTROESOPHAGEAL RELUX DISEASE)

WHAT IS IT?... **GERD i**s a common digestive disorder that affects the muscle between the oesophagus and stomach called the lower oesophageal sphincter, causing chronic heartburn and indigestion.

BODY – EPICURE

- **Fastest...** Water fast for 7–10 days **OR...**
- Cabala juice fast for 28 days.
- Eat a diet of green organic salads with kale, spinach etc., fermented foods such as organic kefirs, olives in brine, kombucha, sauerkraut, tempeh. Also eat raw organic natural yoghurts and organic cheddar cheese.
- Eat sharp cheddar cheese as soon as you feel reflux.
- Eat two apples and one cup of Brazil nuts each day.
- Drink one litre per 22 kilos bodyweight of pure water every day—you can add pure lemon oil to this.
- Sunshine—Develop the darkest suntan you can by covering your body in Divine Body Butter or coconut oil and then exposing at least 70% of your body to the sun for one hour every day (30 mins each side).
- **ESSENTIAL OIL...** lemon, ginger, peppermint, lavender.
- (Divine, Pulse, Ra 24ct See Salt, Himalayan rock salt available in the USA **www.thedontolman.com/store** and Australia **www.lynnienichols.com/shop**)

BODY *FOODS THAT HEAL*	MIND *POSSIBLE EMOTIONAL CAUSE*	SPIRIT *IMBALANCED CHAKRA*
---	---	---
SIGNATURE FOODS... apples, beer, black pepper, cucumbers, flaxseeds, green beans, lentils, okra, plums, psyllium, quinoa, sweet potatoes, sauerkraut, leafy greens, fermented foods	• Are you fearful of change, dreading what's to come? • Are you worried about the past? • Is unforgiveness burning you up inside?	Solar Plexus Chakra-

DIGESTIVE/EXCRETORY SYSTEM
CRUSTED TEMPEH WITH KALE SALAD

Ingredients: 1 packet of organic tempeh, 3 large kale leaves, 1 cup baby spinach leaves, ½ cup pitted Kalamata olives in brine, 2 large green apples, 1 cup sauerkraut, ½ cup tamari, 1 cup Brazil nuts, 1 cup raw organic natural yoghurt, ½ cup organic kefir, ½ cup tahini, pinch Himalayan salt

Method: Pulse the Brazil nuts in a blender until breadcrumb consistency, then place in a bowl. Cut the tempeh into 1 cm sticks and marinate in tamari for a few minutes before frying in coconut oil until golden brown each side. Remove from pan and toss in the nut crumb/ salt mix until well coated. Set aside to cool

In a salad bowl, mix the finely sliced kale, spinach leaves, olives, sauerkraut and finely diced apple. Place a big handful on each plate and lay the crusted tempeh on top. Combine the yoghurt, kefir, tahini and a little salt and drizzle this over the salad just before serving. (serves 2)

HAEMORRHOIDS/PILES

***WHAT IS IT?...** **Haemorrhoids** are inflamed veins in the anus and rectum that cause itching, discomfort and bleeding.

***BODY – EPICURE*

- **Fastest...** Water fast for 7–10 days **OR...**
- Cabala juice fast for 14–21 days.
- Fruit diet—eat and juice locally grown, fresh, raw organic fruits for 30 days, just fruit, juices and water.
- Eat more fibre, especially celery, carrots, apples.
- Drink senna tea.
- Use extra virgin olive oil or Golden ReLeaf oil—put a little on your finger and insert into the anus, pushing everything back up inside. To keep the veins inside where they belong practice kegel exercises by tightening the pelvic floor/anus muscles for 15 seconds at a time then releasing. Do this for one minute at a time 4 x per day.
- Have plenty of nature-made salt in the diet.
- Have a shotglass full of olive oil every day—you can dip this in bread and eat it or put into a smoothie or on a salad as dressing.
- Do a colon cleanse with bentonite clay and herbs for cleaning of the digestive tract/colon and to rid toxic plaque buildup.
- Salt flush—Drink one litre of warm water with two heaped teaspoons of sea salt first thing each morning to flush the digestive tract and colon.
- Drink one litre per 22 kilos bodyweight of pure water every day.
- Sunshine—Develop the darkest suntan you can by covering your body in Divine Body Butter or coconut oil and then exposing at least 70% of your body to the sun for one hour every day (30 mins each side).
- **ESSENTIAL OIL...** frankincense, clove, peppermint, tea tree, myrtle, cinnamon.
- (Divine, Golden Releaf, Colon Cleanses, Pulse, Ra 24ct See Salt, Himalayan rock salt available in the USA **www.thedontolman.com/store** and Australia **www.lynnienichols.com/shop**)

BODY *FOODS THAT HEAL*	MIND *POSSIBLE EMOTIONAL CAUSE*	SPIRIT *IMBALANCED CHAKRA*
---	---	---
SIGNATURE FOODS... apples, beer, black pepper, cucumbers, flaxseeds, green beans, lentils, okra, plums, psyllium, quinoa, sweet potatoes, sauerkraut, leafy greens, fermented foods	• Are you holding on to anger over the past? • Are you feeling burdened or afraid? • Are you afraid to speak your truth for fear of rejection?	Solar Plexus Chakra- / Root Chakra- **colour Red**

DIGESTIVE/EXCRETORY SYSTEM
APPLE AND ALMOND CELERY STICK SNACK

Ingredients: 4 large sticks of celery, 1 jar of organic almond butter, 1 large apple, 1 large carrot

Method: In a processor, process the apple and carrot until chopped well. Mix with the almond butter, then push into the celery sticks and cut into bite-sized pieces.

HEPATITIS A, B & C

***WHAT IS IT?...** **Hepatitis A, B & C** are viral diseases that impact the liver causing inflammation and eventually, if untreated, serious conditions such as cirrhosis, liver cancer, and liver failure.

Hepatitis A can be spread by oral and faecal transmission and even by consuming contaminated water or food. Poor personal hygiene and sanitation is most often the cause. Hepatitis B cannot be spread by interactions such as sharing a meal or eating food prepared by someone who is infected as it is a blood-borne pathogen and therefore is transmitted via direct blood-to-blood contact. Hepatitis C is also spread via contaminated blood, these days most often by contaminated needles.

***BODY – EPICURE*

- **Fastest...** Water fast for 7–10 days **OR...**
- Cabala juice fast for 14–21 days.
- Drink one cup of freshly juiced, with peels on, lemon juice, every single day. You can add water to this to dilute but must be one whole cup of lemon.
- LIVER FLUSH—Drink one litre of grapefruit juice and one cup of organic virgin olive oil blended together 30 minutes prior to going to bed. Typically the next day you will pass gallstones and bile in the stool. You may need to do this two or three days in a row.
- No refined carbohydrates and sugars, sugary drinks and processed foods as these will only damage the liver further.
- No hard alcohol.
- Fruit diet—eat and juice locally grown, fresh, raw organic fruits for 30 days, just fruit, juices and water.
- Yellow—eat all and any yellow foods, such as grapes, apples, squash, bananas, lemons, tomatoes, capsicum.
- Eat a well-balanced diet—if you are having trouble eating or you are experiencing digestive problems, stick to small, simple meals and water throughout the day. Eat plenty of fresh fruits and vegetables, avocados and coconut oil have healthy fats that are needed. Other foods that help are sweet potatoes, bananas, ginger root, and turmeric.
-
- Zinc is necessary for normal liver function and zinc foods are powerful antioxidants that boost immune function, which is important for healing hepatitis C. Foods high in zinc include black-eyed peas, soybeans, lima beans, mushrooms, pumpkin and pumpkin seeds, brightly coloured fruits and vegetables, kelp and organic non-GMO wholegrains.
- Probiotics help to support the liver because the beneficial bacteria in the gut promote the health and functioning of the liver. Probiotic foods include organic yogurt, kefir, organic no-animal-rennet white cheeses, sauerkraut and other fermented veggies, kombucha, garlic-stuffed olives and any other saline ferments.
- Black Seed Oil for its antioxidant, anti-inflammatory, anti-cancer and immune-stimulating effects. A key compound of black seed oil, thymoquinone, protects the liver from damage through several mechanisms like scavenging free radicals and elevating glutathione levels.
- Sunshine/Vitamin D—Develop the darkest suntan you can by covering your body in Divine Body Butter or coconut oil and then exposing at least 70% of your body to the sun for one hour every day (30 mins each side). Eat mushrooms that have been set out in the sun for an hour as they have a high amount vitamin D—eat them raw or cooked.
- Gentle exercise daily can help to relieve symptoms such as tiredness and low energy. Outdoor yoga or walking in the fresh air is beneficial for boosting energy levels and benefiting your mind and emotions.
- Drink one litre per 22 kilos bodyweight of pure water, every day—you can add pure lemon oil to this.
- Take colloidal Silver with fulvic acid.
- **ESSENTIAL OIL...** lemon, peppermint, rosemary, ginger, lavender, turmeric.
- (Divine, Pulse, Ra 24ct See Salt, Nature's Silver Bullet (colloidial silver with fulvic acid), pure essential oils, Himalayan rock salt available in the USA **www.thedontolman.com/store** and Australia **www.lynnienichols.com/shop**)

BODY	MIND	SPIRIT
FOODS THAT HEAL	**POSSIBLE EMOTIONAL CAUSE**	**IMBALANCED CHAKRA**
---	---	---
SIGNATURE FOODS... apples, beer, black pepper, cucumbers, flaxseeds, green beans, lentils, okra, plums, psyllium, quinoa, sweet potatoes, sauerkraut, leafy greens, fermented foods	• Have you got shit on the liver? In other words are you holding anger, resentment, hatred or rage? Are you unable to forgive? • Are you fearful of change?	Solar Plexus Chakra-

***NOTE...** research shows that it's common for people with chronic hepatitis C to have a lack of vitamin D because it needs to be stored in the liver and fatty tissues.*

DIGESTIVE/EXCRETORY SYSTEM
SUNSHINE NOODLES

Ingredients: 2 medium yellow zuchini, 1 cup diced pineapple, ½ cup yellow apple cut into matchsticks with a mandolin, 1 cup yellow cherry tomatoes halved, 1 cup yellow capsicum diced, ½ cup freshly squeezed lemon juice and zest of one lemon, 1 cup olive oil, ½ tsp of Himalayan salt, 1-2 tbsp lemon thyme

Method: Make a dressing out of the olive oil, lemon juice, thyme and salt. Use a spiraliser to make zuchini noodles. Combine all other ingredients and add to the noodles. Gently toss with dressing and serve. (serves 4)

HERNIA

***WHAT IS IT?...** **Hernias o**ccur when there's a weakened area of the abdominal wall that allows for the internal organ/area to protrude outward. The cause of this is often strain from physical movement such as sport/exercise. There are several types of hernias ... these include hiatus hernias of the upper stomach, umbilical- of the belly button, incisional- as a result of incision and inguinal of the inner and outer groin areas.

***BODY – EPICURE*

- **Fastest...** Water fast for 7–10 days **OR...**
- Cabala juice fast for 21 days.
- Massage the area whilst soaking in a hot salt water bath.
- Massage with Healing Chrysm three or four times per day
- For a groin hernia, lie on your back and pull your legs up to the chest then stick your legs in the air and spread them to the left and right as far as you can until it hits the stress point; then pull straight back up again. Do this 12 times x 3 times per day, along with the salt soaks and Healing Chrysm.
- Get the herb 'hawthorn', some lemon seeds, orange seeds, sea kelp and water and make a mix of this in the blender. Drink one cup once or twice per day.
- Drink one litre per 22 kilos bodyweight of pure water every day.
- Drink senna tea or do a salt flush to clear out the bowel.
- Do a colon cleanse with bentonite clay and herbs for cleaning of the digestive tract/colon and to rid toxic plaque buildup.
- Do daily self-administered colonics with an enema bag. (Enema douche travel kits available **www.lynnienichols.com/shop**)
- Sunshine—Develop the darkest suntan you can by covering your body in Divine Body Butter or coconut oil and then exposing at least 70% of your body to the sun for one hour every day (30 mins each side).
- **ESSENTIAL OIL...** lemon, basil, helichrysum, lemongrass, cypress, lavender, geranium.
- (Divine, Pulse, Ra 24ct See Salt, Himalayan rock salt available in the USA **www.thedontolman.com/store** and Australia **www.lynnienichols.com/shop**)

BODY	MIND	SPIRIT
FOODS THAT HEAL	***POSSIBLE EMOTIONAL CAUSE***	***IMBALANCED CHAKRA***
---	---	---
SIGNATURE FOODS... apples, beer, black pepper, cucumbers, flaxseeds, green beans, lentils, okra, plums, psyllium, quinoa, sweet potatoes, sauerkraut, leafy greens, fermented foods	• Are you feeling angry and stuck, unsure of what to do? • Are you straining under life's pressures? • Which relationships are ruptured or rupturing?	Solar Plexus Chakra-

DIGESTIVE/EXCRETORY SYSTEM
CHILLI AVO NUT BUTTER

Ingredients: 4 cups baby spinach leaves, 1 packet of goat's feta, 1 cup green olives stuffed with garlic, 1 cup sauerkraut

Method: Cut the feta into cubes and olives in halves. Place all ingredients together in a salad bowl, toss and serve. (serves 2)

INCONTINENCE

***WHAT IS IT?...** **Incontinence** is when there's a lack of control over the bladder, resulting in urine leakage. There are different types of bladder incontinence. Stress incontinence is where involuntary leakage of urination takes place when pressure is applied to the bladder; for example, when coughing, sneezing, laughing, lifting heavy objects and exercise. Urge incontinence is when there is a sudden urge to urinate that cannot be controlled.

***BODY – EPICURE*

- Drink cranberry juice.
- Eat organic cranberries, fresh or dried, as well as cranberry Pulse.
- Drink one litre per 22 kilos bodyweight of pure water every day.
- Do kegel exercises by tightening the muscles, holding for 10–15 seconds and then letting go for one minute, repeating four or five times. (Women can use a jade egg to strengthen the pelvic floor muscles—available **www.lynnienichols.com**)

- Develop the darkest suntan you can by covering your body in Divine Body Butter or coconut oil and then exposing at least 70% of your body to the sun for one hour every day (30 mins each side).
- **ESSENTIAL OIL...** clary sage, ylang ylang, lavender, pumpkin seed, spearmint, geranium, myrtle, nutmeg, german chamomile.
- (Divine, Cranberry Pulse, Ra 24ct See Salt available in the USA **www.thedontolman.com/store** and Australia **www.lynnienichols.com/shop**)

BODY FOODS THAT HEAL	MIND POSSIBLE EMOTIONAL CAUSE	SPIRIT IMBALANCED CHAKRA
---	---	---
SIGNATURE FOODS... apples, beer, black pepper, cucumbers, flaxseeds, green beans, lentils, okra, plums, psyllium, quinoa, sweet potatoes, sauerkraut, leafy greens, fermented foods	• Are you holding long-suppressed emotions? • Are you feeling unable to be your authentic self? • Are you afraid to go after what you truly want, do you feel it's too late for this?	Solar Plexus Chakra- Sacral Chakra- Colour Orange

DIGESTIVE/EXCRETORY SYSTEM
CRANBERRY & APPLE JUICE

Ingredients: 2 cups dried or fresh cranberries, 4 apples

Method: Put ingredients through a commercial juicer and drink several times per day

INDIGESTION (see GERD)

***WHAT IS IT?...* **Indigestion, also known as dispepsia or heartburn,** is discomfort or a burning pain in the upper abdomen heart area behind the breastbone. Indigestion is often related to emotional issues such as anxiety and fear and can also be a symptom of other diseases such as GERD.

***BODY – EPICURE*

- **Fastest...** Water fast for 7–10 days **OR...**
- Cabala juice fast for 28 days.
- Eat a diet of green organic salads with kale, spinach etc., fermented foods such as organic kefirs, olives in brine, kombucha, sauerkraut, tempeh. Also eat raw organic natural yoghurts and organic cheddar cheese.
- Eat sharp cheddar cheese as soon as you feel reflux.
- Drink one litre per 22 kilos bodyweight of pure water every day—you can add pure lemon oil to this.
- Drink senna tea or do a salt flush to clear out the bowel.
- Do a colon cleanse with bentonite clay and herbs for cleaning of the digestive tract/colon and to rid toxic plaque buildup.
- Do daily self-administered colonics with an enema bag. (Enema douche travel kits available **www.lynnienichols.com/shop**)
- Sunshine—Develop the darkest suntan you can by covering your body in Divine Body Butter or coconut oil and then exposing at least 70% of your body to the sun for one hour every day (30 mins each side).
- **ESSENTIAL OIL...** lemon, ginger, peppermint, lavender.
- (Divine, Pulse, Ra 24ct See Salt, Himalayan rock salt available in the USA **www.thedontolman.com/store** and Australia **www.lynnienichols.com/shop**)

BODY *FOODS THAT HEAL*	MIND *POSSIBLE EMOTIONAL CAUSE*	SPIRIT *IMBALANCED CHAKRA*
---	---	---
SIGNATURE FOODS... apples, beer, black pepper, cucumbers, flaxseeds, green beans, lentils, okra, plums, psyllium, quinoa, sweet potatoes, sauerkraut, leafy greens, fermented foods	• Has fear got a grip on you? • Are you feeling chronic fear and/or anxiety? • What are you dreading?	Solar Plexus Chakra-

DIGESTIVE/EXCRETORY SYSTEM
CUCUMBERS IN FERMENT

Ingredients: 4 large cucumbers diced, 2 cups organic natural yoghurt

Method: Mix the two ingredients together and eat when experiencing indigestion

LACTOSE INTOLERANCE

WHAT IS IT?... **Lactose intolerance** is the reduced ability to digest the carbohydrate naturally found in milk, called lactose, due to insufficient gut enzyme called lactase. Symptoms of lactose intolerance include gas, bloating, diarrhoea and abdominal pain.

BODY – EPICURE

- **Fastest...** Water fast for 7–10 days **OR...**
- Do a cabala juice fast for 28 days—can have coconut water also.
- Eat lots of leafy greens as these have the highest levels of calcium.
- Drink one litre per 22 kilos bodyweight of pure water every day.
- Develop the darkest suntan you can by covering your body in Divine Body Butter or coconut oil and then exposing at least 70% of your body to the sun for one hour every day (30 mins each side).
- **ESSENTIAL OIL...** lemon, fennel, peppermint, ginger, chamomile.
- (Divine, Pulse, Ra 24ct See Salt, Himalayan rock salt available in the USA **www.thedontolman.com/store** and Australia **www.lynnienichols.com/shop**)

BODY *FOODS THAT HEAL*	MIND *POSSIBLE EMOTIONAL CAUSE*	SPIRIT *IMBALANCED CHAKRA*
---	---	---
SIGNATURE FOODS... apples, beer, black pepper, cucumbers, flaxseeds, green beans, lentils, okra, plums, psyllium, quinoa, sweet potatoes, sauerkraut, leafy greens, fermented foods	• Are you having problems digesting life's experiences and feeling unfulfilled? • Are you lacking in compassion and care for others/yourself?	Solar Plexus Chakra-

DIGESTIVE/EXCRETORY SYSTEM
CALCIUM-BOOST SMOOTHIE BOWL

Ingredients: 1 cup each of shredded spinach and kale, 1 cup organic coconut milk or cream, 2 banana. Suggested calcium fruits for garnish: orange, tangerine, dried apricots, kiwifruit, dates, pitted prunes

Method: Place the greens, coconut cream and banana in a blender on high speed until smooth and creamy. Pour into serving bowls and decorate with your selection of garnish fruits. (serves 2)

MELANOMA / SKIN CANCER

WHAT IS IT?... **Melanoma** is most often cancer of the skin originating in melanocytes, which are pigment (melanin)-producing cells which also form moles, and often this is where the melanoma develops.

Skin cancer is a growth of out-of-control abnormal skin cells. It is stated in medical journals that the number one cause of skin cancer is lack of fresh fruit and vegetables eaten in season and second to this are chemical-based sunburn creams.

BODY – EPICURE

- Get off all medication and supplements- herbs in the form of powders or teas are okay, but no pills or capsules!
- Fastest... Water fast for 14–21 days OR...
- Do the five-week 35% food-grade hydrogen peroxide protocol combined with a cabala juice fast for 21–28 days.
- Apply 35% food-grade hydrogen peroxide topically.
- Apply lemon juice to the spot and go out into the sun. Put aloe vera on two hrs before bed.
- Drink lemon, freshly juiced with the peels on, every day.
- Eat and juice a locally grown, fresh, raw organic fruit diet.
- Suck on rock salt every day.
- Drink one litre per 22 kilos bodyweight of pure water every day.
- Have daily a berry, asparaus smoothie, consisting of two cups berries and 12 stalks of asparagus (can add a banana to sweeten) plus water to desired consistency. Drink within 45 minutes of making it. Can eat the foods instead if preferred.
- Salt covenant—Drink one litre of water with two heaped teaspoons of sea salt first thing each morning to flush the digestive tract and colon.
- Joule of Thor—have one shotglass every day.
- Do a colon cleanse with bentonite clay and herbs for cleaning of the digestive tract/colon and to rid toxic plaque buildup.
- Do self-administered daily colonics to remove toxicity. (Enema douche travel kits available www.lynnienichols.com/shop)
- Develop the darkest suntan you can by covering your body in Divine Body Butter or coconut oil and then exposing at least 70% of your body to the sun for one hour every day (30 mins each side).
- **ESSENTIAL OIL...** frankincense, thyme, myrrh, clary sage, lemon and other citrus.
- (Divine, colon cleanses, Pulse, Ra 24ct See Salt, Himalayan rock salt available in the USA **www.thedontolman.com/store** and Australia **www.lynnienichols.com/shop**)

BODY FOODS THAT HEAL	MIND POSSIBLE EMOTIONAL CAUSE	SPIRIT IMBALANCED CHAKRA
---	---	---
SIGNATURE FOODS... apples, beer, black pepper, cucumbers, flaxseeds, green beans, lentils, okra, plums, psyllium, quinoa, sweet potatoes, sauerkraut, leafy greens, fermented foods	• Are thoughts of being not good enough/unworthy eating away at you? • Are you unable to love and accept yourself?	Solar Plexus Chakra-

DIGESTIVE/EXCRETORY SYSTEM
CLEANSING LEMON SMOOTHIE

Ingredients: 2 lemons- zest and juice, ½ cup almonds, ½ cup cashews, 1 tbsp chia seeds, the gel of 1 large aloe vera, 1 small pineapple, 2 large bananas, 1 cup coconut milk, 1 tbsp honey

Method: Place all ingredients together in a blender and whizz on high speed until smooth and creamy. Add extra coconut milk or water to desired consistency. (serves 2)

NAIL FUNGUS / ONYCHOMYCOSIS/TINEA

***WHAT IS IT?...** **Nail fungus/tinea** is a fungal infection that affects the toenails and/or fingernails due to fungal overgrowth, which causes infection and results in thickening, yellowing and crumbling of the nail.

***BODY – EPICURE*

- First and foremost, cut ALL dead nail away as this takes away the humid breeding ground that fungus thrives in.
- Use 35% food-grade hydrogen peroxide neat, once or twice a day, and then oil of oregano.
- Cabala juice fast for 14–28 days.
- 2 cups of natural organic yoghurt and other ferments daily, such as sauerkraut, fermented veggies, kombucha, and kefir, each day to re-establish the flora and fauna of the gut.
- Drink one litre per 22 kilos bodyweight of pure water every day.
- Suck on Himalayan rock salt, the size of the last segment of your little finger, daily.
- Develop the darkest suntan you can by covering your body in Divine Body Butter or coconut oil and then exposing at least 70% of your body to the sun for one hour every day (30 mins each side).
- **ESSENTIAL OIL...** oregano, tea tree, clove, eucalyptus, lavender, cinnamon.
- (Divine, 35% food-grade hydrogen peroxide, Ra 24ct See Salt, Himalayan rock salt available in the USA **www.thedontolman.com/store** and Australia **www. lynnienichols.com/shop**)

BODY *FOODS THAT HEAL*	MIND *POSSIBLE EMOTIONAL CAUSE*	SPIRIT *IMBALANCED CHAKRA*
---	---	---
SIGNATURE FOODS... apples, beer, black pepper, cucumbers, flaxseeds, green beans, lentils, okra, plums, psyllium, quinoa, sweet potatoes, sauerkraut, leafy greens, fermented foods	• Are you stuck in old habits, feeling stale? • Are you knowing you need to make change yet fearful or unsure what to do next?	Solar Plexus Chakra- / Root Chakra- **colour Red**

***NOTE... *Can be contagious.*

DIGESTIVE/EXCRETORY SYSTEM
SAVOURY POTATO WITH FERMENT

Ingredients: 2 large potatoes, 1 large brown onion, 3 cloves garlic, 2 cups mushroom, sea salt and pepper, 4 tbsp fermented vegetables

Method: Bake the potatoes in oven on high temperature so that the outside becomes crunchy and insides soft and creamy. Dice the garlic and brown onions. Fry for a few minutes in coconut oil and then add the sliced mushrooms. Continue to cook for a couple more minutes. Add sea salt and pepper to taste.

Cut the potatoes in half lengthways, drizzle with olive oil and season with sea salt before topping with the savoury mushroom mix. Garnish with a spoon of fermented veggies. (serves 2)

OVERACTIVE BLADDER SYNDROME

***WHAT IS IT?...* **Overactive bladder syndrome** is where there is a problem with the bladder that causes an uncontrollable urge to urinate, causing a leakage of urine (incontinence).

BODY – EPICURE

- **Fastest...** Water fast for 7–10 days **OR...**
- Eat organic cranberries, fresh or dried, as well as cranberry Pulse and drink cranberry juice on a daily basis.
- Drink one litre per 22 kilos bodyweight of pure water every day.
- Develop the darkest suntan you can by covering your body in Divine Body Butter or coconut oil and then exposing at least 70% of your body to the sun for one hour every day (30 mins each side).
- Do kegel exercises by tightening the muscles, holding for 10–15 seconds and then letting go for one minute, repeating four or five times. (Women can use a jade egg to strengthen the pelvic floor muscles—available www.lynnienichols.com)
- Do a colon cleanse with bentonite clay and herbs to remove toxic plaque buildup, which may be affecting optimum bladder function.
- **ESSENTIAL OIL...** clary sage, ylang ylang, lavender, pumpkin seed, spearmint, geranium, myrtle, nutmeg, german chamomile.
- (Divine, Cranberry Pulse, colon cleanses, Ra 24ct See Salt available in the USA **www.thedontolman.com/store** and Australia **www.lynnienichols.com/shop**)

BODY *FOODS THAT HEAL*	MIND *POSSIBLE EMOTIONAL CAUSE*	SPIRIT *IMBALANCED CHAKRA*
---	---	---
SIGNATURE FOODS... apples, beer, black pepper, cucumbers, flaxseeds, green beans, lentils, okra, plums, psyllium, quinoa, sweet potatoes, sauerkraut, leafy greens, fermented foods	• Are you feeling peed off about something or someone? • Are you afraid to let go of old outdated beliefs/past experiences?	Solar Plexus Chakra- / Sacral Chakra- colour Orange

DIGESTIVE/EXCRETORY SYSTEM
CRANBERRY & PEANUT CHOCKY

Ingredients: 1 cup dried cranberries, 1 cup whole roasted peanuts, ½ cup smooth peanut butter, ¾ cup cacao, 3-4 tbsp raw honey, ½ cup coconut oil

Method: Roast the peanuts in an oven or toast in a dry pan on the stove until golden brown. Place all ingredients in a mixing bowl and combine well. Line a casserole dish with banana leaf or greaseproof paper. Pour in the mix, spread evenly, then place in the fridge for 1 hr to set. Cut into squares and store in an airtight container in the fridge or freezer

PARASITES / WORM INFECTION (intestinal)

***WHAT IS IT?...** **Parasitic worms** are organisms that can live in the human body, feeding off the blood or undigested food in the intestines of their host, causing sickness and disease by destroying body tissues and creating their own toxic waste. There are hundreds of parasitic worms that thrive in the environment of the intestines, heart, brain, blood etc. of the human body, and they range in size from minute to meters long. Symptoms of parasitic infection include skin rashes, fatigue, diarrhoea, nervousness, anaemia, asthma and more.

***BODY – EPICURE*

- **Fastest...** Water fast for 7–10 days **OR...**
- Cabala juice fast for 14–21 days then continue on a liquid diet of juices, smoothies and pureed soups.
- Snack on ½ cup of raw pumpkin seeds each day.
- Eat one or two cloves of raw garlic each day and one onion a day—can be red, white or brown.
- Parasites can't handle a lot of fibre so eat two large carrots every day—late afternoon.
- Eat figs daily, fresh or dried.
- Parasites hate coconut oil so make a mix of coconut oil/one clove garlic and oregano, aniseed or clove oil (parasites hate all of these so it doesn't matter which you use) and drink a dose of this daily for as long as necessary. Can also mix one teaspoon of black walnut oil with a few drops of aniseed, clove or oregano oil together with organic natural yoghurt and have a spoonful of this daily.
- Drink fresh juice of lemon, lime, grapefruit and orange—parasites can not stand citrus.
- Drink two tbsp apple cider vinegar in hot water and one tablespoon of raw organic honey two or three times per day during your liquid fast.
- Take 7 mg of Boron per day... Dissolve one level teaspoon of Borax/Boron in one litre of water to make a concentrated solution. Take one teaspoon of this concentrate twice daily with meals.
- Eat and drink ferments such as kefir, kombucha, natural organic yoghurt, sauerkraut, olives in brine, tempeh, and organic blue cheese.
- Do a colon cleanse with bentonite clay and herbs for cleansing of the digestive tract/colon and to rid toxic plaque buildup that parasites thrive in.
- Do self-administered daily colonics to remove toxicity. (Enema douche travel kits available **www.lynnienichols.com/shop**)
- Wash sheets and towels daily for one week to avoid recontamination.
- Drink one litre per 22 kilos bodyweight of pure water every day.
- Sunshine—Develop the darkest suntan you can by covering your body in Divine Body Butter or coconut oil and then exposing at least 70% of your body to the sun for one hour every day (30 mins each side).
- **ESSENTIAL OIL...** citrus, black walnut, aniseed, clove, oregano.
- (Divine, colon cleanses, Ra 24ct See Salt, Himalayan rock salt, essential oils of lemon, orange, lime available in the USA **www.thedontolman.com/store** and Australia **www.lynnienichols.com/shop**)

BODY	MIND	SPIRIT
FOODS THAT HEAL	**POSSIBLE EMOTIONAL CAUSE**	**IMBALANCED CHAKRA**
---	---	---
SIGNATURE FOODS... apples, beer, black pepper, cucumbers, flaxseeds, green beans, lentils, okra, plums, psyllium, quinoa, sweet potatoes, sauerkraut, leafy greens, fermented foods	• Is someone or something eating away at you? • Are you giving your power away to somebody else?	Solar Plexus Chakra-

DIGESTIVE/EXCRETORY SYSTEM
CARROT PEPITA SALAD

Ingredients: 1 cup of raw pumpkin seeds, 2 cloves of garlic, ½ red onion, 4 large carrots, 1 cup dried figs, 1 cup raw cashews

DRESSING; 2 tbsp honey, ⅛ cup apple cider vinegar, ½ cup fresh squeezed orange juice, 1 cup cold pressed organic olive oil, ½ tsp Himalayan salt

Method: Peel and grate the carrots with a coarse grater or mandolin. Finely dice the garlic and onion and slice the figs. Combine all ingredients together. Combine dressing ingredients and toss through the salad. (serves 2)

SALMONELLA FOOD POISONING / SALMONELLOSIS

***WHAT IS IT?...** **Salmonella food poisoning** is a disease affecting the intestinal tract, caused by the group of bacteria called 'salmonella'. Infection occurs through contaminated food and water, especially meat, poultry, fish and eggs. Symptoms include diarrhoea, abdominal cramps, and fever.

***BODY – EPICURE**

- **Fastest...** Water fast for 7–10 days **OR...**
- Cabala juice fast for 14–28 days.
- Salt covenant—Drink one litre of warm water with two heaped teaspoons of sea salt first thing each morning to flush the digestive tract and colon.
- Eat two cups of natural organic yoghurt each day to re-establish the flora and fauna of the gut as well as other ferments such as sauerkraut, organic kefirs and yoghurts, foods preserved in salt brine, and kombucha.
- Suck on Himalayan rock salt.
- Eat foods high in starch and any and all foods that grow under the ground (tubers), especially sweet potato and regular potatoes—can have these raw, fried, mashed or baked. Also eat garlic, onion, carrots and bananas.
- Eat a lot of blueberries, these can be fresh or organic dried.
- Drink one litre per 22 kilos bodyweight of pure water every day.
- Do a colon cleanse with herbs and bentonite clay.
- Develop the darkest suntan you can by covering your body in Divine Body Butter or coconut oil and then exposing at least 70% of your body to the sun for one hour every day (30 mins each side).
- **BEFORE TRAVELLING**—eat lots of berries and have lots of rock salt. Whilst away, keep sucking on rock salt and eat a vegetarian diet.
- **ESSENTIAL OIL...** oregano, thyme, ginger, lemon.
- (Divine, Pulse, Ra 24ct See Salt, Himalayan rock salt available in the USA **www.thedontolman.com/store** and Australia **www.lynnienichols.com/shop**)

BODY	MIND	SPIRIT
FOODS THAT HEAL	*POSSIBLE EMOTIONAL CAUSE*	*IMBALANCED CHAKRA*
---	---	---
SIGNATURE FOODS... apples, beer, black pepper, cucumbers, flaxseeds, green beans, lentils, okra, plums, psyllium, quinoa, sweet potatoes, sauerkraut, leafy greens, fermented foods	• Are you feeling defenceless, unable to protect yourself, attacked?	Solar Plexus Chakra-

DIGESTIVE/EXCRETORY SYSTEM
TUBER STEW WITH FERMENT

Ingredients: 3 large sweet potatoes, 4 yam, 4 large regular potatoes, 1 teaspoon garam masala, 1 teaspoon sweet paprika, ½ teaspoon turmeric, 6 large cloves garlic, 4 large brown onions, 1 cup natural yoghurt, 1 cup keffir, 1 tbsp sea salt, 3 tbsp coconut oil, 5 cups of water, ½ cup coriander

Method: Peel and dice the tubers, be sure to dice the yam into smaller pieces as it takes longer to cook than regular tubers. In a large pot, fry the onions and garlic in coconut oil for a couple of minutes; add the spices and continue to fry for half a minute. Add the vegetables and water to the onion mix. Bring to the boil then turn down and allow to simmer, stirring regularly until all vegetables are soft. Add a little extra water if necessary, remembering it is a stew, not a soup. Taste and add more salt if necessary.

Mix the yoghurt, keffir and coriander in a separate bowl. Serve the stew in bowls topped with a large dollop of the ferment. (serves 4)

VITILIGO

WHAT IS IT?... **Vitiligo** is a skin condition that is caused by a loss of cellular development of melanin production, causing patches of depigmented (white) skin on the body. This condition is almost always caused by chemicals in soaps, shampoos, drinks, insect spray residues, herbicides, pesticides, nail polish remover, moulds especially black mould, chemicals in water supplies, etc.

BODY – EPICURE

- **Fastest...** Water fast for 7–10 days **OR...**
- Cabala juice fast for 14–21 days whilst doing the five-week hydrogen peroxide protocol to oxygenate all 10,000 trillion cells of the body.
- **7 Day External Protocol...** 1 x per day 35% food-grade hydrogen peroxide on the de-pigmented patch; 2-3 x per day put lemon juice on the skin and go into the sun and every night rub fresh aloe vera into the patch of skin and leave this on all night.
- To boost melanin production, eat beans, lentils, legumes, peaches, watermelon and especially apricots as well as deep richly coloured foods such as dark chocolate, organic red wine and organic coffee.
- Different kinds of plants/flowers with dark colours such as beets, henna, black walnut without the shells, crushed and rubbed into the skin can also assist in melanin production.
- Do clay baths on the area ... apply bentonite/diatomaceous earth clay; let dry in the sun then rinse off to remove toxicity from the skin.
- One cup of freshly juiced, with peels on, lemon juice, every single day. You can add water to this to dilute but must be one whole cup of lemon.
- LIVER FLUSH—Drink one litre of grapefruit juice and one cup of organic virgin olive oil blended together 30 minutes prior to going to bed. Typically the next day you will pass gallstones and bile in the stool. You may need to do this two or three days in a row.
- Yellow—eat all and any yellow foods.
- Salt scrub—scrub the body daily with a mix of good oils and salt (you can purchase Renew Body Scrub); once you have rinsed off, pat dry and apply a body butter such as Divine.
- Drink one litre per 22 kilos bodyweight of pure water every day—you can add pure lemon oil to this.
- Sunshine—Develop the darkest suntan you can by covering your body in Divine Body Butter or coconut oil and then exposing at least 70% of your body to the sun for one hour every day (30 mins each side).
- **ESSENTIAL OIL...** babchi (bakuchi), black pepper, curry leaf, radish, lemon, tea tree, black seed, ginger, bergamot, carrot seed.
- (Divine, 35% food-grade hydrogen peroxide, developmental clarity clay (mix of bentonite and diatomaceous clay), Renew Body Scrub, Pulse, essential oil of lemon, Ra 24ct See Salt, Himalayan rock salt available in the USA **www.thedontolman.com/store** and Australia **www.lynnienichols.com/shop**)

BODY *FOODS THAT HEAL*	MIND *POSSIBLE EMOTIONAL CAUSE*	SPIRIT *IMBALANCED CHAKRA*
---	---	---
SIGNATURE FOODS... apples, beer, black pepper, cucumbers, flaxseeds, green beans, lentils, okra, plums, psyllium, quinoa, sweet potatoes, sauerkraut, leafy greens, fermented foods	• Are you feeling hurt and unable to forgive? • Are you feeling like a victim, is this causing you to be angry and judgemental? • Is anger/hatred eating away at you?	Solar Plexus Chakra-

DIGESTIVE/EXCRETORY SYSTEM
SPICY LENTIL AND APRICOT SOUP

Ingredients: 2 cups red lentils, 1 cup organic sulphate free dried apricots, 4 brown onions diced, 6 cloves garlic diced, 2.5cm fresh ginger chopped, 1 tbsp cumin powder, 1 tbsp curry powder, ¼ tsp cinnamon, 2 tsp paprika, 1 tbsp sea salt, 9 cups water

Method: Fry onions and garlic in coconut oil for a few minutes until onion softens. Add ginger, cumin, curry, cinnamon, paprika and stir for a minute or so before adding the lentils. Continue to stir for a further 2 minutes before adding the water and sea salt. Bring to boil then simmer for ½ hour until lentils are soft.

Add the whole dried apricots and turn off the pan. Taste and add extra salt if necessary. Let sit for a few minutes and then serve. (serves 4)

WILSON'S DISEASE

***WHAT IS IT?...** **Wilson's disease** is a condition in which copper accumulates in the tissues, affecting and damaging the liver, nervous system, brain, kidneys and eyes.

***BODY – EPICURE*

- **Fastest...** Water fast for 7–10 days **OR...**
- Cabala juice fast for 14–21 days.
- Drink one cup of freshly juiced, with peels on, lemon juice, every single day. You can add water to this to dilute but must be one whole cup of lemon over the day—can have with hot water and honey.
- LIVER FLUSH—Drink one litre of grapefruit juice and one cup of organic virgin olive oil blended together 30 minutes prior to going to bed. Typically the next day you will pass gallstones and bile in the stool. You may need to do this two or three days in a row.
- Eat a diet with lots of apples, nuts, seeds and avocados—the pectins target the brain where heavy metals accumulate. Also eat lots of potatoes.

- Yellow—eat all and any yellow foods such as grapes, capsicum, squash, banana, pineapple, tomatoes.
- Drink one litre per 22 kilos bodyweight of pure water every day—you can add pure lemon oil to this.
- Sunshine—Get at least 30 minutes of sunshine every day. Develop the darkest suntan you can by covering your body in Divine Body Butter or coconut oil and then exposing at least 70% of your body to the sun for one hour every day (30 mins each side).
- **ESSENTIAL OIL...** lemon, juniper, peppermint, rosemary.
- (Divine, Pulse, Ra 24ct See Salt, essential oil of lemon, Himalayan rock salt available the USA **www.thedontolman.com/store** and Australia **www.lynnienichols.com/shop**)

BODY	MIND	SPIRIT
FOODS THAT HEAL	**POSSIBLE EMOTIONAL CAUSE**	**IMBALANCED CHAKRA**
---	---	---
SIGNATURE FOODS... apples, beer, black pepper, cucumbers, flaxseeds, green beans, lentils, okra, plums, psyllium, quinoa, sweet potatoes, sauerkraut, leafy greens, fermented foods	• Are you feeling hurt and unable to forgive? • Are you feeling like a victim, is this causing you to be angry and judgemental? • Is anger/hatred eating away at you?	Solar Plexus Chakra-

---

DIGESTIVE/EXCRETORY SYSTEM
CRUNCHY SQUISHED POTATO WITH LEMON BUTTER & YELLOW SALSA

Ingredients: 4 large Dutch Cream potatoes, 1 punnet of yellow cherry tomatoes, 1 large yellow capsicum, 4 yellow squash, ½ small pineapple, the juice and zest of 1 large lemon, 1 large clove of garlic, organic butter, 1 cup olive oil, ½ cup coriander, nature-made salt and pepper

Method: Scrub the skins of the potatoes, prick with a fork and place in a hot oven until crunchy on the outside and soft inside. In a small bowl, mix the butter, lemon juice and zest. Once soft, take the potatoes out of the oven and place on a chopping board. Gently squish with the palm of your hand so the potato bursts open a little. Drizzle a generous dose of lemon butter over the smashed potato, season with salt and pepper and place back into the oven for a further 10 minutes until the potato becomes nice and crunchy (vegan; exchange butter with olive oil). If pieces burst out of the potato whilst squishing, don't worry, just add to the tray for further roasting.

To make the salsa, dice the tomatoes, capsicum, pineapple, garlic and parsley and mix together. Serve by placing the crunchy potatoes onto serving plates, topped with a large spoonful of yellow salsa. (serves 4)

'True Livers Are Healthy Livers'!

Did you know that your liver is actually your largest internal organ (it's roughly the size of a football) and responsible for crucial functions like digesting your food, storing energy and removing toxins from your body? Many ancient populations considered the liver to be the most important organ—hence the word 'live' in its name.

One of the hardest-working organs in the body, the liver works tirelessly to detoxify our blood, to produce the bile (anions) needed to digest fat, to break down hormones, and to store essential vitamins and minerals, like iron and vitamin D. If you haven't been eating a vegetable-based diet, regularly getting exercise, and making sure to limit your hard alcohol and toxin exposure—you might be in need of a liver cleanse.

It's the liver's responsibility to process nutrients absorbed by the intestines so they're more efficiently absorbed. The liver also regulates blood composition to balance protein, fat and sugar. Finally, it removes toxins from the blood and breaks down both hard alcohol and toxic medications.

If the fat in your liver makes up 5–10 percent of the organ's weight, you are diagnosed with fatty liver disease.

Today, we're faced with so many environmental toxins in our homes, places of work and food supply, so it's essential for our general health and well-being to keep our livers functioning properly.

Liver disease is a serious problem affecting millions of people. It is one of the top 10 causes of death in the United States yearly, if treated by the cut, burn 'n' poisons of pharma doctors. There are more than 100 types of different kinds of liver diseases including fatty liver syndrome, jaundice, genetic disorders, and various viruses like hepatitis A, hepatitis B and hepatitis C. Liver disease can be caused by a range of factors – many are lifestyle related – including a poor diet, drinking too much hard alcohol, non-organic wines, non-organic additive and preservative beers, drug use, obesity, infections and environmental pollutants.

Liver Disease Symptoms: There are often no symptoms of fatty liver disease, so you may live with the condition and not realize it. Some signs and symptoms may begin to surface over time, these include: fatigue, jaundice, weight loss, loss of appetite, weakness, nausea, vomiting, confusion, trouble concentrating, pain in the centre or right upper part of belly, enlarged liver, bloating and gas, dark urine, bruising easily, excessive sweat, constipation, pale or dark tar-coloured stools, dry and dark patches on neck and under arms, swelling in legs and ankles.

Cirrhosis Symptoms: The buildup of fluid in the body, muscle weakness, internal bleeding, yellowing of the skin and eyes (jaundice), liver failure.

It's so important to add vegetables to your everyday diet. An easy way to do this is by juicing them. With impaired liver function, juicing vegetables has the added benefit of making them easier to digest and more readily available for absorption.

Vegetables ideal for a liver detox include cauliflower, broccoli, leafy greens like kale, spinach, dandelion, watercress, Brussels sprouts or cabbage, celery, asparagus, beets, carrot, cucumber, herbs including parsley, mint, cilantro, basil, ginger root. High-fibre foods help support a healthy digestive tract, speeding up the elimination of toxins in the body. Lemons are #1! Lemons have anions, which the liver makes but it's called bile. *Sweet Potatoes:* Because of their potassium content, they help cleanse the liver. One sweet potato contains nearly 700 milligrams of potassium! It's also rich in vitamins B6, C, D, magnesium and iron. Sweet potatoes are easy to eat because they're naturally sweet. The sugars are slowly released into the bloodstream through the liver, so it won't cause a spike in blood sugar; they are nature's healthy sugars like all fruits have. *Bananas:* Containing 470 milligrams of potassium, they're also great for cleansing the liver and overcoming low potassium levels; plus, bananas assist in digestion and help release toxins and heavy metals from the body. *Dandelion Root:* The vitamins and nutrients present in dandelions help cleanse our livers and keep them working properly. Dandelions also aid our digestive system by maintaining the proper flow of bile. They're natural diuretics and allow the liver to eliminate toxins quickly. Dandelion tea and stems are also high in vitamin C, which helps with mineral absorption, reduces inflammation and prevents the development of disease. *Milk Thistle:* As a liver support and aid, milk thistle is a powerful detoxifier. It helps rebuild liver cells while removing toxins from the body that are processed through the liver. According to a study published in Digestive Diseases and Sciences, milk thistle has the power to improve mortality in patients with liver failure just like lemons do! It's able to naturally reverse the harmful effects of hard alcohol consumption; pesticides in our food supply; heavy metals in our water supply; pollution in the air that we breathe; and even poisons. According to a 2010 study, milk thistle benefits help treat alcoholic liver disease, acute and chronic viral hepatitis, and toxin-induced liver diseases.

Cowboy Don

Follow, Follow The Sun...

Melting beneath the sun's morning kiss, I lie, soaking up every glorious, golden, galactic ray, with love and gratitude for Mother's Angel of Fire, the source of all life on Planet Earth. The Gayatri Mantra floods my mind... *'You who are the source of all power, whose rays illuminate the world, ... illuminate also my heart, so that it too can do your work' and the words of Hafiz ring true in my Soul...'After all this time, the sun never says to the Earth, you owe me! Look what happens with a love like that, it lights the whole sky." '*

Anciently, it was believed that Earth was our Mother and the Sun our Father. It was believed that the Germ of Life (the NTR, pronounced neeter), which is the 'seed of organising intelligence that houses the first indivisible cell upon conception', resides between human lives on the Sun, coming forth to the ovum on conception and returning to the sun the following sunrise after physical death.

Ancient cultures understood that just as plants and all other living creatures and organisms on Earth need sunshine to grow, so too do our bodies in order to develop, regenerate and heal. They knew that suntanning the body for three months of the year would allow the liver to store a three-year supply of vitamin D.

The sun has been around for the entirety of Earth's history. Do you really think it just happened to rise one day with the intention of killing everyone? Mal-illumination, on the other hand, is a very real and serious problem! A study by Swedish researchers have found that people who avoid the sun actually double their risk of dying from health issues, including cancer. This study was published in the Journal of Internal Medicine. It also found that people who avoid the sun actually have a higher risk of skin melanomas. Sunscreen blocks the skin from absorbing rays that are vital for the body's creation of vitamin D, which is critical for the prevention of so many diseases including breast and prostate cancer, heart disease and osteoporosis. Just take a look at our health statistics ... see any correlations here? The sun's rays assist our immune system by increasing white blood cells and helping to control bacterial and viral infection.

The use of sunglasses lowers our visual capacitance and blocks the sun's healing rays from entering the eyes and activating the amygdala, which is the part of the brain that regulates the emotional molecules and makes us feel good! This is why the sun is necessary for our mental health and especially people suffering with depression or schizophrenia. Studies have shown that some of the highest suicide rates in the world are in places with very little sunshine.

Our ancestors understood the incredible power of **sungazing** during the first hour at sunrise and the final hour of sunset. Gazing directly into the sun allows for over one million frequencies of light to enter the brain, causing the pineal gland to secrete chemicals that can activate mental programs that instigate creativity, imagination, intuition and 'innate knowing' that may otherwise lie dormant for the duration of our entire lifetime. The biophotons of light going across the ocular surface and back into the visual cortex electrify the brain and thereby all nerves, which assists in the restoration of full CNS function.

So, there you have it. Don't waste another minute... Get your gear off and get out into that beautiful healing sunshine!

Lynnie

Michelle McKoy Photography

The LYMPHATIC / IMMUNE SYSTEM

Consists of... tonsils, thymus, thoracic duct, lymph nodes/ducts, spleen, bone marrow.

Chakra Heart (green) / Endocrine Gland and Function... The thymus gland produces and secretes the hormone thymosin, which is necessary for the production and development of T Cells. T Lymphocytes (T Cells) target and kill infected host cells and activate other immune cells that secrete cytokines, which are a group of proteins that act as immune chemical messengers.

Holds Emotional Molecules of will, intention and wonder as well as adoration, anxiety, nervousness and impatience.

Foods That Support This System Are... apples, berries, garlic, spring onions, honeydew melon, horseradish, leeks, lemons, limes, orange, peach, prickly pear, radishes, tangerines, garlic, onions, spices.

Support the Emotional/Physical Healing of This System with... YELLOW and PURPLE foods.

YELLOW wholefoods help create strong immunity in this system and strengthen willpower.

PURPLE wholefoods help rectify overwhelm of disease in this system as well as the release of anxiety, nervousness and stress.

***NUGGET... Not only was garlic given to slaves to enhance strength and endurance, but it was also given sacred qualities and placed in the tombs of pharaohs. Eat garlic and onions and your lymphatic system will love you.

LYMPH NODES / DUCTS

BODY *FOODS THAT HEAL*	MIND *POSSIBLE EMOTIONAL CAUSE*	SPIRIT *IMBALANCED CHAKRA*
---	---	---
SIGNATURE FOODS... green leafy vegetables, lime	Are you feeling out of balance, all work and no play? Have you lost touch with the things that are genuinely important?	Heart Chakra- **colour Green**

LYMPHATIC/IMMUNE SYSTEM
NUTMEAL WITH LYMPH FRUIT SALAD

Ingredients: 1 large green apple grated including peel and seeds, ¼ cup LSA, ¼ cup almondmeal, ⅛ cup sunflower seeds, ½ cup chopped walnuts, 1 tsp cinnamon, drizzle of water if necessary

FRUIT SALAD; 1 peach diced, 1 mandarin deseeded and diced, ¼ cup honeydew melon diced.

CASHEW CREAM; **(see recipe under Dressings in back of book)**

Method: Place the coarsely grated apple and any excess juice from grating into a mixing bowl with all other ingredients. Combine well. If the apples are not very juicy you may need to add a drizzle of water to moisten slightly

Fruit Salad; Mix all ingredients together then place atop the meal. Drizzle with cashew cream and serve. Non Vegan Option; use organic natural yoghurt. (serves 1)

SPLEEN

BODY *FOODS THAT HEAL*	MIND *POSSIBLE EMOTIONAL CAUSE*	SPIRIT *IMBALANCED CHAKRA*
---	---	---
SIGNATURE FOODS... sweet potato, green peas and beans, yellow squash	Are you feeling helpless or stuck? Are you feeling obsessive about someone or something?	Heart Chakra- **colour Green** / Sacral Chakra- colour Orange

***NOTE... *The spleen is the septic tank of the body, so it's important to cleanse internally. Do a 10 day water fast or 18 day cabala juice fast, followed by a colon cleanse.*

If the spleen has been removed it is important to eat plenty of good salt to overcome infections. Support this with garlic, onions, capsicums, hot chillies and peppers.

LYMPHATIC/IMMUNE SYSTEM
SPLEENDID IMMUNE BOOSTER JUICE

Ingredients: 1 lemon with peel, 2 limes with peel, 4 oranges, 4 mandarins, ½ honeydew melon, 3 apples, 2 peaches, 2 large kale leaves

Method: Peel the oranges and mandarins; deseed the peaches; remove skin of melon. Chop all ingredients and put through a commercial juicer. (serves 2)

THYMUS

BODY *FOODS THAT HEAL* ---	MIND *POSSIBLE EMOTIONAL CAUSE* ---	SPIRIT *IMBALANCED CHAKRA* ---
SIGNATURE FOODS... mushrooms, thyme	Are you constantly feeling under attack, victimised?	Heart Chakra- **colour Green**

LYMPHATIC/IMMUNE SYSTEM
RAW AVOCADO, LEMON AND LEEK SOUP

Ingredients: 2 avocado, ½ cup water, ½ lemon juiced, ¼ leek juiced, extra water if needed for desired consistency

Method: Juice the leek and lemon with a commercial juicer. In a blender, place the avocado, lemon juice and water. Blend on high until a lovely smooth, creamy consistency. Little by little add the leek juice, tasting after each addition so as not to make the flavour too strong. Serve with organic sourdough. (serves 1)

TONSILS

BODY	MIND	SPIRIT
FOODS THAT HEAL	*POSSIBLE EMOTIONAL CAUSE*	*IMBALANCED CHAKRA*
---	---	---
SIGNATURE FOODS... suck on rock salt	Are you suppressing emotions or feeling fearful?	Heart Chakra- **colour Green** / Throat Chakra- colour Sky Blue
	Are you blocking your creativity?	

LYMPHATIC/IMMUNE SYSTEM
COCONUT & BERRY SMOOTHIE

Ingredients: 2 cups of mixed berries, ¼ cup coconut water, ¾ cup coconut cream

Method: Put all ingredients together in a blender and mix on high speed until smooth and creamy. (serves 1)

DIS-EASES/DISORDERS OF
The IMMUNE SYSTEM

AIDS/HIV

***WHAT IS IT?...* **HIV (human immunodeficiency virus)** is a virus that attacks the body's immune system, which is the body's natural defence system, and is spread through certain body fluids.

Aids (acquired immune deficiency syndrome) is a disease that is caused by HIV.

BODY – EPICURE

- **Fastest...** Water fast for 7–10 days **OR...**
- Cabala juice fast for 28 days then do colon cleanse with herbs and bentonite clay at the end of the fast.
- Drink one cup of freshly juiced, with peels on, lemon juice, every single day for 90 days. You can add water to this to dilute but must be one whole cup of lemon over the day—can have with hot water and honey.
- LIVER FLUSH—Drink one litre of grapefruit juice and 1 cup of organic virgin olive oil blended together 30 minutes prior to going to bed. Typically the next day you will pass gallstones and bile in the stool. You may need to do this two or three days in a row.
- Fruit diet—eat and juice locally grown, fresh, raw organic fruits for 30 days, just fruit, juices and water.
- Yellow—eat all and any yellow foods such as tomatoes, capsicum, squash, banana, pineapple, lemon.
- Drink one litre per 22 kilos bodyweight of pure water every day—you can add pure lemon oil to this.
- Sunshine—Develop the darkest suntan you can by covering your body in Divine Body Butter or coconut oil and then exposing at least 70% of your body to the sun for one hour every day (30 mins each side).
- **ESSENTIAL OIL:** lemon, lavender, frankincense.
- (Divine, colon cleanses, Ra 24ct See Salt, Himalayan rock salt available in the USA **www.thedontolman.com/store** and Australia **www.lynnienichols.com/shop**)

BODY	MIND	SPIRIT
FOODS THAT HEAL	*POSSIBLE EMOTIONAL CAUSE*	*IMBALANCED CHAKRA*
---	---	---
SIGNATURE FOODS... apples, berries, garlic, spring onions, honeydew melon, horseradish, leeks, lemons, limes, orange, peach, prickly pear, radishes, tangerines, garlic, onions, spices	• Are you constantly thinking negative thoughts about yourself/ your body? • Are you unable to be yourself, unable to love yourself? • Do you feel not good enough, unworthy, hopeless?	Heart Chakra- **colour Green**

LYMPHATIC/IMMUNE SYSTEM
IMMUNITY BOWL

Ingredients: 1 lemon juice and zest, 1 orange, 1 lime, 1 cup spinach, 1 green apple, 2 large bananas, 5 deseeded medjool dates, 1 cup of mixed blueberries & raspberries, ½ cup strawberries, granola, 1 extra banana

Method: Peel and deseed the orange and lime and place in a blender, add the lemon juice and zest, spinach, dates, bananas, and apple including skin and seeds and process on high speed until smooth and creamy

Pour into a serving bowl and decorate with banana, berries and granola. (serves 2)

CANDIDA/ YEAST INFECTION

***WHAT IS IT?...** **Yeast infection,** otherwise known as 'thrush', is caused by the parasitic yeast-like fungus, candida albicans. Thrush may develop on the genitals, mouth and throat of both women and men, as well as infecting the skin and nails, which is called cutaneous candidiasis. While not considered a sexually transmitted disease, thrush can be passed from one person to another.

***BODY – EPICURE*

- **Fastest...** Water fast for 7–10 days **OR...**
- Cabala juice fast for 14–28 days.
- Daily, have two cups of natural organic yoghurt and other ferments, such as sauerkraut, fermented veggies, kombucha or kefir to re-establish the flora and fauna of the gut.
- Add to your diet, garlic, thyme, coconut oil, apple cider vinegar.
- Drink one litre per 22 kilos bodyweight of pure water every day.
- Suck on Himalayan rock salt, the size of the last segment of your little finger, daily.
- Salt covenant—Drink one litre of water with two heaped teaspoons of sea salt first thing each morning to flush the digestive tract and colon and do self-administered daily colonics. (Enema douche travel kits available **www.lynnienichols.com/shop**)
- Do a colon cleanse with bentonite clay and herbs to cleanse the digestive tract/colon and to rid toxic plaque buildup.
- Apply topically, a diluted anti fungal essential oil. (as per below)
- WOMEN; insert natural yoghurt vaginally and only wear natural fabric clothing, pads and tampons. Apply topically; diluted apple cider vinegar, coconut oil.
- MEN; apply to the affected area one or more of the following; coconut oil, diluted apple cider vinegar, natural yoghurt.
- Use Colloidal Silver internally and topically.
- Develop the darkest suntan you can by covering your body in Divine Body Butter or coconut oil and then exposing at least 70% of your body to the sun for one hour every day (30 mins each side).
- **ESSENTIAL OIL...** clove, lemongrass, eucalyptus, geranium, thyme, tea tree.
- (Nature's Silver Bullet, Divine, Pulse, colon cleanses, Ra 24ct See Salt, Himalayan rock salt available in the USA **www.thedontolman.com/store** and Australia **www.lynnienichols.com/shop**)

BODY *FOODS THAT HEAL*	MIND *POSSIBLE EMOTIONAL CAUSE*	SPIRIT *IMBALANCED CHAKRA*
---	---	---
SIGNATURE FOODS... apples, berries, garlic, spring onions, honeydew melon, horseradish, leeks, lemons, limes, orange, peach, prickly pear, radishes, tangerines, garlic, onions, spices	• Are you feeling angry/frustrated, or are you being demanding and untrusting of yourself/ your partner? • Are you feeling scattered and unclear?	Heart Chakra- **colour Green** / Sacral Chakra- **colour Orange**

IMMUNE SYSTEM
TIERED YOGHURT AND BERRY GLASS

Ingredients: 1 cup natural organic yoghurt, 1 cup blue berries, 1 cup LSA, ¼ tsp cinnamon

Method: Place a few spoons of natural yoghurt in the bottom of a dessert serving glass; next add a layer of LSA, then a layer of blueberries. Continue to layer in this way until the glass is full. Finish with a dollop of natural yoghurt, a few blueberries and a sprinkle of cinnamon. (serves 2)

COELIAC DISEASE

***WHAT IS IT?...** **Coeliac disease** is an autoimmune disease where the body starts to attack the small intestine when a person eats gluten (a protein found in wheat, rye, barley, and oats). The immune response damages the villi, which line the small intestine, inhibiting the absorption of nutrients into the body.

Gluten Intolerance – Whilst celiac disease is said to be genetic, gluten intolerance is caused by grains that are stored for long periods of time as these are soaked in aluminium-fluoride. No one has gluten intolerance; it's a reaction to the big pharma chemicals.

***BODY – EPICURE*

- **Fastest...** Build autoimmune system by fasting for 20 days on water and then 20 days on cabala juice and at the same time drink two tablespoons of apple cider vinegar and one tablespoon of raw organic honey in hot water 2-3 times per day. Also, have daily a berry, asparagus smoothie, consisting of two cups berries and 12 stalks of asparagus (can add a banana to sweeten) plus water to desired consistency. Drink within 30 mins of making it. Can eat the foods instead if preferred **OR...**
- Cabala juice fast for 14–21 days.
- Continue to drink two tbsp apple cider vinegar in hot water and 1 tablespoon of raw organic honey two or three times per day after your liquid fast.
- Eat and drink ferments such as kefir, kombucha, natural organic yoghurt, sauerkraut, olives in brine, tempeh, and organic blue cheese.
- Drink one cup of freshly juiced, with peels on, lemon juice, every single day. You can add water to this to dilute but must be one whole cup of lemon.
- Drink one litre per 22 kilos bodyweight of pure water every day—you can add pure lemon oil to this.
- Fruit diet—eat and juice locally grown, fresh, raw organic fruits for 30 days, just fruit, juices and water.
- Yellow—eat all and any yellow foods.
- Colloidal silver with fulvic acid—have a dose of this daily for the healing ability of silver ions.
- LIVER FLUSH—Drink one litre of grapefruit juice and one cup of organic virgin olive oil blended together 30 minutes prior to going to bed. Typically the next day you will pass gallstones and bile in the stool. You may need to do this two or three days in a row.
- Sunshine—Develop the darkest suntan you can by covering your body in Divine Body Butter or coconut oil and then exposing at least 70% of your body to the sun for one hour every day (30 mins each side).
- **ESSENTIAL OIL...** lemon, peppermint, ginger, fennel, coriander.
- (Divine, Nature's Silver Bullet (colliodal silver), colon cleanses, Ra 24ct See Salt, Himalayan rock salt available in the USA **www.thedontolman.com/store** and Australia **www.lynnienichols.com/shop**)

BODY *FOODS THAT HEAL*	MIND *POSSIBLE EMOTIONAL CAUSE*	SPIRIT *IMBALANCED CHAKRA*
---	---	---
SIGNATURE FOODS... apples, berries, garlic, spring onions, honeydew melon, horseradish, leeks, lemons, limes, orange, peach, prickly pear, radishes, tangerines, garlic, onions, spices	• Are you feeling that life's too hard, feeling like a victim? • Are you feeling angry, unable to stand up for yourself, unable to forgive others? • Are you punishing yourself for experiences you are unable to forgive?	Heart Chakra- colour Green

LYMPHATIC/IMMUNE SYSTEM
YELLOW SMOOTHIE

Ingredients: 2 bananas, 1 yellow capsicum with pith, 1 cup yellow tomatoes, 2 large yellow apples, 1 small pineapple, 1 cup natural yoghurt, ½ cup kefir, ½ cup water

Method: Pop all ingredients, except the water, into a blender for a few minutes until smooth and creamy. Add water if desired. (serves 2)

CELLULITE

***WHAT IS IT?...** **Cellulite** is subcutaneous fat most commonly seen on women's thighs, hips and buttocks that causes a dimpled texture to the skin.

***BODY – EPICURE*

- **Fastest...** Water fast with added lemon juice for 10 days then 10 days on cabala juice, then 10–20 days on Pulse **OR...**
- Cabala juice fast for 28 days then do colon cleanse with herbs and bentonite clay at the end of the fast.
- Consistent regular water drinking and lymphatic massage are the keys to breaking up cellulite. Massage the cellulite tissue for one or two minutes four or five times per day. While standing still, tighten the bum and hip muscles, let them go, tighten, let go, tighten let go, etc. for 30 seconds at a time; do this repeatedly five or six times per day. It may take two weeks to begin seeing results.
- Drink one cup of freshly juiced, with peels on, lemon juice, every single day for 90 days. You can add water to this to dilute but must be one whole cup of lemon over the day—can have with hot water and honey.
- Infrared blankets and other ultrasonic devices can help to break up cellulite congestion (be aware ultrasound has been proven to cause brain damage in babies, so be careful that way).
- Yellow—eat all and any yellow foods such as tomatoes, capsicum, squash, banana, pineapple, lemon.
- Drink one litre per 22 kilos bodyweight of pure water every day—you can add pure lemon oil to this.
- Do a colon cleanse to remove stored toxicity from the body as well as regular self-administered colonics/enemas. (Enema douche bag travel kits available **www.lynnienichols.com/shop**)
- Sunshine—Develop the darkest suntan you can by covering your body in Divine Body Butter or coconut oil and then exposing at least 70% of your body to the sun for one hour every day (30 mins each side).
- **ESSENTIAL OIL...** lemon, fennel, black pepper, juniper, sage, cedarwood, grapefruit.
- (Divine, colon cleanses, Ra 24ct See Salt, Himalayan rock salt available in the USA **www.thedontolman.com/store** and Australia **www.lynnienichols.com/shop**)

BODY *FOODS THAT HEAL*	MIND *POSSIBLE EMOTIONAL CAUSE*	SPIRIT *IMBALANCED CHAKRA*
---	---	---
SIGNATURE FOODS... apples, berries, garlic, spring onions, honeydew melon, horseradish, leeks, lemons, limes, orange, peach, prickly pear, radishes, tangerines, garlic, onions, spices	• Are you feeling that life's too hard, feeling like a victim? • Are you feeling angry, unable to stand up for yourself, unable to forgive others? • Are you punishing yourself for experiences you are unable to forgive?	Heart Chakra- **colour Green**

LYMPHATIC/IMMUNE SYSTEM
LEMON & HONEYDEW MELON JUICE

Ingredients: 1 honeydew melon, 2 lemons with peel

Method: Juice ingredients with commercial juicer and drink immediately. (serves 2)

COLDSORE/HERPES SIMPLEX VIRUS (HSV)

WHAT IS IT?... **Coldsores** are clusters of tiny blisters that develop around the mouth region, typically caused by the herpes simplex virus 1, which is highly contagious, passed on by close contact/saliva.

BODY – EPICURE

- Get off all medication immediately.
- **Fastest...** Water fast for 7–10 days **OR...**
- Do the five-week 35% food-grade hydrogen peroxide protocol combined with a cabala juice fast for 21–28 days.
- Do a 3% H2O2 mouth rinse several times per day.
- Apply lemon juice to the spot and go out into the sun. Put aloe vera on two hours before bed.
- Drink lemon, freshly juiced with the peels on, every day.
- Eat and juice a locally grown, fresh, raw organic fruit diet.
- Suck on Himalayan rock salt daily, the size of the end segment of your little finger.
- Do the water protocol—one glass of water every hour on the hour, or drink one litre of water per 22 kilos of bodyweight every single day.
- Develop the darkest suntan you can by covering your body in Divine Body Butter or coconut oil and then exposing at least 70% of your body to the sun for one hour every day (30 mins each side).
- **ESSENTIAL OIL...** peppermint, tea tree, oregano, thyme.
- (Divine, Congest Ease, 35% food-grade hydrogen peroxide, Breathe Ez, essential oil of peppermint, Himalayan rock salt, Ra 24ct See Salt, available in the USA **www.thedontolman.com/store** and Australia **www.lynnienichols.com/shop**)

BODY *FOODS THAT HEAL*	MIND *POSSIBLE EMOTIONAL CAUSE*	SPIRIT *IMBALANCED CHAKRA*
---	---	---
SIGNATURE FOODS... apples, artichoke, broccoli, caraway seeds, raw honey, onions, peppermint, potatoes, radish, rosemary, turmeric, yams, carrots	• Is there certain information that you are not wanting to hear? • Are you holding on to angry festering words? • Are you fearful of speaking your truth?	Heart Chakra- **colour Green** / Throat Chakra- colour Sky Blue

IMMUNE SYSTEM
3% H₂O₂ SOLUTION

Ingredients: 35% food-grade hydrogen peroxide, pure water

Method: Mix 1 drop of the 35% hydrogen peroxide with 11 drops of pure water. Store in a glass eye dropper bottle

5 WEEK FOOD GRADE HYDROGEN PEROXIDE PROTOCOL

5 drops x H₂O₂ in a glass of water
5 x per day for 1 week

10 drops x H₂O₂ in a glass of water
5 x per day for 1 week

15 drops x H₂O₂ in a glass of water
5 x per day for 1 week

20 drops x H₂O₂ in a glass of water
5 x per day for 1 week

25 drops x H₂O₂ in a glass of water
5 x per day for 1 week

(recommended for all serious dis-ease)

DENGUE/YELLOW FEVER

***WHAT IS IT?...* **Dengue Fever** is a disease that is spread by mosquitos, typically in tropical and subtropical regions, causing acute joint and muscle pain, fever, headaches and nausea.

Yellow Fever is a tropical viral disease also transmitted by mosquitos that affects the kidneys and liver causing jaundice (yellowing of the skin and eyes), which is why it is called yellow fever.

***BODY – EPICURE*

- **Fastest...** Water fast with added lemon juice for 10 days then 10 days on cabala juice, then 10–20 days on Pulse **OR...**
- Cabala juice fast for 28 days then do colon cleanse with herbs and bentonite clay at the end of the fast.
- Drink one cup of freshly juiced, with peels on, lemon juice, every single day for 90 days. You can add water to this to dilute but must be one whole cup of lemon over the day—can have with hot water and honey.
- Take 7 mg of Boron per day... Dissolve one level teaspoon of Borax/Boron in one litre of water to make a concentrated solution. Take one teaspoon of this concentrate twice daily with meals.
- Put lemon juice on the mozzie bite topically.
- Salt Covenant—Drink one litre of water with two heaped teaspoons of sea salt first thing each morning.
- Suck on Himalayan rock salt, the size of the last segment of your little finger, each day.
- Yellow—eat all and any yellow foods such as tomatoes, capsicum, squash, banana, pineapple, lemon.
- Drink one litre per 22 kilos bodyweight of pure water every day—you can add pure lemon oil to this.
- Walk barefoot outside on the grass/sand.
- Sunshine—Develop the darkest suntan you can by covering your body in Divine Body Butter or coconut oil and then exposing at least 70% of your body to the sun for one hour every day (30 mins each side).
- **ESSENTIAL OIL...** lemon. As a mosquito repellent; lemon, eucalyptus, lemongrass, peppermint, cinnamon, aniseed, lavender, tea tree.
- (Divine, colon cleanses, Ra 24ct See Salt, Himalayan rock salt available in the USA **www.thedontolman.com/store** and Australia **www.lynnienichols.com/shop**)

BODY *FOODS THAT HEAL*	MIND *POSSIBLE EMOTIONAL CAUSE*	SPIRIT *IMBALANCED CHAKRA*
---	---	---
SIGNATURE FOODS... apples, berries, garlic, spring onions, honeydew melon, horseradish, leeks, lemons, limes, orange, peach, prickly pear, radishes, tangerines, garlic, onions, spices	• Are you literally burning up with anger?	Heart Chakra- **colour Green** / Solar Plexus Chakra-

LYMPHATIC/IMMUNE SYSTEM
DAILY DOSE OF BORON

Ingredients: Borax/boron, 1 litre pure water

Method: Dissolve one level teaspoon of Borax/Boron in one litre of water to make a concentrated solution. Take one teaspoon of this concentrate twice daily with meals

EBOLA VIRUS

***WHAT IS IT?...** **Ebola,** previously known as Ebola hemorrhagic fever, is a contagious viral disease spread via body fluids and characterised by fever and severe internal bleeding.

***BODY – EPICURE*

- Get off all medication and supplements- herbs in the form of powders or teas are okay.
- **Fastest...** Water fast for 7–10 days **OR...**
- 21–28 day cabala juice fast whilst snacking on raw pumpkin seeds.
- Stop eating pig. Avoid food/drinks that have pig/monkey fats/gelatins, which are put in so many products now. Some of these products are clarified olive oil, citric acid, lip balms, ice creams, candies, breads, chewing gum with aspartame, wine, beers that are clear, toothpaste, collagen in makeup, laundry conditioners, and marshmallows.
- FOR PARASITES—Snack on ½ cup of raw pumpkin seeds each day. Eat one or two cloves of raw garlic each day and 1 onion a day—can be red, white or brown. Parasites can't handle a lot of fibre so eat two large carrots every day, late afternoon. Eat figs daily, fresh or dried. Parasites hate coconut oil so make a mix of coconut oil/one clove garlic and oregano, aniseed or clove oil (parasites hate all of these so it doesn't matter which you use) and drink a dose of this daily for as long as necessary. Can also mix one teaspoon of black walnut oil with a few drops of aniseed, clove or oregano oil together with organic natural yoghurt and have a spoonful of this daily. Drink fresh juice of lemon, lime, grapefruit and orange—parasites cannot stand citrus.
- Drink one glass of water every hour on the hour for 10 hours of each day, for 30 days or drink one litre of water per 22 kilos of bodyweight.
- Have lots of nature-made salt (Ra 24ct Gold See Salt is especially healing).
- Salt Covenant—have two teaspoons of sea salt in one litre of water first thing in the morning before you eat to clear toxicity.
- Do a colon cleanse with bentonite clay and herbs for cleaning of the digestive tract/colon and to rid toxic plaque buildup.
- Do self-administered colonics daily. (Enema travel douche kit available **www.lynnienichols.com/shop**)
- Sungazing morning and evenings in 13-second intervals; look at the sun until it reaches a 10-degree arc, or a clenched fist sitting on horizon as sun comes up, stop at top of fist. At night, start gazing as sun hits top of fist until it's gone.
- Develop the darkest suntan you can by covering your body in Divine Body Butter or coconut oil and then exposing at least 70% of your body to the sun for one hour every day (30 mins each side).
- **ESSENTIAL OIL...** citrus, tea tree, oregano, eucalyptus, cinnamon, thyme, clove, black walnut, aniseed.
- (Divine, colon cleanses, Ra 24ct See Salt, Himalayan rock salt available in the USA **www.thedontolman.com/store** and Australia **www.lynnienichols.com/shop**)

BODY *FOODS THAT HEAL*	MIND *POSSIBLE EMOTIONAL CAUSE*	SPIRIT *IMBALANCED CHAKRA*
---	---	---
SIGNATURE FOODS... apples, berries, garlic, spring onions, honeydew melon, horseradish, leeks, lemons, limes, orange, peach, prickly pear, radishes, tangerines, garlic, onions, spices	• Are you giving your power away to others? • Who/what's eating away at you?	Heart Chakra- **colour Green**

***NOTE...** *Originally Ebola was a parasite called the trichina worm found in pigs, monkeys and flat fish. Now this is used as a GMO so be sure to wash all non-organic produce with a mix of water and apple cider vinegar to remove GMO sprays. Since 2011 most gelatin was switched from cow to pig fat. Marshmallows are pure gelatin!*

***NUGGET...** *Parasites cannot live in the presence of plants, they only survive in animals. The fluids of plants are the worst environment for parasites, especially citrus, particularly lemons.*

LYMPHATIC/IMMUNE SYSTEM
APPLE & RADISH SALAD WITH LEMON ANISEED DRESSING

Ingredients: 4 large green apples with skin and seeds, 1 cup whole walnuts, 4 red radishes, 1 cup dried figs, ½ large red onion, 1 large clove garlic, a little bit of fresh mint, juice of 2 lemons and the zest of 1, ½ cup organic cold pressed olive oil, 1 drop essential oil of aniseed

Method: Dice the apples into cubes, finely slice the radish, figs and onion, and dice the garlic. Mix all of these ingredients together in a salad bowl. In a jar, mix the olive and aniseed oils, lemon zest and juice and shake well. Drizzle over the salad just before serving. (serves 2)

GLANDULAR FEVER/INFECTIOUS MONONUCLEOSIS

***WHAT IS IT?...** **Glandular Fever** is an infectious viral disease caused by the Epstein-Barr virus (EBV) and is characterised by swelling of the lymph nodes and glands, sore throat, fatigue and fever.

***BODY – EPICURE*

- **Fastest...** Water fast with added lemon juice for 10 days then 10 days on cabala juice, then 10–20 days on Pulse **OR...**
- Cabala juice fast for 28 days then do colon cleanse with herbs and bentonite clay at the end of the fast.
- Drink one cup of freshly juiced, with peels on, lemon juice, every single day for 90 days. You can add water to this to dilute but must be one whole cup of lemon over the day—can have with hot water and honey.
- Salt Covenant—Drink one litre of water with two heaped teaspoons of sea salt first thing each morning.
- Suck on Himalayan rock salt, the size of the last segment of your little finger, each day.
- Drink orange juice with salt added to it.
- Absolutely no refined sugars and chemical sweeteners.

- Yellow—eat all and any yellow foods such as tomatoes, capsicum, squash, banana, pineapple, lemon.
- Drink one litre per 22 kilos bodyweight of pure water every day—you can add pure lemon oil to this.
- Walk barefoot outside on the grass/sand.
- Sunshine—Develop the darkest suntan you can by covering your body in Divine Body Butter or coconut oil and then exposing at least 70% of your body to the sun for one hour every day (30 mins each side).
- **ESSENTIAL OIL...** lemon, orange, frankincense, rosemary, eucalyptus, thyme, cinnamon, oregano.
- (Divine, colon cleanses, Ra 24ct See Salt, Himalayan rock salt available in the USA **www.thedontolman.com/store** and Australia **www.lynnienichols.com/shop**)

BODY *FOODS THAT HEAL*	MIND *POSSIBLE EMOTIONAL CAUSE*	SPIRIT *IMBALANCED CHAKRA*
---	---	---
SIGNATURE FOODS... apples, berries, garlic, spring onions, honeydew melon, horseradish, leeks, lemons, limes, orange, peach, prickly pear, radishes, tangerines, garlic, onions, spices	• Are you holding on to suppressed anger? • Are you lacking in self-love and care? • Are you seeing new experiences through negative eyes?	Heart Chakra- **colour Green**

***NUGGET...** *PREVENTION... Anciently, they would eat foods grown in the season they come forth in order to support, protect and heal the body. For example, in the colder months they would eat tubers and beans, pulses and legumes as well of lots of citrus, which grows in the colder months. Then in spring they would eat berries of every type... The Latin word for berry is vaccinium, which means 'to heal and protect'.*

LYMPHATIC/IMMUNE SYSTEM
STUFFED CAPSICUM WITH SWEET & SOUR JACKFRUIT

Ingredients: 2 cups of ripe jackfruit, ½ cup Braggs amino liquid or tamari, ¼ cup raw honey, ⅛ cup apple cider vinegar, 1 tsp sea salt, 2 yellow capsicums cut in halves and de-seeded, 1 small pineapple, 4 cloves garlic, 2 large spring onion, ¼ cup coriander, 1 punnet yellow cherry tomatoes

Method: Dice the garlic and place in a pan with a little coconut oil. Fry until golden then add the jackfruit, tamari, honey, salt and ACV. Sauté for 20 mins or so until the mix becomes caramelised; set aside to cool.

Dice the pineapple into small cubes, quarter the cherry tomatoes, finely slice the spring onions and tear the coriander. Mix all ingredients together with the cool jackfruit. Spoon into the capsicum halves, garnish with a sprig of coriander. (serves 2-4)

LUPUS

***WHAT IS IT?...* **Lupus** is an autoimmune disease where the body's immune system attacks its own normal, healthy tissue causing inflammation and swelling as well as a variety of other symptoms.

***BODY – EPICURE*

- **Fastest...** Build autoimmune system by fasting for 20 days on water and then 20 days on cabala juice and at the same time drink two tablespoons of apple cider vinegar and one tablespoon of raw organic honey in hot water two or three times per day. Also have daily, a berry, asparagus smoothie, consisting of two cups berries and 12 stalks of asparagus (can add a banana to sweeten) plus water to desired consistency. Drink within 30 mins of making it. Can eat the foods instead if preferred **OR...**
- Cabala juice fast for 14–21 days.
- Continue to drink two tbsp apple cider vinegar in hot water and one tablespoon of raw organic honey two or three times per day after your liquid fast.
- Eat and drink ferments such as kefir, kombucha, natural organic yoghurt, sauerkraut, olives in brine, tempeh, and organic blue cheese.
- Drink one cup of freshly juiced, with peels on, lemon juice, every single day. You can add water to this to dilute but must be one whole cup of lemon.
- Drink one litre per 22 kilos bodyweight of pure water every day—you can add pure lemon oil to this.
- Fruit diet—eat and juice locally grown, fresh, raw organic fruits for 30 days, just fruit, juices and water.
- Yellow—eat all and any yellow foods.
- Colloidal silver with fulvic acid—have a dose of this daily for the healing ability of silver ions.
- LIVER FLUSH—Drink one litre of grapefruit juice and one cup of organic virgin olive oil blended together 30 minutes prior to going to bed. Typically the next day you will pass gallstones and bile in the stool. You may need to do this two or three days in a row.
- Sunshine—Develop the darkest suntan you can by covering your body in Divine Body Butter or coconut oil and then exposing at least 70% of your body to the sun for one hour every day (30 mins each side).
- **ESSENTIAL OIL...** lemon, orange, peppermint, lavender.
- (Divine, Nature's Silver Bullet (colliodal silver), colon cleanses, Ra 24ct See Salt, Himalayan rock salt available in the USA **www.thedontolman.com/store** and Australia **www.lynnienichols.com/shop**)

BODY	MIND	SPIRIT
FOODS THAT HEAL	*POSSIBLE EMOTIONAL CAUSE*	*IMBALANCED CHAKRA*
---	---	---
SIGNATURE FOODS... apples, berries, garlic, spring onions, honeydew melon, horseradish, leeks, lemons, limes, orange, peach, prickly pear, radishes, tangerines, garlic, onions, spices	• Are you feeling like a victim, like life's too hard? • Are you feeling angry, unable to stand up for yourself and unable to forgive others? • Are you punishing yourself for experiences you can't forgive yourself for?	Heart Chakra- **colour Green**

LYMPHATIC/IMMUNE SYSTEM
FERMENT PLATTER

Ingredients: ½ cup sauerkraut, ½ cup kim-chi, 1 cup olives in brine, 2 packets of tempeh, a few drops tamari (until desired taste), ¾ cup organic natural yoghurt, 1 lime- juice and zest, ¾ cup coconut keffir, 1 packet organic blue cheese, sea salt

Method: Make the tamari dipping sauce by mixing the yoghurt and tamari together. Make the lime dipping sauce by mixing the kefir, lime juice and zest together. Cut the tempeh into long strips and gently fry in coconut oil until golden brown each side. Season with sea salt

Arrange the warm tempeh, dipping sauces, sauerkraut, kim-chi, olives and blue cheese on a serving platter with some dehydrated flax crackers and serve. (serves 2)

LYME DISEASE

***WHAT IS IT?...* **Lyme disease** is said to be an infection caused by the bacteria Borrelia when a person is bitten by a tick; however, this was exposed to be a total medical and pharmaceutical scam years ago ... every one of the symptoms could be diagnosed as over 300 diseases!

***BODY – EPICURE*

- **Fastest...** Water fast for 7–10 days **OR...**
- Cabala juice fast for 14–21 days then continue on a liquid diet of juices, smoothies and pureed soups.
- Drink two tbsp apple cider vinegar in hot water and one tbs of raw organic honey two or three times per day during your liquid fast.
- Take 7 mg of Boron per day. Dissolve one level teaspoon of Borax/Boron in one litre of water to make a concentrated solution. Take one teaspoon of this concentrate twice daily with meals.
- Eat and drink ferments such as kefir, kombucha, natural organic yoghurt, sauerkraut, olives in brine, tempeh, and organic blue cheese.
- Colloidal silver with fulvic acid—have a dose of this daily for the healing ability of silver ions.
- Develop the darkest suntan you can by covering your body in Divine Body Butter or coconut oil and then exposing at least 70% of your body to the sun for one hour every day (30 mins each side).
- Drink one cup of freshly juiced, with peels on, lemon juice, every single day. You can add water to this to dilute but must be one whole cup of lemon.
- Drink one litre per 22 kilos bodyweight of pure water every day—you can add pure lemon oil to this.
- Sunshine—Develop the darkest suntan you can by covering your body in Divine Body Butter or coconut oil and then exposing at least 70% of your body to the sun for one hour every day (30 mins each side).
- **ESSENTIAL OIL...** lemon, oregano, cinnamon, clove, garlic.
- (Divine, Nature's Silver Bullet (colloidal silver), colon cleanses, Ra 24ct See Salt, Himalayan rock salt available in the USA **www.thedontolman.com/store** and Australia **www.lynnienichols.com/shop**)

| **BODY** | **SPIRIT** |
FOODS THAT HEAL	*IMBALANCED CHAKRA*
SIGNATURE FOODS... apples, berries, garlic, spring onions, honeydew melon, horseradish, leeks, lemons, limes, orange, peach, prickly pear, radishes, tangerines, garlic, onions, spices	Heart Chakra- **colour Green**

LYMPHATIC/IMMUNE SYSTEM
CITRUS CIDER SLUSHIE

Ingredients: ⅛ cup apple cider vinegar (with the mother), 1 large lemon, 5 large oranges, 4 lime, 3 tbsp raw honey

Method: Peel and remove seeds from the oranges before putting through a commercial juicer. Juice the lemon and limes with skins on. Mix the citrus with the ACV and honey. Add more honey if necessary. Put in a shallow bowl in the freezer for half hour until just frozen, then take out and mash. Place in a glass and serve immediately. (serves 1)

OEDEMA (FLUID/WATER RETENTION)

***WHAT IS IT?...* **Oedema** is where swelling occurs, most often of the feet, legs, ankles, arms and hands, caused by excess fluid retention due to long periods of immobility and lack of water intake.

***BODY – EPICURE*

- **Fastest...** Water fast for 7–10 days **OR...**
- Salt Covenant—drink one glass of water every hour for 8–10hrs of the day/alternatively, drink one litre per 22 kilos bodyweight of pure water every day.
- Suck on Himalayan rock salt, the size of the last segment of your little finger, daily and have lots of good nature-made salt in the diet. Get Ra 24ct Gold See Salt.
- Elevate the legs above the heart when lying down.
- Have a hot water bath morning and night with one cup of epsom salt and one cup of bicarb soda added.
- Deep interstitial lymphatic massage.
- Get lots of sunshine—Develop the darkest suntan you can by covering your body in Divine Body Butter or coconut oil and then exposing at least 70% of your body to the sun for one hour every day (30 mins each side).
- (Divine, Ra 24ct See Salt, Himalayan rock salt available in the USA **www.thedontolman.com/store** and Australia **www.lynnienichols.com/shop**)

BODY *FOODS THAT HEAL*	MIND *POSSIBLE EMOTIONAL CAUSE*	SPIRIT *IMBALANCED CHAKRA*
---	---	---
SIGNATURE FOODS... apples, berries, garlic, spring onions, honeydew melon, horseradish, leeks, lemons, limes, orange, peach, prickly pear, radishes, tangerines, garlic, onions, spices	• Are you thinking negatively, feeling not good enough? • Are you severely lacking in self-love and approval?	Heart Chakra- **colour Green**

LYMPHATIC/IMMUNE SYSTEM
SALT COVENANT

Ingredients: Water, sea salt

Method: Drink 1 glass of pure water with a pinch of sea salt every hour for 8–10 hrs of the day. Alternatively, drink one litre per 22 kilos bodyweight of pure water with a pinch of salt, every day

RHEUMATOID ARTHRITIS

***WHAT IS IT?...** **Rheumatoid arthritis** is chronic autoimmune condition where the body's immune system attacks the joints, causing inflammation that can deform the fingers, feet, wrists and ankles and results in pain and immobility.

***BODY – EPICURE*

- Get off all medication and supplements- herbs in the form of powders or teas are okay, but no pills or capsules!
- **Fastest...** Water fast for 14–21 days to rid the body of pain **OR...**
- Cabala juice fast for 40 days.
- For the pain, eat two or three cups of organic cherries each day – these can be fresh, dried or frozen – or eat cherry Pulse.
- Eat and juice a locally grown, fresh, raw organic vegan diet for 90 days. Especially beneficial are celery, bok choy, and rhubarb. Eat mushrooms after placing them in the sun for a couple of hours.
- Do a colon cleanse with bentonite clay and herbs to remove the toxic plaque and heavy metals from the body.
- Salt—have plenty of good, nature-made salt in the diet and suck on Himalayan rock salt the size of the last segment of your little finger each day.
- Take 7 mg of Boron per day. Dissolve one level teaspoon of Borax/Boron in one litre of water to make a concentrated solution. Take one teaspoon of this concentrate twice daily with meals.
- Take hot water salt baths with 1 cup epsom salts and 1 cup bicarb soda first thing in the morning, and again at night if necessary. Soak in the ocean.
- Massage the areas several times daily with essential oils, or use Healing Chrysm and Golden ReLeaf.
- Sunshine—lie in the sun to assist the liver and neuroendorine glands to stimulate strength to the muscles.
- **ESSENTIAL OIL...** peppermint, eucalyptus, lavender, rosemary.
- (Divine, Cherry Pulse, Mango Pulse, Healing Chrysm, Golden ReLeaf, Ra 24ct See Salt, Himalayan rock salt, essential oils of peppermint, eucalyptus available in the USA **www.thedontolman.com/store** and Australia **www.lynnienichols.com/shop**)

BODY	MIND	SPIRIT
FOODS THAT HEAL	*POSSIBLE EMOTIONAL CAUSE*	*IMBALANCED CHAKRA*
---	---	---
SIGNATURE FOODS... apples, berries, garlic, spring onions, honeydew melon, horseradish, leeks, lemons, limes, orange, peach, prickly pear, radishes, tangerines, garlic, onions, spices	• **Rheumatoid Arthritis-** Are you feeling unloved and resentful? • Are you being inflexible? • Are you feeling shame/guilt, having difficulty forgiving yourself and others? • Are you feeling limited but afraid to make change?	Solar Plexus Chakra- and other chakras

---

*** TESTIMONIAL...** *'Four years ago, I started to experience chronic Rheumatoid Arthritis symptoms. A year ago, I became a ringleader and it changed my life. Following your advice, I have fasted on water, juice and pulse; I have completed a clay cleanse and a parasite cleanse; I have removed mercury fillings and done some mental healing and I can very happily say that I am completely pain and symptom-free and have been for six months. I no longer fear disease. I am forever grateful for your courage to speak out and share your amazing knowledge in spite of what you're up against because now you have given me the courage to walk alongside you. My children, who are three and 18 months tell me that they heal themselves; they've never been to a doctor and they crave salad and fresh juices. S, you can add them to your list of admirers, Don. Thank you from the bottom of our hearts. I hope we meet some day.' Nicole Rose*

LYMPHATIC/IMMUNE SYSTEM
PAIN RELIEF OIL

Ingredients: coconut oil, essential oils of peppermint, eucalyptus, lavender and rosemary

Method: Please check with the oil company as far as strength and any contraindications before using direct on the skin. Alternatively, dilute with a little coconut oil and massage regularly into the area

STAFF INFECTION/ MRSA

***WHAT IS IT?...** **Staff infection** is caused by the bacteria 'staphyloccus', which lives on surfaces such as skin, up your nose, on the ground etc. When the bacteria enters the body via a cut, scratch, insect bite etc, the area may become infected. Methicillin-resistant staphylococcus aureau (MRSA) is caused by a strain of staph bacteria that has become resistant to antibiotics, antibacterials and antiseptics.

***BODY – EPICURE*

- Get off all medication and supplements- herbs in the form of powders or teas are okay, but no pills or capsules!
- Bath in warm water with 2 cups epsom salts for 20 minutes.
- Mix equal amounts of essential oils of tea tree and eucalyptus, apply directly to the skin.
- Mix 2tbsp apple cider vinegar in clean warm water with 1 tbsp of manuka honey and drink. This kills the MRSA superbug caused by anti bacterials, antibiotics and antiseptics.
- Applying coconut oil and essential oils of oregano and basil can help.
- Mix turmeric and ginger organic powders with warm water and drink 2 x per day.
- Apply ACV directly to the skin.
- Rub cinnamon essential oil over the area several times per day.
- **ESSENTIAL OIL...** cinnamon, tea tree, eucalyptus, oregano, basil.
- (Essential oils of tea tree, eucalyptus, basil available in the USA **www.thedontolman.com/store** and Australia **www.lynnienichols.com/shop**)

BODY *FOODS THAT HEAL*	MIND *POSSIBLE EMOTIONAL CAUSE*	SPIRIT *IMBALANCED CHAKRA*
---	---	---
SIGNATURE FOODS... apples, berries, garlic, spring onions, honeydew melon, horseradish, leeks, lemons, limes, orange, peach, prickly pear, radishes, tangerines, garlic, onions, spices	• Are you feeling angry or irritated?	Solar Plexus Chakra- and other chakras

LYMPHATIC/IMMUNE SYSTEM
SUPERBUG KILLER

Ingredients: 2 tbsp apple cider vinegar, 1 tbsp of manuka honey, 1 cup warm water

Method: Mix all ingredients together and drink daily

Getting Back To Nature...
'All for One, One for All.' United We Stand, Divided We Fall.

Originally the word, 'Law' meant: The 'Energy Powers' or 'Forces of the Cosmos', today called: The 'Physics of Nature' that controls all energetic and three-dimensional physical existence throughout space and time. Time being the measure of Distance in Space. All of existence is based on the frequencies of sound.

The seven notes of the Octave once sounded as: Do, Re, Me Fa, So, La, Ti.

This is where the word Time comes from, 'Ti' being the 7th note sound frequency and 'Me' being the 3rd note sound frequency hence, TI-ME, TIME.

La(law) is the 6th note... The number six was called the 'Number of Man'.

All of this was anciently called the Law of Time.

Sounds condense into Light frequencies, hence the seven notes of sound creating the seven colours of the Rainbow of Light (red, orange, yellow, green, blue, indigo and violet).

Light condenses into the seven major Gases—Nitrogen, Oxygen, Carbon Dioxide, Argon, Hydrogen, Helium and Neon. Gases condense into Liquids and Liquids condense into Solids meaning: Made of Light. Sol-ids comes of Sol, one of the names of the Sun. Hence, 'Mother Earth and Father Sun' are the Cosmic Creators of all Life.

If you are a member of a Patriarchal (God is a Man) Religion please don't be offended; keep reading please. TIME spelled backwards is EMIT, meaning the energy radiating over time and distance in space to Create all things under the Sun.

The Law of Time is, was, and always will be the Cosmic Principle of Synchronization.

The Law of Time distinguishes between nature's timing frequency that governs the Cosmic Order and an artificial timing frequency that sets modern human civilization apart from the rest of its environment, the bio-sphere (Life).

The effect of basing a civilization on artificial timing factors – an irregular calendar and the mechanical clock – has resulted in the creation of an artificial global mantle, the technosphere.

By consuming nature's resources faster than they can be replaced and creating more waste than can be eliminated, the technosphere operates at the expense of the biosphere, hence the current global crisis and chaos.

'We are no longer One.' E Pluribus Unum, meaning, 'All for One, One for All.' United we Stand, Divided we Fall.

The Law of Time affirms and confirms that all of the planetary upheavals and social chaos that we are experiencing today are directly related to giving precedence to 'human man-made laws' and machine technology, rather than divine Cosmic order and nature's law. This is due to living a collective misperception of time known as the 12:60 frequency. This refers to the 12-month cycle of the irregular Gregorian calendar, paced by the 60-minute clock. Living in artificial time disconnects us both as a species and individually from our true nature. We always feel like we never have 'enough time'.

In the 12:60 frequency, 'Time is Money.' None of the names of the Gregorian 'months' fit their meaning.

September means seven and now it's the 9th month, October means eight and it's the 10th month, December means 10 and it's the 12th month, etc.

The Ancients wrote 'Mankind will lose Nature's Cosmic Law of Time, which is a 13:20 frequency of Energy, but in the year 2029(13) it will return to humans Globally.'

The 13:20 ratio of the natural timing frequency is coded into the Tzolk'in Lunar calendar of the Mayans, but it has been taken from most villages.

The Law of Time, the 13:20 ratio, is the 260-unit harmonic matrix, which is the number of days for a foetus to grow in the mother and to be born. This 13:20 frequency can also be found in our body/temple:
In the synchronic order, the holographic 'soul' element (Sound and Light) of any given form – human, planet, star or galaxy – is called a holon.

The human holon is the holographic 'soul' element of the human form (Solar Plexus).

The 20 Solar Seals are contained in our 20 fingers and toes.

The 13 Galactic Tones are contained in our 13 main articulations: two ankles, two knees, two hips, two wrists, two elbows, two shoulders, one neck. We also have 13 doorways, the way things get in and out of the body—two eyes, two ears, two nostrils, one mouth, two nipples, one urinary doorway, one intestinal doorway, the skin, and imagination = 13. Imagination creates thoughts; thoughts create emotions; emotions create behaviours.

E-nergy factored by T-ime equals Art. In this equation, (E) refers to all phenomena in their processes of unfoldment; (T) is the present moment of functioning according to the ratio constant to 13:20. Everything that is shaped by time is the Art of Existence. Take time to look at the Sun, Moon and Stars. Get out of the city and observe Nature. You will radiate/glow with the 13:20 Cosmic Energy.

Pleasure is the Greatest Good. Humour is the Best Medicine.

The only Evil is Violence against Innocents.

Cowboy Don

Sounds condense into Light frequencies, hence the seven notes of sound creating the seven colours of the Rainbow of Light (red, orange, yellow, green, blue, indigo and violet).

Cowboy's True Understandings- Etymologies of Words

Pre religion, all of these words were the symbolic representations of the forces of nature that are around us and indicators of the path we are following. Are we following the path of health, light and longevity or are we embracing things that are toxic and creating deficiencies?

People need to understand that the ancient scholars, healers, builders, gardeners, and brilliant scholastic communities looked at the nature around them and each culture gave words that represented in English what would be gods and goddesses. There were many forces of nature—wind, tide of the ocean, new moon, full moon, quarter moon, gravity, etc.

The ancients carved in stone and also wrote on papyrus scrolls the 'TWO LAWS of LIFE.'
Law #1. PLEASURE IS THE GREATEST GOOD.
Law #2. THE ONLY EVIL THAT EXISTS IS VIOLENCE AGAINST INNOCENTS.

Devil... was over the kingdom of disease and death ... the energies of Pain, Dis-comforts, and Diseases. Reverse the spelling of 'Devil' and it spells the word 'Lived'.

Evil... is 'Live' backwards. When you embraced behaviours that were against the life of human body and function, you were doing something that was 'Evil'. If you were sick, you had embraced things that were 'Evil', meaning toxic, or creating deficiency in the body—you were following the practice of the 'Devil', meaning the path of death and illness. Eventually religion switched the original meaning to what most believe today in regards to evil and going to hell.

Demon... literally meant 'The Full Moon' because ancient scholars knew that the full moon activates the breeding of the communities of parasites in the body and these activated 'Demons' in the heart and brain, making people behave weirdly. The energy of the moon is what's in charge of the ebb and flow of the ocean ... the earth is 70% water and we are 70% water. The moon affects all waters! Women's menses are every 28 days ... because of the cycle of the moon!

Satan... was God/ess over darkened mysteries... Things that people were thinking about and all of the things that had not yet been revealed. Hidden knowledge is kept behind a 'Veil of Forgetfulness', meaning the 'Brain'. Satan had a brother called 'Lucifer'.

Lucifer... meant the 'Greatest Shining Light', the bright shining one/star. The sun in a noonday blue sky with no clouds was 'Lucifer'. Lucifer lights up the darkness of Hidden Knowledge and you experience epiphanies, moments of AH HA discovery, sought-after answers, creative enlightenments, even memories of the future being downloaded in night dreams, etc. This is where the word 'lucky' comes from.

Sol... was one of the names of the sun. It meant brightness/answer to that which they were seeking and had been sitting in darkness on. The scholars were excited; they wanted to find answers; they wanted to find 'SOLutions'.

Lucky... literally meant 'moments when thoughts pop into your head', the moment you downloaded the 'solution' to what had been hidden in darkness with no answers. This meant 'Lucifer' had shown up and shined a bright light into the dark cave of mysteries controlled by 'Satan', the force of darkness, and illuminated it and brought it to your understanding.

Spirit... literally meant breath, or air, the aura of something that can be smelled... When you breathe, it keeps the NTR inside of you.

NTR... the seed of the seed, the undivisable first cell that comes forth at the moment of conception.

Evil Spirit... literally meant the smell of dead rotting decay and filth. They believed anciently that this was an indicator that cleansing, clearing and healing needed to take place. Wherever the smell of death showed up, this was literally what they were talking about... It wasn't the devil in a red skin-tight outfit with horns and a long tail, carrying a pitchfork.

Sun... 'Father'- nothing new under the 'Son\Holy Ghost'

Holy Ghost... is the 'spirit'/air inside of you.

The Archangels were the seven Senses: Sight, Hearing, Smelling, Tasting, Touching, Intuition, and Imagination. These deliver your 3-Dimensional Life Experience.

The Administering Angels were: Air, Water, Sunshine, Movement, Plant Foods, Healthy Relationships, Passions.

Cowboy Don

Eating With Your Hands Is Healthy!

Eating with your hands has many health benefits, including weight loss.

According to Ayurvedic and other ancient texts, each finger is an extension of one of the five elements. The thumb is space. Before children are at an age where they can chew, they tend to suck their thumb as nature's way of aiding digestion. The forefinger is air, the ring finger is earth, mid finger is fire and the little finger is water.

Imbalance of any of these elements can actually lead to many diseases or disorders in the body. When we eat with our hands, we normally stick our fingers and thumb together and by using all five fingers to eat, we have all five elements energising the food and helping to keep our body organs in balance.

If you suffer from poor digestion, try eating with your hands. The moment we touch our food with our hands, the brain signals the stomach that we are about to eat. This, in turn, prepares the stomach to digest the food it will receive, aiding in better digestion. If you suspect that you might be eating too fast, ditch utensils and focus on eating with your hands. You will be amazed by how soon you will get full with less food if you eat with your hands. But do make sure that your hands are washed with clean water before touching your food! However, NEVER use antibacterial soaps or antiseptics of any kind.

Sometimes I Suck at The Game of Life!

From the moment I opened my eyes I was engulfed by fear and a low energetic feeling as if someone had thrown a blanket of darkness over my Soul, leaving nothing more than a slither of light shining through... Unbeknownst to me, I had subconsciously, overnight, signed up for a game of life with Ego as my opponent, and I have to tell you it was absolutely flogging me!

That slither of light, or in other words 'truth', peeking out from the darkness was not enough to outplay my Ego opponent, and somehow, I managed to forget everything I teach, every bit of knowledge I have, every single tool I have in my kit and everything that I am! In fact, if the game of life was snakes and ladders, I felt like I'd landed on the biggest, most venomous adder and slid all the way down to its tail where the darkness blinded me from everything I know to be true and authentic and powerful and honest and beautiful ... and instead I fell into the trap of the Ego Mind and its bullshit stories of fear, not good enough, can't do it, it's too hard and, ultimately, the negative core belief that 'If I'm not perfect, I'm not good enough!'

And do you believe all of this was triggered by my past fear of technology... I'm saying past as my affirmation this year is 'Technology and I absolutely love each other.' When I look back now, I cannot believe that I allowed such a trivial thing to have so much power over me ... but then I realise it wasn't actually the technology part that had the power, it was my core belief of 'not good enough' that had been triggered and Ego saying, 'Ha ha—checkmate! Got you again baby!'

Even with my Spiritual Journey being one of the most important aspects of my life, the thing I am

MOST passionate about, here I was, for two days of my life, allowing Ego to dominate my game! As that light of truth within me grew and I was able to climb my way up the ladder and out of the darkness, all thanks to emotional healing and cleansing of the energy body, I felt so cranky at myself for getting sucked into playing by Ego's rules again... I refuse to do that these days simply because I have more awareness and I know full well of its dirty tactics and incessant desire to drag up any unhealed dregs from the past in order to hold it against me like a wild card, unhealed dregs based on past indoctrination of someone else's truth as well as my perception of any particular experience at the time it took place during childhood, or, in other words, mistakes, lies and bullshit!

There is but one truth and that is LOVE! I have no religion. I don't believe in the man-made rules and regulations society enforces upon us in order to create fear and control. Truth is found in the heart, not the Ego mind. Yep, Ego is a dirty player, there's no doubt about that, and yet most of us play by its rules every single day of our lives simply because we don't have the awareness or tools to play a different game! I wanted to share this with you as I know, for many people, the game of life feels like an exhausting tournament, a constant fearful battle! This book is designed to empower you with the tools necessary to heal on the deepest level, and begin to play the game differently.

From My Heart to Yours, Have a love-filled, empowered day

Lynnie

The MUSCULAR / SKELETAL SYSTEM

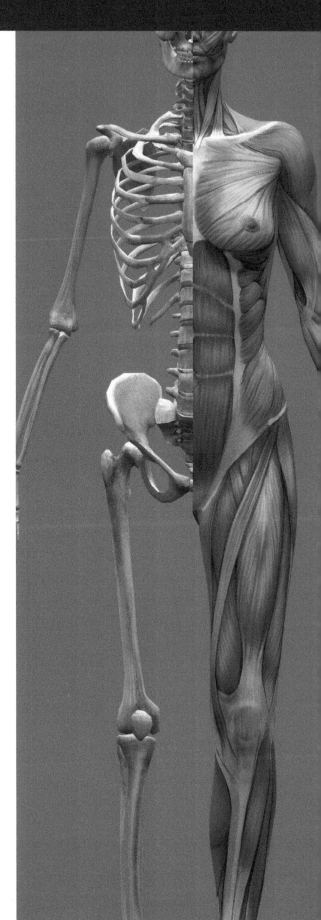

Consists of... muscles, ligaments, tendons, bones

Chakra- Root (red) /**Endocrine Gland and Function...** There are two adrenal glands located at the top of each kidney. The inner part of each gland is called the medulla, which secretes adrenaline and controls the fight or flight response. The outer area is called the cortex and secrete the steroids cortisol, which helps regulate metabolism, and aldosterone, which helps to control blood pressure. The adrenal glands also maintain salt levels and the overall fluid concentration of the body.

Holds Emotional Molecules of kindness, happiness, curiosity, fear, worry and doubt.

Foods That Support The Muscular System Are... apples, asparagus, beans, lentils, legumes, bean sprouts, cashews, eggs, chickpeas, oats, rye, sprouts, spelt, spinach, soybeans, tomatoes, tubers.

Foods That Support The Skeletal System Are... apples, beans, lentils, legumes, bok choy, celery, corn, jicama, kohlrabi, pistachios, pumpkin seeds, rhubarb, sesame seeds, sunflower seeds, Swiss chard, tubers.

Support the Emotional/Physical Healing of This System with... ORANGE and BLUE foods.

ORANGE wholefoods support this system by promoting feelings of joy and curiosity.

BLUE wholefoods help release disease in this system as well as emotional feelings of fear and worry.

***Did you know** that every two years you have a new skeleton?

***NUGGET...** Salt is the fourth most critical element to the human body after air, water and movement. All 10,000 trillion cells operate because of salt functioning as an electrolyte. If you don't have enough good earth-made salt in your diet, your body will need to use stored salt from the bones.

ARMS

BODY *FOODS THAT HEAL*	MIND *POSSIBLE EMOTIONAL CAUSE*	SPIRIT *IMBALANCED CHAKRA*
---	---	---
SIGNATURE FOODS... celery, bok choy, rhubard and salt	Are you struggling through life, unable to trust and enjoy the process? Is fear making you inflexible, do you need to relax?	Root Chakra- **colour Red** / Heart Chakra- **colour Green**

MUSCULAR/SKELETAL SYSTEM
CURRIED CHICKPEA AND APPLE SALAD

Ingredients: 400 g cooked chickpeas, 1 green apple diced, 1 cup cashews, 1 cup baby spinach leaves, 1 cup Swiss chard coarsely shredded, ½ cup bean sprouts, 1 cup assorted sprouts, 1 heaped tsp curry powder, coconut oil.

DRESSING; 1/8 cup apple cider vinegar, ¼ cup olive oil, 1 tsp sea salt

Method: In a mix of coconut oil, sea salt and curry powder, gently fry the chickpeas until golden brown. Allow to cool and then combine with all ingredients in a salad bowl. Combine the dressing ingredients and drizzle over the salad just before serving. (serves 2)

BONES

BODY	MIND	SPIRIT
FOODS THAT HEAL	*POSSIBLE EMOTIONAL CAUSE*	*IMBALANCED CHAKRA*
---	---	---
SIGNATURE FOODS... celery, bok choy, rhubard and salt	Are you feeling controlled, mentally pressured, inflexible? Are you hard on yourself and others? Are you punishing yourself due to painful memories from the past?	Root Chakra- **colour Red**

MUSCULAR/SKELETAL SYSTEM
PISTACHIO AND APPLE BONE-STRENGTHENING STICKS

Ingredients: 2 large sticks of celery, 1 apple diced, 1 cup salted pistachios, ¼ cup mixture of pumpkin and sunflower seeds, 2 large Swiss chard leaves finely shredded

LEMON DRESSING; **(see recipe under Dressings in back of book)**

Method: Place the apple, pistachios and seeds in a food processor on medium to high until chopped finely. Spoon the mixture into the celery centres. Place the shredded chard onto a small platter and drizzle with dressing. Cut the celery into smaller pieces and arrange on the chard

Serve as a snack

HANDS

BODY *FOODS THAT HEAL*	MIND *POSSIBLE EMOTIONAL CAUSE*	SPIRIT *IMBALANCED CHAKRA*
---	---	---
SIGNATURE FOODS... celery, bok choy, rhubard and salt	Are you handling life well or are you living from fear, worry and lack of faith? If you have arthritis in your fingers, are you feeling like a victim and wanting to blame and punish others?	Root Chakra- **colour Red** / Heart Chakra- **colour Green**

MUSCULAR/SKELETAL SYSTEM
ORANGE BIRCHER MUESLI

Ingredients: 3 cups rolled oats, 5 oranges juiced, 4 mandarins juiced, 1 lemon juiced, 4 apples grated. Granola: ½ cup whole walnuts, ½ cup pepitas, sprinkle of chia seeds, sprinkle of flaxseeds, ½ tsp cinnamon

Method: Place the oats in a bowl. Juice the lemon and pour over the grated apple before combining with the oats. Juice the oranges and mandarins and add, mixing well (juice should just cover the mix, if not, add extra juice).

Place in the fridge overnight. In the morning, mix well before placing in serving bowls topped with granola and cashew cream (see recipe in book). Granola: chop the walnuts a little then combine with remaining ingredients

*For a non-vegan option, serve with organic natural yoghurt

Serves 4

KNEES

BODY	MIND	SPIRIT
FOODS THAT HEAL	***POSSIBLE EMOTIONAL CAUSE***	***IMBALANCED CHAKRA***
---	---	---
SIGNATURE FOODS... celery, bok choy, rhubard and salt	Are you being stubborn or inflexible?	Root Chakra- **colour Red**
	Are you controlling, blaming or judging others?	
	Are you unable or unwilling to forgive?	

MUSCULAR/SKELETAL SYSTEM
APPLE & RHUBARB CRUMBLE

Ingredients: 5 apples grated with peel and seeds, 4 sticks of rhubarb steamed until soft-allow to cool

CRUMBLE; 1 cup rolled oats, 1 cup salted pistachios, ½ tsp cinnamon, ½ cup coarsely dessicated coconut, 2 tbsp coconut oil, 1 heaped tsp honey

CASHEW CREAM **(see recipe under Dressings in back of book)**

Method: Combine the cooled rhubarb and grated apple then place in a casserole dish.

Crumble; Place the oats in a food processor on high speed until chopped; add the pistachios and continue to process for another 5 seconds. In a mixing bowl, combine the oat/pistachio mix, coconut, cinnamon, honey and coconut oil.

Use your hands to rub the coconut oil into the mix, creating the crumble. Spread the crumble over the apple and rhubarb mixture and serve as is, or, for a warm version, place in the oven for 10 minutes until crumble is slightly golden. Serve with cashew cream. (serves 4)

LEGS

BODY *FOODS THAT HEAL* ---	**MIND** *POSSIBLE EMOTIONAL CAUSE* ---	**SPIRIT** *IMBALANCED CHAKRA* ---
SIGNATURE FOODS... celery, bok choy, rhubard and salt	Are you feeling fearful about the future, unsure how you will survive? Is fear or a lack of confidence keeping you stuck?	Root Chakra- **colour Red**

MUSCULAR/SKELETAL SYSTEM
BEAN AND ROSEMARY BRUSCHETTA

Ingredients: Organic spelt sourdough, 1½ cups of cooked assorted beans (kidney, butter, black), 1 large celery stick diced finely, 1 organic corn cob, 2 cloves garlic diced finely, finely diced chilli to taste, 4 tomatoes finely diced, 1 tablespoon finely chopped rosemary, ½–1 tsp sea salt, pepper, organic olive oil.

Method: Cook the assorted organic beans in boiling water until soft, allow to cool. In a jar, mix the olive oil and rosemary. Combine the diced celery, tomato, onion, garlic, sea salt, rosemary and chilli in a bowl with the bean mix. Using a knife, slice the corn from the cob and add to the mixture. Season with extra sea salt if needed.

Toast the sourdough then top with a generous serving of the bean mixture. Drizzle with a good dose of rosemary oil and serve

*For a non-vegan version, top with crumbled organic feta

MUSCLES

BODY *FOODS THAT HEAL*	MIND *POSSIBLE EMOTIONAL CAUSE*	SPIRIT *IMBALANCED CHAKRA*
---	---	---
SIGNATURE FOODS... beans, lentils, legumes, eggs, asparagus, apples, cashews, chickpeas, oats, rye, sprouts, spelt, edamame, spinach, tomatoes	Are you resisting change, trying to control life rather than trusting and going with the flow? Are you feeling powerless? Are you feeling stuck, unable to move?	Root Chakra- **colour Red**

MUSCULAR/SKELETAL SYSTEM
ROSEMARY EGGS ON SPELT SOURDOUGH

INGREDIENTS: 1 or 2 organic eggs per serving, 2 pieces of organic spelt sourdough per serving, 1 bunch of fresh asparagus, baby spinach leaves, avocado, Himalayan salt, 1 cup organic olive oil, one large stick of fresh rosemary diced finely

METHOD: In a bowl or glass jar, combine the finely diced rosemary with olive oil. Smash avocado in a bowl with a couple of pinches of Himalayan salt; then spread a thick layer onto each piece of toast. Place the poached eggs on top of the avocado and drizzle with a generous dose of rosemary oil. Add a little more salt and some cracked pepper to serve.

*An alternative to toast is to serve the poached eggs on a bed of wilted baby spinach leaves.

*Optional extra to assist this system ... raw or lightly steamed asparagus.

DIS-EASES/DISORDERS OF
The MUSCULAR/SKELETAL SYSTEM

ANKYLOSING SPONDYLITIS (AS)

***WHAT IS IT?...* **Ankylosing spondylitis** is an inflammatory arthritis that affects the spinal joints, beginning at the base of the spine with the sacroliliac joint and eventually affecting the other vertebrae, leading to severe discomfort and pain.

BODY – EPICURE

- Get off all medication and supplements- herbs in the form of powders or teas are okay, but no pills or capsules!
- **Fastest...** Water fast for 7–10 days or cabala juice fast 14–28 days **OR...**
- Eat and juice a locally grown, fresh, raw organic vegan diet for highest nutritional force. Especially beneficial are celery, bok choy, and rhubarb. Eat mushrooms after placing them in the sun for a couple of hours.
- Exercise by doing rotational stretching movements and lifting legs etc. before getting out of bed in the morning. Do similar exercises once or preferably twice a day (ocean, stream, pool).
- Salt—have plenty of good, nature-made salt in the diet and suck on rock salt during the day.
- Take hot water salt baths first thing in the morning and again at night if necessary.

- Find the day of the week you were born (day of Sabbath) and fast on liquids on this day each week to give the body time to rest and heal.
- Take 7 mg of Boron per day. Dissolve one level teaspoon of Borax/Boron in one litre of water to make a concentrated solution. Take one teaspoon of this concentrate twice daily with meals.
- Massage the spine several times daily with anit-inflammatory essential oils, or use Healing Chrysm and Golden ReLeaf.
- **ESSENTIAL OIL...** helichrysum, eucalyptus, roman chamomile, clove, thyme, turmeric, ginger.
- (Divine, colon cleanses, Ra 24ct See Salt, Himalayan rock salt, essential oils of lemon, orange, lime available in the USA **www.thedontolman.com/store** and Australia **www.lynnienichols.com/shop**)

BODY *FOODS THAT HEAL*	MIND *POSSIBLE EMOTIONAL CAUSE*	SPIRIT *IMBALANCED CHAKRA*
---	---	---
SIGNATURE FOODS... apples, asparagus, beans, lentils, legumes, bean sprouts, cashews, eggs, chickpeas, oats, rye, sprouts, spelt, spinach, soybeans, tomatoes, tubers	• Are you feeling unloved and unsupported? • Are you feeling unable to stand for or support yourself?	Base Chakra- **colour Red**

***NOTE...** Good nature-made sea or rock salt targets restructuring of the bones and clears inflammation. Celery is 21–30% phytolitical plant sodium, perfect signature for the bones.*

MUSCULAR/SKELETAL SYSTEM
MUSHROOM, CASHEW & CHICKPEA STIR-FRY

Ingredients: 2 cups of mushrooms, 2 cups chopped bok choy, 2 cups finely sliced celery, 1 cup cooked chickpeas, 1 cup cashews, ¼ cup tamari, 4 cloves garlic, 1 tsp sea salt, 1 tbsp coconut oil

Method: Marinate the chickpeas in the salt and tamari for 2 hrs. Place 2 cups of mushrooms in the sun for a minimum of 2hrs before slicing and frying them for 2 minutes with the garlic, coconut oil and chickpeas. Add the tamari from the chickpea marinade and the remaining ingredients and stir-fry for a further 2 minutes, leaving a little crunchy. Taste and add extra tamari or sea salt if desired. (serves 2)

BROKEN BONE

WHAT IS IT?... **Broken bone** is the term given to any size fracture, from a hairline fracture to a complete snap. When the broken bone actually punctures the skin, it is referred to as an open fracture or compound fracture, and when a break occurs due to prolonged force against the bone, this is called a stress fracture.

BODY – EPICURE

- Get off all pain relief after 7 days! Eat one or two cups of cherries each day which contain natural aspirin.
- **Fastest...** Water fast for 7–10 days, or cabala juice fast 14–28 days **OR...**
- Eat three or four stalks of celery every day and other stalk foods such a rhubarb and bok choy.
- Use ice for swelling only ... or can do heat/ice/heat/ice and not too hot.
- Salt—have plenty of good, nature-made salt in the diet and suck on rock salt during the day.
- Have a shot glass of Joule of Thor each day or fresh aloe vera gel with 24ct Ra gold See Salt.
- Use Golden ReLeaf each morning and evening and Healing Chrysm five or six times per day.
- Soak in a hot salt water bath every day.
- Drink celery juice and green juices often, include berries in juices and smoothies.
- Eat and juice a locally grown, fresh, raw organic vegan diet for highest nutritional force. Eat mushrooms after placing them in the sun for a couple of hours.
- **ESSENTIAL OIL...** helichrysum, clove, ylang ylang, frankincense, marjoram, cypress, nutmeg, ginger.
- (Divine, colon cleanses, Ra 24ct See Salt, Himalayan rock salt, essential oils of lemon, orange, lime available in the USA **www.thedontolman.com/store** and Australia **www.lynnienichols.com/shop**)

BODY *FOODS THAT HEAL*	MIND *POSSIBLE EMOTIONAL CAUSE*	SPIRIT *IMBALANCED CHAKRA*
---	---	---
SIGNATURE FOODS... apples, asparagus, beans, lentils, legumes, bean sprouts, cashews, eggs, chickpeas, oats, rye, sprouts, spelt, spinach, soybeans, tomatoes, tubers	• Are you holding supressed resentment and not doing anything about it? • Are you rebelling against authority?	Base Chakra- **colour Red** and other chakras

TESTIMONIAL – *After a cycling accident in 2008, Sam wound up in hospital with a broken shoulder, punctured lung, broken ribs and 4 broken vertebrae. As you can imagine, the doctor's were insisting he have surgery, however, after consulting with Don, Sam refused. Supported by Don, Sam walked out of hospital 10 days later, in a brace, but free from surgery. 3-4 months later, Sam had regained full mobility. See Sam's video testimonial here* **https://youtu.be/Fp4R-Si2-VM**

MUSCULAR/SKELETAL SYSTEM
ALOE & BERRY SMOOTHIE BOWL

Ingredients: 2 cups mixed berries, 1 cup rhubarb, gel from a large aloe vera leaf, 2 large bananas, 5 medjool dates (keep a little of the berries and banana aside for decorating the smoothie bowl)

GRANOLA; 1 cup salted cashews chopped, ¼ cup sprouted lentils, 1 cup chopped dried apple, ½ cup shredded coconut, 5 dates chopped finely

Method: Steam the rhubarb until soft and then refrigerate. Once cold, place in a blender with the berries, aloe vera gel, dates and banana and process until smooth and creamy. Pour the smoothie into a serving bowl and decorate with the granola, extra berries and banana . (serves 2)

FIBROMYALGIA

***WHAT IS IT?...** **Fibromyalgia** is a painful musculoskeletal condition of the joints and muscles that creates pain and stiffness in localised areas of the body.

***BODY – EPICURE*

- Get off all medication and supplements- herbs in the form of powders or teas are okay, but no pills or capsules!
- **Fastest...** Water fast for 10 days then Cabala for 10 days and then 28 days on fruit, nuts and seeds or cherry Pulse **OR...**
- Cabala juice fast for 28–40 days.
- Eat two or three cups of organic cherries each day- these can be fresh, dried or frozen or eat cherry Pulse.
- Eat and juice a locally grown, fresh, raw organic fruit diet for 90 days.
- Salt—have plenty of good, nature-made salt in the diet and suck on Himalayan rock salt the size of the last segment of your little finger each day.
- Take 7 mg of Boron per day. Dissolve one level teaspoon of Borax/Boron in one litre of water to make a concentrated solution. Take one teaspoon of this concentrate twice daily with meals.
- Take hot water salt baths with one cup epsom salts and one cup bicarb soda first thing in the morning, and again at night if necessary. Soak in the ocean.
- Massage the areas several times daily with essential oils, or use Healing Chrysm and Golden ReLeaf.
- Sunshine—lie in the sun to assist the liver and neuroendorine glands to stimulate strength to the muscles.
- **ESSENTIAL OIL...** peppermint, eucalyptus, lavender, rosemary, sandalwood, ginger.
- (Divine, Cherry Pulse, Mango Pulse, Healing Chrysm, Golden ReLeaf, Ra 24ct See Salt, Himalayan rock salt, essential oils of peppermint, eucalyptus available in the USA **www.thedontolman.com/store** and Australia **www.lynnienichols.com/shop**)

BODY	MIND	SPIRIT
FOODS THAT HEAL	***POSSIBLE EMOTIONAL CAUSE***	***IMBALANCED CHAKRA***
---	---	---
SIGNATURE FOODS... apples, asparagus, beans, lentils, legumes, bean sprouts, cashews, eggs, chickpeas, oats, rye, sprouts, spelt, spinach, soybeans, tomatoes, tubers	• Are you feeling unloved and resentful? • Are you being inflexible? • Are you feeling shame/guilt, having difficulty forgiving yourself and others? • Are you feeling limited but afraid to make change?	Base Chakra- **colour Red** and other chakras

MUSCULAR/SKELETAL SYSTEM
FRUITY NUT MUESLI WITH TOFFEE CASHEWS

Ingredients: 2 cups organic dried fruits of apple, cherries, mango and peach, ½ cup chopped almonds, ½ cup chopped Brazil nuts, 1 cup whole cashews, 3 cups organic rolled oats, 1 cup of shaved coconut, ½ cup coconut oil, 1 heaped tsp cinnamon, 1 tbsp honey

Method: Place the oats in a bowl with the coconut oil, cinnamon and shaved coconut. Using your hands, rub the mix until the oats are coated with the oil. Add a little extra oil if needed. Spread the mix onto a large baking tray and place in a moderate oven for 20 mins, tossing now and then so the oats become lightly toasted. Remove and allow to cool before adding the chopped dried fruit, almonds and Brazil nuts

Toffee Cashews: place the cashews and a pinch of Himalayan salt in a dry pan on low heat and stir until the cashews become lightly golden. Allow to cool slightly then add the honey. Set aside until they become hard and crunchy then add to the muesli mix. Keep a few aside to garnish. Serve with cashew, almond or coconut milk and fresh fruit if desired. (serves 4)

MUSCULAR DYSTROPHY (MD)

***WHAT IS IT?...** **Muscular dystrophy** is the term used for more than 30 genetic disorders that weaken the muscles and cause wasting, due to missing information that prevents the body making the proteins needed for healthy muscles.   MD is the most common muscle disease in children.

***BODY – EPICURE*

- Get off all medication and supplements- herbs in the form of powders or teas are okay, but no pills or capsules!
- **Fastest...** Water fast for 10 days then Cabala for 10 days and then 28 days on fruit, nuts and seeds or cherry Pulse **OR...**
- Cabala juice fast for 28–40 days.
- Eat two or three cups of organic cherries each day, these can be fresh, dried or frozen, or eat cherry Pulse.
- Eat and juice a locally grown, fresh, raw organic fruit diet for 90 days.
- Salt—have plenty of good, nature-made salt in the diet and suck on Himalayan rock salt the size of the last segment of your little finger each day.
- Take 7 mg of Boron per day. Dissolve one level teaspoon of Borax/Boron in one litre of water to make a concentrated solution. Take one teaspoon of this concentrate twice daily with meals.
- Take hot water salt baths with one cup epsom salts and one cup bicarb soda first thing in the morning, and again at night if necessary. Soak in the ocean.
- Walk every day for 30–45 minutes. Exercise by doing rotational stretching movements and lifting legs etc. before getting out of bed in the morning. Do similar exercises for one hour every day or twice a day preferrably (ocean, stream, pool); walk up and down stairs three or four times per day or use a rebounder trampoline for 15 minutes at a time. Do star jumps, bent knee push-ups, rotations of the neck, shoulders, arms, legs and ankles five or six times every day.
- Massage the areas several times daily with essential oils or use Healing Chrysm and Golden ReLeaf.
- Sunshine—lie in the sun to assist the liver and neuroendorine glands to stimulate strength to the muscles.
- **ESSENTIAL OIL...** peppermint, eucalyptus, lavendar, rosemary oil.
- (Divine, Cherry Pulse, Mango Pulse, Healing Chrysm, Golden ReLeaf, Ra 24ct See Salt, Himalayan rock salt, essential oils of peppermint, eucalyptus available in the USA **www.thedontolman.com/store** and Australia **www.lynnienichols.com/shop**)

BODY *FOODS THAT HEAL*	MIND *POSSIBLE EMOTIONAL CAUSE*	SPIRIT *IMBALANCED CHAKRA*
---	---	---
SIGNATURE FOODS... apples, asparagus, beans, lentils, legumes, bean sprouts, cashews, eggs, chickpeas, oats, rye, sprouts, spelt, spinach, soybeans, tomatoes, tubers	• Are you allowing fear/sadness to eat away at you? • Is life just too hard or scary? • Are you harbouring guilt?	Base Chakra- **colour Red** and other chakras

*** NUGGET... *Life is movement; the less you do, the less you can do!*

MUSCULAR/SKELETAL SYSTEM
APPLE & MANGO CRUMBLE

Ingredients: 2 red apples, 2 green apples, 2 large sweet mangoes, 1 cup dried cherries

CRUMBLE; 1 cup organic oats, ½ cup coconut oil, 1 tsp nutmeg, 1 cup crushed salted cashews, 1 cup coarsely shredded coconut, 2 tbsp raw honey

Method: Grate the apple with peel and cores; cut the mango into cubes; dice the dried cherries. Mix these ingredients together. Place into serving bowls and top with a generous amount of crumble

Crumble: mix all ingredients together in a bowl then rub together with your hands until it becomes a crumb-like consistency

If desired, add a drizzle of Cashew Cream **(see recipe uncer Dressings in back of book).** (serves 2)

OSTEOARTHRITIS

WHAT IS IT?... **Osteoarthritis** is degeneration of joint cartilage and the underlying bone, mostly of the knees, hips, lower back and neck, causing stiffness and pain.

BODY – EPICURE

- Get off all medication and supplements- herbs in the form of powders or teas are okay, but no pills or capsules!
- **Fastest...** Water fast for 14-21 days to rid the body of pain **OR...**
- Cabala juice fast for 40 days.
- Stop eating meat—urea creates crystals in the body that attract around the joints and creates pain.
- For pain, eat two or three cups of organic cherries each day, these can be fresh, dried or frozen, or eat cherry Pulse.
- For cartilage, two or three weeks eating only mangoes and peaches.
- Eat and juice a locally grown, fresh, raw organic vegan diet for 90 days. Especially beneficial are celery, bok choy, and rhubarb. Eat mushrooms after placing them in the sun for a couple of hours.
- Salt—have plenty of good, nature-made salt in the diet and suck on Himalayan rock salt the size of the last segment of your little finger each day.

- Take 7 mg of Boron per day....Dissolve one level teaspoon of Borax/Boron in one litre of water to make a concentrated solution. Take one teaspoon of this oncentrate twice daily with meals.
- Take hot water salt baths with one cup epsom salts and one cup bicarb soda first thing in the morning, and again at night if necessary. Soak in the ocean.
- Massage the areas several times daily with essential oils, or use Healing Chrysm and Golden ReLeaf.
- Sunshine—lie in the sun to assist the liver and neuroendorine glands to stimulate strength to the muscles.
- **ESSENTIAL OIL...** peppermint, eucalyptus, lavender, rosemary, marjoram.
- (Divine, Cherry Pulse, Mango Pulse, Healing Chrysm, Golden ReLeaf, Ra 24ct See Salt, Himalayan rock salt, essential oils of peppermint, eucalyptus available in the USA **www.thedontolman.com/store** and Australia **www.lynnienichols.com/shop**)

BODY *FOODS THAT HEAL*	MIND *POSSIBLE EMOTIONAL CAUSE*	SPIRIT *IMBALANCED CHAKRA*
---	---	---
SIGNATURE FOODS... apples, asparagus, beans, lentils, legumes, bean sprouts, cashews, eggs, chickpeas, oats, rye, sprouts, spelt, spinach, soybeans, tomatoes, tubers	• **Osteo-arthritis-** Are you putting everybody else's needs before your own? • Are you fearful of experiencing life? • Are you feeling guilty about past actions, worried about what others think?	Base Chakra- **colour Red** and other chakras

MUSCULAR/SKELETAL SYSTEM
PAIN-RELIEF CHOCKY BALLS

Ingredients: 1 ½ cup cashews, 1 cup dried cherries, ¾ cup medjool dates, ¾ cup cacao powder, dessicated coconut for coating

Method: Place the cashews in a processor and pulse to a fine texture, add the cherries and cacao and process. Gradually add the dates then process until the mix forms a smooth ball. Roll into small balls and coat with coconut. Keep in airtight container in the fridge

Makes approximately 15

OSTEOPOROSIS

WHAT IS IT?... **Osteoporosis** is a disease that affects bone density and quality due to the loss of minerals such as calcium. The lack of the body's ability to replace these minerals causes bone fragility and, therefore, a high risk of fractures.

BODY – EPICURE

- Get off all medication and supplements- herbs in the form of powders or teas are okay, but no pills or capsules!
- **Fastest...** Water fast for 14–21 days to rid the body of pain **OR...**
- Cabala juice fast for 40 days.
- Eat two or three dark leafy greens for phytolitic plant calcium and lots of fruit as this dialates the blood vessels and extends them and allows for blood supply to speed up the healing process.
- Eat and juice a locally grown, fresh, raw organic vegan diet for 90 days. Especially beneficial are celery, bok choy, and rhubarb. Eat mushrooms after placing them in the sun for a couple of hours.
- Salt—have plenty of good, nature-made salt in the diet and suck on Himalayan rock salt the size of the last segment of your little finger each day.
- Take hot water salt baths with one cup epsom salts and one cup bicarb soda first thing in the morning, and again at night if necessary. Soak in the ocean.
- Drink one litre per 22 kilos bodyweight of pure water every day.
- Take 7 mg of Boron per day. Dissolve one level teaspoon of Borax/Boron in one litre of water to make a concentrated solution. Take one teaspoon of this concentrate twice daily with meals.
- Develop the darkest suntan you can by covering your body in Divine Body Butter or coconut oil and then exposing at least 70% of your body to the sun for one hour every day (30 mins each side). (Divine available at www.thedontolman.com/store)
- Sungazing morning and evenings in 13-second intervals; look at the sun until it reaches a 10-degree arc, or a clenched fist sitting on horizon as sun comes up, stop at top of fist. At night, start gazing as sun hits top of fist until it's gone.
- **ESSENTIAL OIL...** rosemary, thyme.
- (Divine, Cherry Pulse, Mango Pulse, Healing Chrysm, Golden ReLeaf, Ra 24ct See Salt, Himalayan rock salt, essential oils of peppermint, eucalyptus available in the USA **www.thedontolman.com/store** and Australia **www.lynnienichols.com/shop**)

BODY *FOODS THAT HEAL*	MIND *POSSIBLE EMOTIONAL CAUSE*	SPIRIT *IMBALANCED CHAKRA*
---	---	---
SIGNATURE FOODS... apples, asparagus, beans, lentils, legumes, bean sprouts, cashews, eggs, chickpeas, oats, rye, sprouts, spelt, spinach, soybeans, tomatoes, tubers	• Are you feeling angry, resentful or unsupported?	Base Chakra- **colour Red**

NOTE: *Salt ionises into calcium and the bones store calcium. If there's not enough salt in the body, it pulls calcium from the stores in the bones, so salt, water and sunshine are crucial!*

MUSCULAR/SKELETAL SYSTEM
MEGA BONE-SUPPORT STIR-FRY

Ingredients: 4 stalks of celery, 1 cup mushrooms placed in the sun for 2 hrs, 1 bok choy, ½ cup sprouted lentils, 1 cup bean sprouts, 1 cup cashews, 6 stalks asparagus, ½ cup cooked chickpeas, 2 cups spinach, 1 cup organic soybeans, 2 eggs, ¼ cup coconut oil, 1 tbsp ginger, 2 large cloves garlic, 1 tsp sea salt, 1 tsp cracked pepper.
DRESSING: ¼ cup organic cold pressed olive oil, ½ tsp sea salt, ½ cup tahini

Method: Boil the eggs then peel and cut into halves or quarters. Finely slice the celery and mushrooms. Dice the ginger and garlic. Using a knife or mandolin cut the apple into matchsticks. Dice the asparagus into 2cm lengths; slice the bok choy and spinach. In a pan with coconut oil, gently fry the chickpeas, garlic and ginger until slightly golden. Add the bok choy, spinach, asparagus, salt and pepper and continue to fry for a further 2 minutes. Add the remaining ingredients of celery, apple, soybeans, bean sprouts, lentils and cashews and stir-fry for a further minute just to heat through. Add the dressing, garnish with boiled egg and serve. (serves 2)

DRESSINGS / SAUCES

LEMON OR ORANGE DRESSING

Ingredients: 1 cup olive oil ½ cup lemon juice (or ½ cup orange juice), 2 teaspoons grainy mustard, 1 clove of garlic finely diced, pinch of sea salt

Method: Place all ingredients together in a glass jar or bottle and shake well.

*** For orange dressing, just replace the lemon in this recipe with orange juice.

TAHINI DRESSING

Ingredients: 2 heaped tbsp tahini, ½ cup olive oil, ¼ teaspoon sea salt, 1 tsp nutritional yeast, pinch sea salt

Method: Combine all ingredients together in a glass jar or bottle and shake well.

CASHEW MAYONNAISE

Ingredients: 1 cup cashews-soaked, 1 clove garlic, juice of 1 lemon, ¼ cup water, drizzle of apple cider vinegar, ⅛ cup nutritional yeast, ½ tsp sea salt, extra water if necessary, depending on desired consistency

Method: Blend all ingredients together on high-speed in a blender until mixture reaches a smooth consistency

BASIL PESTO

Ingredients: 250g basil, 1 cup raw cashews,1 tsp sea salt, ½ - ¾ cup olive oil, extra salt to taste, extra olive oil depending on desired consistency

Method: Place the cashews in a food processor and pulse until finely chopped. Add the basil leaves, olive oil and sea salt and blend again. Taste and add more salt if necessary. Add extra olive oil until you reach the desired consistency. (I like my pesto quite moist)

RED CAPSICUM PESTO

Ingredients: 1 large red capsicum including pith and seeds- stem removed, 1 clove garlic chopped, 1 cup of cashew nuts, ½ tsp sea salt

Method: Place the cashews in a food processor and pulse until finely chopped. Add the other ingredients. Pulse again until well blended.

OLIVE TAPANADE

Ingredients: 1 cup pitted Kalamata olives, 3 tbs capers, 3 cloves garlic- crushed, 1 tbs thyme, juice of ¼ lemon, 5 tbs olive oil

Method: Place the garlic in a food processor and process well, add the olives, capers, thyme and lemon juice until finely chopped. Continue to blend whilst adding the olive oil.

HUMMUS

Ingredients: 1 cup cooked chickpeas, 1 large clove garlic, 1-2 tsp tahini, ¼ cup organic olive oil, juice of 1 lemon, ½ - 1 cup water depending on desired consistency, 1 tsp nature made salt (option; ¼ cup roasted sweet potato or pumpkin)

Method: In a blender, on high speed, puree the chick peas with lemon juice and ¾ cup of water. Add all other ingredients and blend on high until a nice smooth consistency. Add extra salt and water if desired.

CASHEW CREAM

Ingredients: 1 cup cashews- soaked, ¼ cup coconut milk, 2 tbs raw honey, 3 tbs coconut oil, 1 tsp pure vanilla

Method: Soak cashews for at least 2hrs. Process all ingredients in a blender on high speed until desired creamy consistency.

HERB DRESSING

Ingredients: 1 cup olive oil, ½ cup parsley, 1/8 cup ACV, ½ tsp Himalayan salt, 1 tbs honey

Method: Place all ingredients in a blender on high speed until smooth. Store in a glass jar in the fridge.

Heirloom Seeds and the Tree of Life

Anciently, our bodies were called the Tree of Life, the Tree of Knowledge. We have four limbs and a trunk, and the brain bears 'fruits of imagination and creativity/inventions, art, music, technologies' and more. A dead human body was never meant to have over 100 pharma chemical preservatives put into it and then be laid in a wooden box in an underground Cement-tary Vault. It's all about the money!

Anciently, 'the body' was placed three feet down in the ground with a fruit tree planted on top of it. This was so that the deceased person's DNA could come up into that tree and into the fruit and seeds. This is where the term Heirloom Seeds originated. Children eating these fruits would have memories of the person buried.

Other options were: to first compost the body, place this into the ground and plant a fruit tree over it, or burn the body, place the ashes in the soil and then plant the fruit tree.

We have close to 98% of the same DNA as plants. We are meant to be healthy plant-eating vegans or healthy organic vegetarians.

No one should ever eat dead animal bodies, and yes, fish, sea food and chickens are animals.

Michelle McKoy Photography

Life and Death...The History and Herstory of Halloween

Halloween is celebrated each year on October 31st.

October, meaning eight, was the symbol for infinity, which meant 'The Return of the Dead, To Life'.
13 meant Life; 31 meant Death.

Halloween originated with the ancient Celtic festival of Samhain, where people would light bonfires symbolising 'The Light of Intelligence of the Individual Returning to Life' in the future, and they would wear costumes of ghosts, meaning 'The Womb of the Female Creatrix Will Allow You to Return and Stay Again on Mother Earth.'

The evening before was known as 'All Hallows' Eve' and later Halloween.

They taught that all departed souls of the preceding year were finally freed from 'Earthly Ties' and will live on the 'Sun, Until THEY Choose to Return.'

Over time, Halloween evolved into a day of activities such as trick-or-treating and carving Jack O' Lanterns. The 'Pumpkin' meant your 'Kin or Relatives' will 'Pump the Seeds of Your Return in the Future'.

The 'Pumpkin Seeds' represented 'LIFE', so they 'Pulled the Seeds Out of the Pumpkin' and carved a 'Smiling Face with Eyes Wide Open' and 'THE FIRE OF LIFE WITHIN IS SEEN'.

Because the 'Seeds of Life' come from the Male, this is called a 'Jack O' Lantern'.

As the days grew shorter and nights got colder in the northern countries of the world (winter) this was a symbol of 'DEATH Shall Return'.

Winter symbolised the death of most plants and those who had died during that year.

Gardeners knew that winter 'Ends One Planting Cycle and Begins Another'. Seeds for the next year were often planted at the same time.

The Romans used this day to honour Pomona, the goddess of fruit and trees. The symbol of Pomona is the Apple.

Apples have a Five-Pointed Star, the shape the Human body stands in.

Women 'Bear the Fruit of Life', which are the 'Trees of Knowledge Returning'.

People continue to usher in the season with gatherings, costumes and sweet treats, meaning

'Pleasure Is the Greatest Good.'

Cowboy Don

Love Life and Life Will Love You Back!

Ask and desire of Earth Mother, that body and emotions become as perfect as those of the Creative Force.

Pray; may all life continue to bless me with its unfolding vision of true joy, pleasure of the sun, rain, wind on my face and earth beneath my feet- the pleasure of watching a seed grow and my own growth and intelligence.

I am grateful for my beautiful physical body and may I continue to improve its structure and life force, that one day I will see my full potential...

Thankyou to the forces of life!

ACKNOWLEDGEMENTS

I would love to say a HUGE thankyou to the beautiful people that have allowed us to share their stories and testimonials throughout this book. It is you, and so many others like you, that have concreted my faith in the body's ability to heal naturally.

A massive heartfelt thankyou to these beautiful talented women... my sister Michelle McKoy @ **www.michellemckoyphotographer.com.au** for her professional food and landscape photography, to Tuuli Kaunisluonto for her raw unedited jungle recipe photography, to Rebecca May for the creative profile photography, to Dora Debrecini for her beautiful Goddess graphics **www.behance.net/dorcidebre203c/** and to Rebecca Ashcroft for creating our beautiful book cover exactly as I had envisioned it! A huge thank you also to the amazing Adi Bustaman @ **www.adibustamandesign.com** for putting up with my chopping and changing during the process of designing this book and creating something beyond my wildest dreams.

Last but not least, a huge thankyou to the incredible people who have taught and inspired me in the area of healing Mind, Body and Spirit; Brandon Bays, Louise Hay and of course, my teacher & co-author, Don Tolman. The teachings of these people, along with my own first-hand experience have become the basis of my holistic healing retreats and 'The Recipe...Healing in the Age of Aquarius'.

RESOURCES

For Private Consultations and Don's Online Store; **www.thedontolman.com**

For Private Emotional Healing Sessions, Upcoming Retreat Info and Online Store; **www.lynnienichols.com**

Journey Emotional Healing; The Journey- *by Brandon Bays*

Find a Journey Emotional Healing Practitioner Near You; **www.thejourney.com/find-a-practitioner/**

Resource on colon cleansing and reflex points of the colon; **Cleanse and Purify Yourself**- *by Richard Anderson*

Resources on the **Emotional Causes of Physical Illness**; **You Can Heal Your Body**- *by Louise Hay*

The Body is the Barometer of the Soul- *by Annette Noontil*

The Secret Language of Your Body- *by Inna Segal*

Printed in the USA
CPSIA information can be obtained
at www.ICGtesting.com
LVHW071732200824
788736LV00027B/491

9 780645 171419